Bumper FAMILY QUIZ BOOK

LOTS OF FUN FOR KIDS AND GROWN-UP KIDS, WITH OVER **5000** QUESTIONS

PaRragon

Bath • New York • Cologne • Melbourne • Delhi
Hong Kong • Shenzhen • Singapore • Amsterdam

This edition published by Parragon Books Ltd in 2015

Parragon Books Ltd
Chartist House
15–17 Trim Street
Bath BA1 1HA, UK
www.parragon.com

ISBN 978-1-4723-8049-4

Printed in China

Contents

Introduction

This quiz book contains over 5,000 quiz questions, with a range of difficulties and topics to ensure there is something suitable for every member of the family.

There are 314 separate quizzes, one per page, and full solutions are given at the back of the book so you can check your answers if you wish.

Questions particularly suitable for younger children are marked with a lightbulb symbol, 💡, so that you can find them immediately when you turn to a particular quiz. However these are certainly not the only questions suitable for children.

Good luck!

The Bumper Family Quiz Book
Quiz 1

① What Mexican political party was voted out of office in 2000, after 71 years in power?

② In the *Mr Men* books, what colour is Mr Bump?

③ In the movie *Ghost*, who plays the charlatan medium Oda Mae Brown?

④ Which country's capital is Kampala?

⑤ More than 50% of all the lakes in the world are in which country?

⑥ Egyptian sphinxes have the head of a ram or person and the body of what animal?

⑦ Which animal's young is called an 'elver'?

⑧ What is the name of the album on which John Mayer's song *Say* appears?

⑨ What is the capital of Mozambique?

⑩ What is the first name of the half-giant, Hagrid, in the *Harry Potter* novels?

⑪ In *Alice's Adventures in Wonderland*, who says 'Oh dear! Oh dear! I shall be too late!'?

⑫ In January 2013, Boeing 787 aircraft were grounded worldwide over concerns about what?

⑬ Who wrote *The Prime of Miss Jean Brodie*?

⑭ What school of art was born out of social problems following the end of World War 1?

⑮ In which Shakespeare play would you find Titania, Queen of the Fairies?

⑯ What was the first North American city to host the modern Olympic games?

The Bumper Family Quiz Book
Quiz 2

1. In Japan, what is 'raku'?

2. Achluophobia is the fear of what?

3. What animal is a pink bird that eats with its head upside down? 💡

4. In Salvador Dali's 'Meditative Rose', what is the rose doing?

5. What inert groups of compounds are known for short as CFCs?

6. By how many countries is Afghanistan landlocked?

7. Where do Chile's coastal mountains run in relation to the Andes?

8. How deep was the wreck of the *Titanic* when it was discovered?

9. Which King of England died in February 1685?

10. You should watch out for what prickly items on a blackberry bush? 💡

11. What former employee returned to Apple and then introduced the iMac in 1998?

12. How often is biannually?

13. In what year did Brazil earn the right to keep a World Cup trophy permanently?

14. During the time of the Pearl Harbor attack what was the berthing area on Ford Island nicknamed?

15. What character does Ellen Page portray in *Juno*?

16. Who became UK Poet Laureate in 1999?

The Bumper *Family* Quiz Book
Quiz 3

1. Ancient Roman aqueducts brought water to Rome from how far away: 5 miles, 27 miles or 57 miles?

2. What Croatian player got three yellow cards in one match during the 2006 World Cup?

3. On which continent is Norway located?

4. What colour is a Samoyed dog?

5. What nation has no US embassy, but has an honorary consulate in Honolulu: Cuba, Fiji or Kiribati?

6. A dugong's flippers are as long as what percentage of its body?

7. Which actor was in both *The Truman Show* and *The Firm*?

8. Which of these animals is native to Australia: grizzly bear, koala, panda or polar bear?

9. What is 'Turkish coffee'?

10. In Hinduism and Buddhism, what is a 'deva'?

11. Which famous supermodel tripped at her first fashion show?

12. Who was Australia's Prime Minister at the time of the Japanese attack on Pearl Harbor?

13. What does 'oracular' mean?

14. In a house, what is a 'parlour'?

15. Which capital city is the only one located on the equator?

16. What is the measure of phone line transmission speed?

The Bumper *Family* Quiz Book
Quiz 4

1. The Light Brigade made their famous charge during which war?

2. What was the name of Crowded House's debut album?

3. In music, what is a 'segue'?

4. What is an animal doing if it is moving to a new location for a warmer climate?

5. The iron ore, magnetite, was formerly called what?

6. Orange juice is a good source of which vitamin?

7. In British slang, what is a 'facer'?

8. What French author wrote the play *No Exit*?

9. Which country is Rabat the capital of?

10. How can you share 6 biscuits equally among 4 people?

11. Which ingredient is not found in a classic 'salade niçoise': chicken, olives or tuna?

12. Rivaldo and Miroslav Klose both scored 5 goals in which World Cup: 1994, 1998, 2002 or 2006?

13. Which city is the capital of Burkina Faso?

14. What art did Hitler partake in during his youth?

15. What cellblock held Princess Leia in *Star Wars*?

16. In which Euripidean play does a woman kill her children for her husband's betrayal?

The Bumper Family Quiz Book
Quiz 5

1. On what label was the first recorded use of the bass drum in jazz used, and by whom?

2. What river runs into Victoria Falls?

3. Who was the father of Henry VIII?

4. At what stadium does the English soccer team Derby County play their home games? 💡

5. What did courier firm Federal Express change their name to in 1994?

6. What country's high-ranking officers were once 'pashas'?

7. On average, how far can a skunk spray?

8. The Indian film industry is often called what?

9. How many 2014 Formula One circuits were run in an anti-clockwise direction? 💡

10. What title does the leader of Mexico hold?

11. What legendary Atari founder also created US chain Chuck E. Cheese?

12. What is the name of the former police chief in the 1975 film *Sholay*?

13. Leonardo da Vinci was hired by the Duke of Milan when he said he could build a portable what?

14. What two countries border the UAE?

15. Which continent includes Cambodia?

16. In which sport could you play at silly point, cover, midwicket or gully?

Quiz 6

1. What does SLR stand for in reference to a camera?

2. Which character did Superman defeat in the Marvel vs. DC series?

3. What disaster is usually caused by earthquakes: blizzard, hurricane or tsunami?

4. In what year did Kodak introduce the Folding Pocket Kodak: 1898, 1925, 1948 or 1963?

5. Who coached Spain when they won the UEFA European Football Championship in 2008?

6. What nation is sometimes referred to as the 'Rainbow Nation'?

7. How does a cricket hear?

8. Which is the largest living land animal?

9. Authorities in which country released gas into a theatre, killing 116 hostages in 2002?

10. What sort of electricity do you get when you rub two balloons and they stick together?

11. Which of these was the first Scooter song to reach the top 20 in Britain: *Back In The UK* or *Back In the Day*?

12. What does 'piscatorial' mean?

13. In heraldry, what colour is 'azure'?

14. What does TASER stand for?

15. What is the capital of the picturesque island of Saba, in the Netherlands Antilles?

16. Who was the commander of Allied forces in the Persian Gulf in 2003?

The Bumper Family Quiz Book
Quiz 7

1. On the Internet, what is the IMAP email protocol short for?

2. Which two colours make up the Scottish flag?

3. What type of scientist studies microscopic plants and animals?

4. What is the name of the high school in *Glee*?

5. How many U-boats did Germany lose in operations in World War 2?

6. At what rate does muscle turn to fat without exercise?

7. In what weight class did Ricky Hatton fight his debut match?

8. Bernini, Correggio and Botticelli were all artists from what nation?

9. When was Marks & Spencer first founded?

10. What do you call a large underwater formation made by corals?

11. Which Norwegian painter lived from 1863-1944?

12. Which African capital city contains the Al-Zaytuna Mosque?

13. In cosmetics, what is titanium dioxide used as?

14. What was the name of the band William wrote about in *Almost Famous*?

15. If I 'lave', what am I doing?

16. What are the only mammals that can fly?

The Bumper *Family* Quiz Book
Quiz 8

1. What ocean did European explorers cross to get to the New World?

2. What do you traditionally give for a fifth anniversary?

3. Who plays the titular role in the 2014 film *Lucy*?

4. Which is the heaviest snake: Anaconda, boa constrictor or Indian python?

5. What is the main form of energy produced by a laser?

6. What World War 1 'Ace' was known as the 'Sentinel of Verdun'?

7. During the Crimean War, who was 'The Lady with the Lamp'?

8. What decade is the hit single *Desire* by U2 from?

9. Kuala Lumpur is the capital of which south-east Asian nation?

10. What has to be visible from the front of a car according to Formula One rules?

11. Many paintings of the Italian Renaissance dealt with what theme?

12. Vatican City, where the Pope resides, is a city-state entirely contained within what country?

13. In *X-Men: First Class*, who plays Magneto?

14. What is the official currency of Somalia?

15. What is in a Tequila Sunrise?

16. In Russia, what is a 'mir'?

The Bumper *Family* Quiz Book
Quiz 9

1. Which country features a famous safari hotel built into the treetops: Congo, Egypt, Ghana or Kenya?

2. Which of the following is not commonly found as a garden plant: begonia, orchid, rose or tulip? 💡

3. What two days of the month can the 'ides' fall upon?

4. What is *Lihaperunasoselaatikko*?

5. In medicine, what does 'tumid' mean?

6. Finish the Jackson 5 lyric 'But now since I see you in his arms'?

7. Which musical features the music of Michael Jackson? 💡

8. When did the third Punic War end?

9. Maracaibo is located in which South American country?

10. How many 10-minute periods are played in Olympic basketball games?

11. In what year were the Torres Strait Islands annexed to the Colony of Queensland?

12. Which type of tree can grow the tallest?

13. What military conflict features in the 1966 film *The Battle of Algiers*?

14. In 1959, the USSR launched a rocket with two of which animals aboard?

15. From what two-word phrase is the term 'pixel' derived?

16. What is the name of the founding patriarch of Saudi Arabia?

The Bumper *Family* Quiz Book
Quiz 10

1. Which racehorse won the Grand National in 1973, 1974 and 1977?

2. In France, what was an 'aune'?

3. What title is usually given to the chief executive official of a town or city: Mayor or President? 💡

4. Who is the Greek goddess of the harvest?

5. What sedimentary rock is composed primarily of sand-sized grains?

6. What was the name of the only ship captured at sea during the Korean War?

7. What adjective means 'belonging to or associated with a flower'? 💡

8. Which Stuart King continued to reign after the death of his wife, Mary II?

9. The book *Way Station* was written by whom?

10. The 2014 single *Braveheart* is a song by which British girl group?

11. Which actor played coach Clay Driscoll in the film *Believe In Me*?

12. How old was the youngest-ever Han emperor?

13. Which bubbly beverage is fermented twice?

14. How much longer, on average, do American women live than men?

15. How fast can an ostrich run?

16. What was Disney's 25th in-house animated feature?

The Bumper Family Quiz Book
Quiz 11

1. According to the title of a 2011 film, which planet *Needs Moms*?

2. A famous panel of the Sistine Chapel features the creation of who?

3. Which former communist dictator executed his Prime Minister, his wife and nine children?

4. What percentage of a coal power plant's energy is typically lost as waste heat?

5. Which four colours feature on a 'Twister' mat?

6. Rob Ford made headlines worldwide in 2013. What job did he hold?

7. What does 'noisome' mean?

8. Which of these kitchen utensils would be best used for spreading icing on a cake: A fork, a sieve or a spatula?

9. What is in the Newfoundland meal, 'fish and brewis'?

10. Who was the only player to score in every World Cup in the 1990s?

11. How long is the US-Canadian border?

12. What relation is coach David Pierce to tennis pro Mary Pierce?

13. The Gilbert Islands are now known as what country?

14. Which bird is also known as the South American ostrich?

15. What two creatures make up the body of a griffin?

16. Who is the protagonist of 'Nineteen Eighty-Four'?

The Bumper Family Quiz Book
Quiz 12

1. Who was Ebenezer Scrooge's business partner in *A Christmas Carol*?

2. What is the national flower of England, which by any other name smells as sweet? 💡

3. What is a 'synchronism'?

4. Blood diamonds are named as such for what reason?

5. What is the SI unit for frequency?

6. Which Beatle sang the lead vocal on *Here Comes the Sun*?

7. What is the UK Prime Minister's London address? 💡

8. The largest natural satellite in our solar system belongs to which planet?

9. Who voices Hades in Disney's *Hercules*? 💡

10. Which city hosted the 2014 Winter Olympic Games?

11. Roughly what percentage of Afghanistan lies higher than 6,500 feet above sea level?

12. Who discovered Vinland in around 1000AD, an area in North America?

13. What year did the Panama Canal open for shipping traffic?

14. Which of Edvard Munch's paintings is sometimes known as 'The Cry'?

15. In which desert was there once no rain for 10 years: Desla, Sahara or Sonoran?

16. The line, *If you build it, he will come*, is from which film?

The Bumper Family Quiz Book
Quiz 13

1. Corbin Bernsen made his directorial debut with what film?

2. In cooking, what does 'etoufee' mean?

3. What 2008 US law aimed to limit harmful emissions from sea-going vessels?

4. If a letter is 'SWAK', what is it?

5. From what language do we get the food term *hors d'oeuvre*? 💡

6. Which prayer-ending word comes from the Hebrew for 'so be it'?

7. Rio's 'Carnival' takes place at the same time as what US event?

8. What animal lives in a sett?

9. What type of picture did Thomas Gainsborough mostly paint?

10. Which is the only country whose name ends in the letter 'k'? 💡

11. Which African country's highest elevation point is Bikku Bitti?

12. What happens to air pressure as you increase your altitude?

13. Which country is an East Asian island nation: Libya, Suriname, Taiwan or Uruguay?

14. Who succeeded Oliver Cromwell as Lord Protector in 1658?

15. Luxury vehicles such as Ferrari, Maserati, and Lamborghini are manufactured in what country?

16. What is the tennis term for 'zero points'?

The Bumper Family Quiz Book
Quiz 14

1. What 2013 film starred Henry Cavill as Clark Kent?

2. On which continent is Oman located?

3. In text chat, what does IRL mean?

4. Which of these words means 'ornamental glass': mille-feuille, millefiori or millefleur?

5. Which of the following is not an operetta by Gilbert and Sullivan: Bolero, Iolanthe or The Mikado?

6. Which part of the human eye is stored in an 'eye bank'?

7. What is the incubation period for measles?

8. What does a 'dipsomaniac' suffer from?

9. What do you call a corner where three or more edges meet in a solid figure?

10. Colombia is part of which region, notorious for its volcanoes and earthquakes?

11. When was the LPGA Tour Hall of Fame established?

12. Who is the Roman god of the sea?

13. In what year did Edward V ascend the English throne, at the age of 12?

14. Which British supermodel was born on January 16, 1974?

15. What three colours are on the flag of the Netherlands?

16. What ferry sank in the Baltic Sea in 1994?

The Bumper Family Quiz Book
Quiz 15

1. Which Nordic country formerly ruled Iceland?

2. What is the name of the lion in *The Lion, The Witch and the Wardrobe*?

3. The spice 'mace' is derived from the shell of what other spice?

4. Who was US President immediately prior to George W. Bush?

5. Which element has the chemical symbol O?

6. Which film won the Best Picture Oscar for 2007?

7. What was the name of Russia's Military Academy in World War 2?

8. What colour is the middle stripe on the Latvian flag?

9. Finish this song line in Disney's *Aladdin*: 'I steal only...'?

10. The 83-floor Aon Centre, at 346m (1136ft) tall, is found in which US city?

11. Which is the second largest city in the UK, by population?

12. Which ocean liner sank on her maiden voyage in 1912?

13. In biology, what is an 'imago'?

14. What would you call an animal with hair that feeds milk to its babies?

15. Who wrote the sci-fi book *The Uplift War*?

16. How many times did Lloyd Honeyghan lose his world boxing title before retiring?

The Bumper Family Quiz Book
Quiz 16

1. Who is the patron saint of carpenters?

2. If it looks like a lemon, but is green, it's probably what?

3. Which Australian mammal swallows large amounts of soil with its food?

4. Who was China's first emperor?

5. What Portuguese province did Prince Henry the Navigator govern?

6. Druk Air is the flag-carrier airline of which country?

7. What geometric shape has seven sides?

8. Who won the European Nations Cup in 1968?

9. Part of the Impressionist movement, Claude Monet focused on the changes in which natural element?

10. What is the only insect with four equally sized wings?

11. In the film *The Doors*, who played Pam, Jim's girlfriend?

12. Which electronic duo released the Middle Eastern-flavoured hit 'Living on the Ceiling'?

13. Where is the wettest area of the world?

14. Why should you never eat polar bear liver?

15. What year was the United Nations founded?

16. Who wrote *Suite Française*?

The Bumper Family Quiz Book
Quiz 17

1 What type of video game is 'Pong'?

2 Perfume distillation is a major industry in what country: Afghanistan, Comoros, Indonesia or Niger?

3 What yoga posture is named the Sethu Bandhasa?

4 A poultry farmer raises which animals?

5 What is foie gras?

6 What does the word 'Koran' mean, literally?

7 In UNIX, what is the /etc directory used for?

8 What US talk show host played themselves in *The Long Kiss Goodnight*?

9 What is a 'baguette'?

10 In which country was Adam Scott born?

11 What number comes next in the pattern: 3, 6, 9?

12 If you 'ideate', what do you do?

13 Who collected the first major statistics for wind and ocean currents?

14 Gulf Air is the flag-carrier airline of which country?

15 What good-luck symbols were sewn into Princess Diana's wedding dress?

16 Which one of these is not an external territory of Australia: Lord Howe Island or Norfolk Island?

The Bumper Family Quiz Book
Quiz 18

1. What, in printing, is a 'pica'?

2. What ocean does the River Congo discharge into?

3. What are the ladies doing in the song *The Twelve Days of Christmas*?

4. What were the main ingredients in the UK Ministry of Food's 'mock marzipan' recipe?

5. What is the boundary between two air masses called?

6. What is the most populous city in Canada?

7. Which of the following is an oven used to fire pottery or ceramics: clone, kiln, kilt or kite?

8. What vehicle is famously recreated on stage in the musical *Miss Saigon*?

9. Mount Karthala is an active volcano in what African island nation?

10. In what year did *One Flew Over the Cuckoo's Nest* win the Academy Award for Best Picture?

11. Gorditas are included in which cuisine?

12. What is a 'roister'?

13. What was Salvador Dali's wife's name?

14. On which Spanish island did Rafael Nadal win his first tennis title?

15. Who recruited sailors for *Legio I Adiutrix*, the 'helper' legion, in 66 AD?

16. Which of these is not a part of the process of investigation via the scientific method: hypotenuse, hypothesis or theory?

The Bumper Family Quiz Book
Quiz 19

1. In which year did the Great Fire of London occur?

2. Which band launched a 2011 tour to support the album *The Whole Love*?

3. What was Disney's fifth animated feature, about a deer?

4. Which wild cat was often kept as a pet by the forest Indians of South America?

5. Who was the Russian city of St. Petersburg founded by?

6. Which powerful magical artefact is destroyed by Harry Potter at the end of *The Deathly Hallows*?

7. Which future Formula One driver earned the Star of Tomorrow title in the 1989 British Formula Ford series?

8. Which infamous Nazi commanded the 'Death Squadron'?

9. Joan Miro's brightly coloured paintings often filled shapes with what: patterns or objects?

10. What is the official language of Argentina?

11. Who wrote *The Portrait of a Lady*?

12. How many sides does a dodecahedron have?

13. Which mammal is renowned for its ability to fight snakes?

14. Which is not an island in the Bahamas: Andros, Cat, Crooked or Palm?

15. What is the largest mangrove forest in the world, located in India, called?

16. What three colours are on the flag of Ireland?

The Bumper *Family* Quiz Book
Quiz 20

① What kind of tree does an acorn come from?

② What desert-ready animal is a main product of Iraqi agriculture?

③ In the board game *Cluedo*, what is the blue piece called? 💡

④ Which film won the Best Picture Oscar for 2009?

⑤ What is the name of the cup that New Zealand and Australia play for in rugby?

⑥ Where is Australia's Scotland Island located?

⑦ Who wrote the book *Simple Abundance*?

⑧ In text chat, what does NP mean? 💡

⑨ How many stomachs does a llama have?

⑩ In geography, what is 'esparto'?

⑪ The statues Michelangelo made for Lorenzo de Medici's tomb are 'Dawn', 'Evening', 'Day' and what?

⑫ What gas do plants take in that humans give off when they breathe?

⑬ 'The boy looked at' who in a song title by The Libertines?

⑭ Which country has Kuala Lumpur as its capital city?

⑮ What type of vegetable is the US state of Idaho famous for producing?

⑯ In the court of Louis XIV, what was prestige measured by?

The Bumper Family Quiz Book
Quiz 21

1. Many who knew Raphael referred to him as 'The Prince of' what?

2. In what film did Gary Busey play Ty Moncrief?

3. Who kills the title character in Shakespeare's *Macbeth*?

4. Which artist is featured on the 2014 release of Michael Jackson's song *Love Never Felt So Good*?

5. If you drove from Melbourne to Adelaide along the coast, what scenic Australian road would you travel on?

6. In which country are you likely to hear the cheer or toast 'Opa!' during a celebration?

7. What would you call 'by way of the intestines' in a medical context?

8. A 'pride' is a group of which animals?

9. Challah bread is typically associated with which religion?

10. What year did the first man go into orbit?

11. In World War 2, what island did Great Britain designate 'Island X'?

12. What Egyptian ruler sided with Mark Antony at the Battle of Actium?

13. What vegetable is also called bhindi or gumbo?

14. Where did Maria Sharapova train to be a tennis pro?

15. What breed is the smallest 'working' terrier: Australian Terrier, Norfolk Terrier or Yorkshire Terrier?

16. In heraldry, what do you call a hunting dog?

The Bumper Family Quiz Book
Quiz 22

1. What was the first product ever released by Sony?

2. In what year did the last Space Shuttle launch?

3. Which David Bowie song has the lyrics 'pace their rooms like a cell's dimensions'?

4. What is the name for a group of foxes? 💡

5. Tripoli is the capital of which northern African country?

6. Which oranges have a button-like opening on one end?

7. Which river's water is controlled by the Aswan Dam?

8. Carl Sandburg is generally known for being what?

9. Which breed of dog was bred for chasing rats?

10. In text chat, what does ATM mean? 💡

11. In *The Shawshank Redemption*, what is Red's cell number?

12. Boxer Joel Casamayor turned pro in 1992 shortly after achieving what?

13. The Japanese word for 'planted in a tray' describes what type of tree?

14. How long did it take to construct the Cathedral of Notre Dame?

15. Peru, the third largest country in South America, has which capital city?

16. Which woman was runner-up in the 2014 Australian Open singles championship?

The Bumper Family Quiz Book
Quiz 23

1. Which heavyweight boxing champion held the title for a record 11 years 8 months?

2. How many inches are there in one foot?

3. Which of these bodies of water would it be easiest to float in: lake, sea or swimming pool?

4. The film *Hellraiser* was directed by whom?

5. Based on Kepler's first law, the path of a planet is defined as what shape?

6. Who wrote the novels about James Bond?

7. Which company introduced the first hard drive?

8. What do we call a baby duck?

9. How many children does Queen Elizabeth II have?

10. Which fruit is called 'hala kahiki' in Hawaiian and has been grown in Hawaii since the early 1800s?

11. In Buddhism, what is 'satori'?

12. As of 2014, how many MOBO Awards has Leona Lewis won?

13. What is the capital of Mongolia?

14. Which British overseas territory has George Town as its capital city?

15. Who became leader of Germany after the death of Adolf Hitler, by his order?

16. What ingredients are in the garnish called gremolata?

The Bumper Family Quiz Book
Quiz 24

① Which author wrote *Robinson Crusoe*?

② Removal of signs of facial ageing is commonly known as what?

③ The kuna is a currency in what nation?

④ In what year did Graham Norton take over commentating the Eurovision Song Contest?

⑤ If a two-dimensional shape is 'regular', what does this mean?

⑥ Who played Derek Smalls in *This Is Spinal Tap*?

⑦ Who painted 'The Last Supper' in 1497?

⑧ What country forms a 2000-mile archipelago along the east coast of Asia?

⑨ How long is a decade?

⑩ What did scientists in Geneva create for the first time in 1995?

⑪ What is the largest country in the Caribbean?

⑫ Which 2001 hit single by Moby featured Gwen Stefani on vocals?

⑬ What is the smallest country by size in South America?

⑭ Which branch of yoga advocates the path of action?

⑮ What are the colours of the Turkish national soccer team?

⑯ Colombia has the second largest Spanish-speaking population in the world behind which country?

The Bumper *Family* Quiz Book
Quiz 25

1. What does 'MSN' stand for in the URL http://www.msn.com/?

2. What is the national flower of France?

3. How many keys with numbers on them are found on a typical telephone keypad? 💡

4. The islands of Inishmore, Inishmaan and Inishere lie off the coast of which European country?

5. In the film *Sixteen Candles*, who plays Farmer Ted?

6. As an artist, who did Pablo Picasso say it was most dangerous to copy?

7. In which year was William IV crowned King of the United Kingdom?

8. Which film features Clint Eastwood, Hilary Swank and Morgan Freeman?

9. How many holes are there in a ten pin bowling ball? 💡

10. What do you call a system of naming things?

11. El Salvador is considered to be part of which continent?

12. Which international politician officially opened the 1984 Summer Olympics?

13. Which philosopher wrote *Nausea*?

14. What is the minimum threshold for the depth of a 'deepwater' operation?

15. Who was the first Australian astronaut to successfully conclude a space walk?

16. 'Parfum' is the French word for what scented cosmetic?

The Bumper *Family* Quiz Book
Quiz 26

1) What is a 'sai'?

2) Which Italian company took control of Acorn Computers in 1985?

3) What is a 'sporran'? 💡

4) What were the 'Pickelhaube' in World War 1?

5) Eucalyptus oil is used most often to relieve which condition?

6) What type of dish is a chowder?

7) What Saki story is named after a talking cat?

8) Which strait in the Caribbean Sea separates Cuba and Haiti?

9) Who voices C-3PO in *The Lego Movie*? 💡

10) The airport code EWR designates which international airport?

11) What are the werewolf-like creatures in *Underworld Evolution* called?

12) Chiang Kai-shek led which country?

13) How is the constellation *Aquarius* known in English?

14) What animal did Ancient Egyptians worship as the daughter of the sun god?

15) What was the name of the 1978 World Cup mascot?

16) What U2 song was the first to chart in the US?

Quiz 27

1. Which Spanish King launched the Spanish Armada against England in 1588?

2. In what year did France become the fourth nuclear power?

3. Who is Cinderella's helpful friend in traditional pantomime? 💡

4. What was Michael Jackson's first multi-platinum solo album?

5. In *Doctor Who*, the 10th Doctor grants the Family of Blood what wish?

6. Which natural landmark acts as a divider between Bolivia's geographic zones?

7. What are 'colossi'?

8. What does a konimeter measure?

9. What is the chemical symbol for sulphur?

10. Aesop's fable about a slow-mover beating a faster creature is called what? 💡

11. How many stars are there on the flag of New Zealand?

12. Who became President and Chief Operating Officer of Viacom in 2010?

13. Loyalty to which clothing sponsor caused Kim Clijsters to miss tennis matches in 2003?

14. Crown caps for bottles were first made from what?

15. In *The Deathly Hallows* the character Griphook is a member of what magical species?

16. Who is the Greek god of hunting and animals?

The Bumper *Family* Quiz Book
Quiz 28

1. What year was the North American Free Trade Agreement signed?

2. What English patriotic song was used as the English victory anthem at the Commonwealth Games prior to 2010?

3. What country did Iraq invade in 1990, based on claims of disputed oil?

4. What colour flag, when shown to a Formula One driver, means to let the faster car overtake?

5. In the board game *Cluedo*, what is the red piece called?

6. In which modern-day country would you find the ancient city of Carthage?

7. What is *stilchester*?

8. A line of equal or constant air temperature is called what?

9. Where in the body can you find a 'utriculus'?

10. British currency shares its name with what unit of weight?

11. What type of drug promotes blood clotting?

12. What was the name of the first Britney Spears-branded perfume?

13. What item of clothing is an 'obi'?

14. When did the International Geophysical Year occur?

15. What is the flowering plant, 'khat', used for in the Arabian peninsula?

16. *Rocky* films featured the song *Eye of the* what?

The Bumper *Family* Quiz Book
Quiz 29

1. In what century did the Impressionistic movement in art take place?

2. What is the term for the top limit of an interest rate?

3. Which world river discharges the most water?

4. What was the world's first RISC-based home computer?

5. At what temperature on the Celsius scale does water freeze? 💡

6. In golf, what is a 'bogie'?

7. Who played the voice of Shrek in the film *Shrek*?

8. Who was Mike Tyson's first professional opponent?

9. In literary terms, what does 'subfusc' mean?

10. What metal object would you traditionally hide in a Christmas pudding? 💡

11. In Russian history, who are the Tatars?

12. What tube carries urine from the kidney to the urinary bladder?

13. Nelson Mandela apologized for neglecting what medical crisis during his presidency?

14. In the book *Lisey's Story*, written by Stephen King, what was Scott Landon's profession?

15. Of these Asian countries, which has access to the sea: Afghanistan, Bangladesh, Laos or Tajikistan?

16. How many hours behind London is New York City?

The Bumper Family Quiz Book
Quiz 30

1. What is the capital of the Canadian territory Nunavut?

2. Which of the following types of Italian pasta is hollow: linguine, penne or vermicelli?

3. Who was the first man to walk on the moon?

4. If something is 'agleam', what is it?

5. What type of animal is a guppy?

6. Which British rower won gold medals at five consecutive Olympic games from 1984 to 2000?

7. Who was the voice of Iago the Parrot in Disney's *Aladdin*?

8. In *101 Dalmatians*, what duo tried to capture the puppies?

9. Who succeeded John Major as UK Prime Minister?

10. In which year was the Turkish Super Lig soccer league founded?

11. In what year did Christina Aguilera first have a top 20 album in the UK?

12. Which Tokyo hotel was designed by American architect Frank Lloyd Wright?

13. In the *Odyssey*, how does Odysseus escape the storm created by Poseidon?

14. What country became the 150th member of the World Trade Organization in 2007?

15. What city is the capital of Papua New Guinea?

16. What colours are Boston terriers?

The Bumper Family Quiz Book
Quiz 31

1. How do wasps hold on to stems while sleeping?

2. In 1953, Communists ordered the deportation of 200,000 unproductive persons from what Romanian city?

3. What is edible as a young shoot but is better food for pandas when it's larger? 💡

4. Mary I ascended the English throne in which year?

5. Which display connector is electrically compatible with HDMI: Coaxial, DVI or RCA?

6. What shape is a bacterium if it is a cocci?

7. What do you call the extra amount added onto an item's price by the government?

8. Who won the Pichichi Trophy for being the top scorer in the 2013-14 season of the Spanish La Liga?

9. Approximately how many paintings did Vincent van Gogh create?

10. What seafaring warriors raided Europe during the 8th-11th centuries? 💡

11. Which French island has Saint-Denis as its capital?

12. In music, what does 'con brio' mean?

13. In *The Great Gatsby*, what sport does Jordan play?

14. Which country has Apia as its capital city?

15. What was the name of the microcomputer kit offered by MITS in 1975?

16. A mezzo-soprano range is between the soprano and which other range?

The Bumper *Family* Quiz Book
Quiz 32

1. Which painter did Gertrude Stein make a portrait of?

2. What would a doctor usually do to look at your bones? 💡

3. What kind of medical condition continues for a long time?

4. What might an English speaker call the people the French refer to as 'mere' and 'pere'?

5. Budapest is the capital of which country?

6. What country uses the gourde as its currency?

7. In Ancient Greece, what was an 'obol'?

8. What does the Tin Man wish that he had in *The Wizard of Oz*? 💡

9. What is the name of the central conflict in *Starship Troopers*?

10. *The Comforts Of Madness* was the 1990 debut LP for which short-lived British pop act?

11. Who was the first American to go into space, in 1961?

12. What type of reproduction uses only one parent cell?

13. What is the only nation that has participated in every World Cup finals tournament?

14. What nautical fleet did Spain send to attack Britain in 1588? 💡

15. For which film did Colin Firth win an Academy Award?

16. Which Byzantine emperor outlawed the worship of icons?

The Bumper Family Quiz Book
Quiz 33

1. On her maiden voyage, which British city did *Titanic* depart from?

2. 'Creme de Abacate' is a Brazilian dessert made from which green fruit?

3. On average, how long does a butterfly live?

4. How many feet off the ground do vampire bats generally fly?

5. Which two chemical elements make up water? 💡

6. Which London lawyer produced the first multi-shot gun?

7. *Mystic River* stars Sean Penn along with which *Ladder 49* actor?

8. Which emperor was the child of Agrippina?

9. What does 'hoar' mean, when used as an adjective?

10. Which Disney villain sings *Kill The Beast*? 💡

11. Which city has suburbs named Nunawading, Murrumbeena, Mordialloc and Brunswick?

12. Where does Emily Brontë fit in among the Brontë sisters, in terms of age?

13. A picture of what is featured on the cover of Buckcherry's *15* album?

14. Ronaldo is a Goodwill Ambassador for the UN, fighting for which global concern?

15. What must a meteor do in order to become a meteorite?

16. La Gioconda is an alternative name for which painting?

The Bumper Family Quiz Book
Quiz 34

① What is pesto?

② As of 2014, Coldplay have won how many Grammy Awards?

③ Who during the Wars of the Roses, was known as the 'King-maker'?

④ How many Academy Awards did Walt Disney personally win?

⑤ Which vegetable produces bright purple juice when cut?

⑥ Which is generally true about persons with Type 1 diabetes?

⑦ The dram is a currency for which of the following nations: Armenia, Iraq or Uzbekistan?

⑧ In the *Little Miss* books, what colour is Little Miss Sunshine?

⑨ How many seasons of *The West Wing* were produced?

⑩ Kodak introduced the Brownie roll-film camera in what turn-of-the-century year?

⑪ In what year did Harold II become King of England?

⑫ What royal collection is housed in St James's Palace: butterflies, bibles, stamps or gowns?

⑬ What was Robert Plant's debut 1982 solo album entitled?

⑭ Which club did Graeme Souness leave Liverpool to become manager of in 1995?

⑮ Who wrote *Scoop*?

⑯ Which scientific term means 'curved inwards'?

The Bumper Family Quiz Book
Quiz 35

1. What is the name given to a special French wedding cake, made of profiteroles?

2. What are the claws of a bird of prey called?

3. What is a region of Earth in which all areas share the same time called?

4. Which of these objects did Claude Monet not paint a famous series of: children, cathedrals, haystacks or water lilies?

5. What English monarch was deposed in December 1688?

6. If you referred to someone as 'unco' in Scotland, what would it mean?

7. Which Disney attraction, later a film series, was originally envisaged as a wax museum?

8. In what century was the first English Poet Laureate appointed?

9. In which country were Fabergé Eggs made?

10. What kind of little red car did Prince sing about in the 1980s?

11. In music, what do you call the horizontal lines on which notes are written?

12. What is the proper name for a 'sundog', an atmospheric optical phenomenon?

13. Which birds are left in the care of Jim Carrey in a 2011 family comedy?

14. What type of cloud is fog?

15. Which Formula One driver was the only World Champion on both two and four wheels?

16. The majority of immigrants to Australia in recent years have come from which country?

The Bumper Family Quiz Book
Quiz 36

1. Which mythological Greek's face 'launched a thousand ships'?

2. What is guacamole made from?

3. In text chat, what does IDK mean?

4. What electronic device only allows current to flow in one direction?

5. Which of the following is an example of a biometric device: fingerprint scanner, thumbdrive or wireless mouse?

6. The 1953 book, *The Adventures of Augie March*, was written by?

7. In legal terms, what do you do if you 'estop'?

8. What company manufactures Oil of Olay products?

9. What ocean is on the eastern border of Canada?

10. What does the Scarecrow wish that he had in *The Wizard of Oz*?

11. What part of the body do salamanders use for hearing?

12. Who was Henry VIII's second wife?

13. Alberto Fujimori was the President of which country from 1990-2000?

14. What was Nirvana's first album?

15. What team didn't want to play in the Merconorte Cup due to security concerns?

16. In what year was the film *Atlantic City* released?

The Bumper Family Quiz Book
Quiz 37

1. Which type of dance resembles a fast foxtrot: hula, peabody or swing?

2. Brunei is a wealthy nation due to what natural resource?

3. Burkina Faso won its independence in what year?

4. Which bank do Sophie and Robert go to in *The Da Vinci Code*?

5. What was Disney's fourth animated feature, about an elephant?

6. Which two letters are used to indicate years that occurred before the birth of Jesus?

7. What was the first concentration camp to be liberated by US troops in World War 2?

8. What type of picture does an artist make using a pencil: Collage, Drawing, Painting or Photograph?

9. Which volcano in Iceland was once thought to be a gateway to the underworld?

10. What is the federal weather agency in Canada called?

11. What is the name of the largest aquarium in North-West England?

12. Which children's character reached number one in the UK Singles Chart with *Can We Fix It*?

13. What is an 'ulu'?

14. What is the most common form of Chinese spoken in the south of China, in Hong Kong and in Macau?

15. Great Britain won the gold medal in hockey at which Winter Olympics?

16. What are 'dowds'?

The Bumper Family Quiz Book
Quiz 38

1. Which African country's highest point is Tahat?

2. Who wrote *Midnight's Children*?

3. In the *Harry Potter* universe, what is the term for a non-magical person?

4. What is a baby turkey called?

5. What is Tiger Woods' real name?

6. Through what process did many nations spread their cultures to new countries?

7. What are the two official languages of Chad?

8. A group of lions is called a what?

9. Who plays Casey Carlyle in the *Ice Princess*?

10. What kind of animal is a klipspringer?

11. Which English monarch was born in June 1566?

12. Which company is responsible for the CPU core used in the Apple iPhone?

13. In what year were the words 'Under God' added to the US Pledge of Allegiance?

14. In 1948, what did Henri Matisse design for the St. Dominique Church?

15. Which bone in the arm is the longest?

16. What is a Sudoku puzzle with alternatively shaped regions often called?

The Bumper Family Quiz Book
Quiz 39

1. Prime Minister Kim Campbell was the nineteenth Prime Minister of what country?

2. In 1990, fax machines became commercially available that could transmit what?

3. Who painted 'The Scream'?

4. Which Disney animated feature centres on arcade game characters? 💡

5. What is the name of the 1994 short film made by the musical group Portishead?

6. Where are 75% of the world's pineapples grown?

7. Which capital city is furthest south?

8. What gas that you breathe, necessary for life, is also dissolved in sea water? 💡

9. In heraldry, what do you call a seated animal?

10. What consecutive letters were Will Smith and Tommy Lee Jones' characters named after in *Men In Black*?

11. Who voices the satyr, Philoctetes, in Disney's *Hercules*?

12. Which Brontë sister wrote *Jane Eyre*?

13. Which country hosted the FIFA World Cup in 2014?

14. What country became the leading coffee supplier in the mid-19th century?

15. Pope Francis was elected Pope on which day of the 2013 papal conclave?

16. Which element has the chemical symbol Li?

The Bumper Family Quiz Book
Quiz 40

① In which year did tennis player Nikolay Davydenko turn professional?

② What year did the Treaty of Ghent end the War of 1812?

③ Which of these cities is not in Europe: Berlin, Helsinki, Sydney or Warsaw?

④ Which of the following is a small organism that can make your body sick: bacterium or melanin?

⑤ What is the definition of the word 'buck'?

⑥ What word was written on the Sydney Harbour Bridge during the fireworks to celebrate the year 2000?

⑦ What was the name of the prince in Disney's *The Little Mermaid*?

⑧ In which 2001 film did Peter Boyle play the character Buck Grotowski?

⑨ Indonesia is considered to be part of which continent?

⑩ When was the first Crufts Dog Show held?

⑪ What does a lion-fish keep in its spiny fins to deter predators?

⑫ Edgar Degas made over 700 copies of what?

⑬ In which American television series did British theatre actress Fiona Shaw appear in 2011?

⑭ In what year was Selfridge & Co. founded?

⑮ What is the capital of Bermuda?

⑯ Who was Ian Walmsley's wife on the show *Footballers' Wives*?

Quiz 41

1. Who won the first British Touring Car Championship in 1958?

2. The term 'polecat' is a misnomer because the polecat is really what?

3. Which side of a boat is starboard, when facing forward?

4. What is the most northern place on Earth? 💡

5. What kind of bird plays Paulie in the film *Paulie*?

6. What does 'agglutinate' mean?

7. What colour Formula One flag warns of a slow car? 💡

8. Reykjavik, Akureyri and Keflavik are cities in what remote island country?

9. A radio broadcast of which book caused hysteria on October 30th, 1938 in the eastern US?

10. In 2007, which Rage Against the Machine song took the Christmas number one slot in the UK Singles Chart?

11. Which country has Paramaribo as its capital?

12. Isadora Duncan is known best as what?

13. After the decline of the Maya, which people controlled northern Mexico?

14. What does a cubra libra have that a rum and coke does not?

15. People who move from one country into another are called what?

16. When were the first world climate maps charted: 1835, 1853, 1869 or 1875?

The Bumper Family Quiz Book
Quiz 42

1. Which city, located at the foot of the snowy Elburz Mountains, is the capital of Iran?

2. What is the fourth book in the *Harry Potter* series called? 💡

3. Who plays Jon Snow in *Game of Thrones*?

4. What contain almost 97% of the world's water?

5. Who is the Patron Saint of Scotland?

6. What yearly event helped provide arable land in Egypt?

7. Which Scottish player joined the English Football Hall of Fame in 2014?

8. Which number was the title of Adele's debut full-length album? 💡

9. What type of cat is referred to as a Foreign White?

10. In what film did Dana Carvey play Garth Algar?

11. Moosehead Breweries are found in what country?

12. To be called a *troglodyte* is to be called what?

13. According to a 2002 David Holmes song title, 'This Could Be Your' what?

14. What is the word to describe the height above sea level of a geographic point?

15. How many classes are there in the Hierarchy of the Order of the Knights of Malta?

16. In which Marilyn Monroe film is the iconic white dress subway scene?

The Bumper Family Quiz Book
Quiz 43

1. Which social group in ancient Sparta was lowest in status?

2. Which vehicle follows *Rock & Roll* in the title of a 2011 Urge Overkill album?

3. Who discovered the smallpox vaccine?

4. In what year did William the Conqueror invade England from Brittany? 💡

5. What was the name of Nala's mother in the film *The Lion King*?

6. Brine pools in the ocean have an unusually high level of what?

7. Where does Sherlock Holmes live?

8. Which is the largest US city on the Canadian border?

9. Who voices Batman in *The Lego Movie*? 💡

10. Who plays Dr John 'J.D.' Dorian in *Scrubs*?

11. Which of these methods would work best to cook a very tough cut of meat: braising, sautéing or tempura?

12. What is the most common program used to read PDF files?

13. What landmark is known to natives as 'Uluru'?

14. Who patented the electric tattoo machine?

15. What country did Czar Nicholas lead?

16. How many games were played in the course of the 1994 World Cup?

The Bumper Family Quiz Book
Quiz 44

1. In which film did singer, Jewel, make her acting debut?

2. How many colours of ball are used in snooker?

3. In 2004, what did the French National Assembly ban in schools?

4. In the *Mr Men* books, what colour is Mr Tickle?

5. Where does the name of the region of Johannesburg called Soweto come from?

6. In what European country did President Reagan meet Mikhail Gorbachev for a summit meeting in 1986?

7. Who wrote *Cold Comfort Farm*?

8. Which European country's name begins with the letter D?

9. Whose body does Christoffer go to Prague to retrieve in Ole Christian Madsen's 2006 film *Prague*?

10. What currency was used in the Netherlands before the adoption of the euro?

11. How many moons does Mars have?

12. What animals were worshipped like gods by Egyptians?

13. Which of the following is not a metric measurement: centimetre, kilogram, pound, litre?

14. In medicine, what does the adjective 'orbital' mean?

15. What is Italian mascarpone cheese made with?

16. What type of root does a carrot have?

The Bumper Family Quiz Book
Quiz 45

1. What does the acronym 'HTTP' stand for?

2. Easter Island is an island in what ocean?

3. What is the length of the Suez Canal?

4. What is the national flower of Egypt?

5. Where will you find the British Crown Jewels?

6. Who wrote the 1924 novel *A Passage to India*?

7. A screwdriver becomes a fuzzy screw when what is added?

8. Green is created by blending what two paint colours?

9. In Disney's *Pinocchio* what was the name of Geppetto's fish?

10. Which American actor is featured in the music video for Dido's *White Flag*?

11. Rene Lacoste founded what sportswear label?

12. The 2010 Ryder Cup was held in which country of the United Kingdom?

13. What is the capital of Croatia?

14. What do you traditionally give for a thirtieth anniversary?

15. What year was Mandela first convicted with 19 others for his role in the Defiance Campaign?

16. What feature was added to London's City Hall in 2007, to make the building more energy efficient?

The Bumper Family Quiz Book
Quiz 46

① Which company invented the frappuccino?

② Who won Chelsea 'player of the year' for both 2012 and 2013?

③ Which prequel to the *X-Men* trilogy was released in 2011?

④ What is New Year's Eve called in Germany?

⑤ Echolocation is used for navigation by what flying animal?

⑥ *Life In A Day* was the debut album by which Scottish band led by Jim Kerr?

⑦ American Airlines merged with which airline in 2013, making it the world's largest?

⑧ What is the practice of supplying arable land with external water called?

⑨ Which element has the atomic number 12?

⑩ The Azores belong to which country?

⑪ What year did Emperor Wilhelm I of Germany die?

⑫ *Be Cool* is a sequel to which film?

⑬ On the Internet, what does a 'domain name server' do?

⑭ What type of weather event is a 'sirocco'?

⑮ When is the holiday Cinco de Mayo held?

⑯ Who was the author of *Under the Net*?

The Bumper *Family* Quiz Book
Quiz 47

1. What is the slang term for a photo taken of yourself, by yourself?

2. If I had a 'mote' in my eye, what would that be?

3. John Langdon-Down, who first identified Down's Syndrome, was a physician from which country?

4. Which country won the 1990 World Cup in Rome?

5. Spaghetti is a variety of what food type? 💡

6. What city did Constantine choose for a new imperial city?

7. Who wrote Nelly Furtado's *I'm Like a Bird*?

8. The ancient Phoenician city of Constantine is located in what modern-day Arab country?

9. You can find the US Yankee Stadium in which state?

10. What 2014 film is about a toy thought to be 'The Special'? 💡

11. What is the capital city of Georgia?

12. Which Tudor monarch ruled from 1509 to 1547?

13. What is the largest crocodile in the world?

14. The medical term 'prognosis' is best defined as what?

15. Which New York Art Deco building is home to the Rockettes?

16. What was the name of the ape in *George of the Jungle*?

The Bumper Family Quiz Book
Quiz 48

1. Which city hosted the 1988 Olympic Games?

2. Which island is not part of the Greater Antilles: Jamaica, Puerto Rico or Trinidad?

3. In Greek Mythology, who was Oedipus' mother?

4. In text chat, what does BRB mean?

5. What are the broken-off pieces of glaciers that make it to the open sea called?

6. In what year was Cilla Black born?

7. What is the name of Google's online-only notebooks?

8. What is one of ten equal parts: a half, a quarter, a tenth or a twentieth?

9. Who succeeded Vitellius as Roman Emperor in the Year of the Four Emperors?

10. What are triglycerides?

11. Which Northern European country's point of highest elevation is Haltiatunturi?

12. What is the modern name of the country once known as Basutoland?

13. What film earned River Phoenix an Academy Award nomination?

14. Who was William Shakespeare married to?

15. Which diet fad limits a person to eating only foods produced within a certain radius?

16. The British Museum houses which of these famous artefacts: Hope Diamond, Mona Lisa or Rosetta Stone?

Quiz 49

1. Which of these was a hit song from Portishead's debut album: *Sad Times*, *Sour Times* or *Sweet Times*?

2. Cranachan and bannock are foods associated with which country?

3. In World War 2, what country invaded East Timor on December 16, 1941?

4. In which country was the Berlin Wall located?

5. Who is the Roman version of Aphrodite?

6. In which year did Ernie Els win the US Open?

7. Which solid figure has the shape of a round ball?

8. What Spanish Cubist painter and sculptor lived from 1881-1973?

9. What obscure term is used for otter dung?

10. How many times in the twentieth century did Lake Eyre, Australia, have significant amounts of water in it?

11. What part of the plant gets water and nutrients to the rest of the plant?

12. Which film is the character Batgirl from?

13. How many hours behind London is Los Angeles?

14. Where in Africa might you find an 'oba'?

15. The US invaded Afghanistan in 2001 to topple what political movement?

16. Anorexia is to eating disorder as lymphoma is to what?

The Bumper Family Quiz Book
Quiz 50

1. Who was the first astronaut to go into orbit?

2. The value of a company's employees is sometimes referred to as what?

3. In what year did Microsoft ship the first *Windows*?

4. What toppings are used on a Hawaiian pizza? 💡

5. How long was Poland able to resist German forces during World War 2?

6. Who discovered that a moving magnet generates electric current in wires?

7. Which city hosted the 2006 Winter Olympic Games?

8. What sort of vehicle is a 'tumbril'?

9. How many books are there in the *Harry Potter* series? 💡

10. What type of food is 'halva'?

11. In what country would you most likely be if paying for something with an afghani?

12. In which city is the Peace Tower, part of the Canadian Parliament Buildings?

13. How many 20th-century British Prime Ministers fathered legitimate children while in office?

14. *Prince Caspian* followed which *Chronicles of Narnia* book? 💡

15. What was the title of the first album that PJ Harvey released?

16. In *Pulp Fiction*, what was the name of Jimmy's wife?

The Bumper Family Quiz Book
Quiz 51

1. Garrincha, Pele and Vava were the stars of which 1962 World Cup team?

2. In geography, what is an 'arroyo'?

3. What year was Alan Greenspan first nominated as US Federal Reserve chairman: 1955, 1968, 1987 or 1992?

4. Who is the Patron Saint of Ireland?

5. What is the name of the Good Witch in *Wicked*?

6. What kind of competition did Guy Pearce win as a teenager?

7. What were the 'new breed' of young women who wore short skirts and bobbed hair called?

8. How many noses does a slug have?

9. Which of these terms best describes Brazil within South America: driest country or largest country?

10. What colour is Angel food cake?

11. Comoros won its independence in what year in the 1970s?

12. Renaissance artist Raphael's first painting teacher was what relation?

13. The narrowest part of the English Channel (The Strait of Dover) is how wide?

14. How many structural isomers does propane have?

15. Canberra is the capital of which country?

16. What are the main two elements that undergo fusion to power the sun?

The Bumper Family Quiz Book
Quiz 52

1. Which is the only major city in Australia that has trams running on its streets?

2. What was the name of the first probe to escape Earth's gravity?

3. Which is not a primary colour: blue, orange, red or yellow?

4. Which explorer first mapped the eastern coast of Australia?

5. Who was the first Angevin monarch to rule on the English throne?

6. Who killed Ash by throwing him off a balcony in the 2014 film *Dawn of the Planet of the Apes*?

7. In what year did Robbie Fowler make his international debut versus Bulgaria?

8. Although sand can comprise any particle, the majority of it consists of what?

9. How many siblings does Peter Rabbit have?

10. What does a Spanish 'floristeria' sell?

11. Into which body of water does the Yukon River discharge?

12. Salvador Dali believed that which feeling set creativity free?

13. What is a 'proem'?

14. What is 'mulct' a formal term for?

15. What, technically, does vitamin D do for your body?

16. What U2 song asks 'Have you come to raise the dead'?

The Bumper *Family* Quiz Book
Quiz 53

1. A 2005 Goldfrapp single is titled *Ride a White* what?

2. A serious, potentially life-threatening allergic reaction is known as what condition?

3. Which vegetable grows in a pod: carrot, corn, pea or potato?

4. In *The Wizard of Oz*, the Wicked Witch of the West wants Dorothy's what?

5. What award was presented to the people of Malta for bravery during World War 2?

6. What gas makes up the majority of the atmosphere on Earth?

7. Who is the current editor of *Vogue* Magazine in America, as of 2014?

8. Who succeeded Titus as Roman Emperor in 81AD?

9. What is a 'time line'?

10. What is the name of the main character in the 1959 French film *The 400 Blows*?

11. What is 'spheksophobia'?

12. In 1981, Prince Charles married Lady Diana Spencer at what church?

13. What type of precipitation occurs when sulphur dioxide builds up in the clouds?

14. What country hosted the 1984 UEFA European Football Championship?

15. What Bohemian religious thinker was burned in 1415 in Constance, Germany, for heresy?

16. Where did Claude Monet build a studio?

The Bumper Family Quiz Book
Quiz 54

1. In Italian cooking, what are salvio, timo, prezzemolo and basilico?

2. How many heart cards are there in a deck of playing cards? 💡

3. Robert Wyatt performs with Bjork on what song?

4. How many days do ants live on average?

5. In what year did William II become King of England?

6. What Australian bird often sounds like it is laughing?

7. In *Harry Potter*, what was the name of Fleur Delacour's sister? 💡

8. Under which codename were German rocket scientists brought to the US in 1945?

9. The Chapel Bridge is a famous tourist attraction in which European country?

10. Where were The Beatles famously photographed on a zebra crossing?

11. Which actor directed the film *The Monuments Men*?

12. Where did the 1945 World Zionist Conference call for a Jewish state?

13. Which World Cup was the first to be televised?

14. Which of these plants captures insects to get necessary nutrients: oak tree, sundew or tulip?

15. Which is not a type of dress: cheongsam, jodhpur or sheath?

16. In medieval times, what was a 'seigneur'?

The Bumper Family Quiz Book
Quiz 55

1. When cool or cold air suddenly drops to the ground, it is known as a what?

2. Which golfer is known as the 'Great White Shark'?

3. Where is the indigenous habitat of the small kawakawa tree?

4. What does #TBT on Twitter stand for? 💡

5. To the nearest 100 miles, what is the distance between Los Angeles, California, and Seattle, Washington?

6. What country dominates the Jutland Peninsula?

7. Which Disney animated feature tells the story of Ariel? 💡

8. The book *Flowers for Algernon* was written by whom?

9. Which country has Dakar as its capital city?

10. Which famous Australian bush ranger wore metal armour at his last stand?

11. In the film *Raiders of the Lost Ark*, why does Indy say he is afraid of snakes?

12. Who organized the Salt March (or Satyagraha) in India in 1930?

13. The Irish suffered a failure of what crop between 1845-1849, leading to famine?

14. What also means 'negative': adverse, converse or obverse?

15. What is the name of the sauce that traditionally accompanies souvlaki?

16. How many Primetime Emmys did *Orange Is The New Black* win in 2014?

The Bumper *Family* Quiz Book
Quiz 56

1. Who popularized the use of crop rotation to preserve soil fertility?

2. 'Botox' is used as a means of removing what?

3. According to the title of a 2011 film, which character played by Nick Swardson is *Born to be a Star*?

4. What geometric shape has ten sides?

5. What is a 'hotchpotch'?

6. What is the currency of India?

7. Tower Palace Three, completed in 2004 at 264m (865ft) high, is located where?

8. Who are the 'Teenage Mutant Ninja Turtles' named after?

9. What is unusual about pumice rock?

10. Where was golfer Annika Sorenstam born?

11. What was the name of Hillary Duff's first clothing line?

12. What was Mercator's profession?

13. How tall is Tom Cruise?

14. What is a 'Kugelhupf'?

15. What is chanted in the chorus of The Wombats song *Lost in the Post*?

16. In *Long Walk to Freedom*, what did Nelson Mandela say was a 'formidable combination'?

The Bumper Family Quiz Book
Quiz 57

1. During which geologic period was the Alpine orogeny?

2. What is the name of the ancient ocean that surrounded the Pangea land mass?

3. In which city was the United Nations charter drawn up in 1945?

4. What does a ruler measure?

5. On what part of your body would you wear a yarmulke?

6. Which Backstreet Boys song contains the well-known lyric 'Backstreet's back, all right!'

7. Which emperor came after Trajan?

8. Which room is not in a game of 'Cluedo': ballroom, billiard room, conservatory or observatory?

9. What country does 'dal' come from?

10. Which country has Damascus as its capital city?

11. In what year was Pluto discovered?

12. Joseph Stalin used what nickname to describe his 'right-hand man', Vyacheslav Molotov?

13. Which city will host the 2020 Olympic Games?

14. Who starred in the film *Downhill Racer*?

15. What were Gary Gilmore's last words?

16. Which of the following is not a form of pasta: linguini, mascarpone, penne or ziti?

The Bumper Family Quiz Book
Quiz 58

1. Which of these is not one of the four lobes in the hemispheres of the brain: lateral, occipital, parietal or temporal?

2. What type of creature is an 'inca'?

3. Where were the 1996 Summer Olympics held?

4. Which Nazi fugitive did the Israelis capture in Argentina in 1960?

5. Which one of the following is not a parallelogram: circle, rectangle, rhombus or square?

6. What is the biggest city in Pakistan?

7. Who sang reggae single *I Can See Clearly Now*?

8. What was Disney's second animated feature?

9. What insect transmits sleeping sickness?

10. France is about the same size as what US state?

11. Heathrow Airport serves which city?

12. Which footballer and presenter regularly promotes Walkers crisps?

13. Rihanna's single, *SOS*, was used in her endorsement of what sports brand?

14. On September 22, 2013, what prominent Chinese politician was sentenced to life in prison?

15. In *Whip It*, what sport does Bliss take up?

16. Who was the author of *Catch-22*?

The Bumper Family Quiz Book
Quiz 59

① In *The Dark Knight*, who plays Harvey Dent?

② What colour is the Hogwarts Express train?

③ Who was named Prime Minister of Iraq in 2014?

④ When was Industrial Light and Magic founded?

⑤ Who was US President at the outbreak of World War 2?

⑥ Where was the 1970 World Cup final played?

⑦ Based on French words, the terms 'blonde' and 'brunette' describe what personal feature?

⑧ Which two oceans lie east and west of Argentina?

⑨ Which type of building is designed to keep birds?

⑩ In the film *Jaws*, what is the name of Chief Brody's secretary?

⑪ The People's Revolutionary Armed Forces is a military branch in what nation?

⑫ What was the name of NASA's quest, begun in 1958, to put a man in space?

⑬ In archaic English, what did 'reck' mean?

⑭ What is the nickname of the John Updike character, Harry Angstrom?

⑮ Who was the third wife of Henry VIII?

⑯ Who has had the second-most UK Singles Chart number ones?

The Bumper *Family* Quiz Book
Quiz 60

1. Who preceded Marcus Aurelius as Roman Emperor?

2. In *Star Trek: First Contact*, what did Data say the atmosphere of Earth consisted of?

3. What table shows the days, weeks and months of the year? 💡

4. In the *Twilight* book *Breaking Dawn*, what does Bella name her baby?

5. In what year did Turkey expel 1.75 million Armenians?

6. What is the second largest Canadian island?

7. As of 2014, how many movies have Tim Burton and Johnny Depp made together?

8. The diameter of an atom is best measured with which: angstroms, centimetres or feet?

9. Which of these animals goes through incomplete metamorphosis: butterfly or grasshopper?

10. What European country is shaped like a boot? 💡

11. Which was the only World Cup of the 20th century to end in a penalty shoot-out?

12. What are 'tempi'?

13. Why has Emperor Ch'in Shih Huang been regarded poorly by Chinese throughout the centuries?

14. What do you call an Oriental tower, often used as a shrine?

15. What decade is the hit single *Fingertips, Pt. 2* by Stevie Wonder from?

16. Who is the Greek god of music, arts and knowledge?

The Bumper Family Quiz Book
Quiz 61

1. What was the name of the estate in Henry James' *The Turn of the Screw*?

2. Which number is a multiple of 4: 22, 23, 28 or 32?

3. Who was Henry VIII's third wife?

4. Which theory states that living things come only from other living things?

5. What is 'pietism'?

6. Which artist said 'I paint in order not to cry'?

7. Estonia has what capital?

8. What does 'bedim' mean?

9. What is the chemical symbol for chlorine?

10. What country did King Hussein rule?

11. Who did Anwar Sadat succeed as President of Egypt in 1970?

12. At the 2004 Olympics, Misty May competed in which sport for the USA?

13. Who was King Henry married to in *The Other Boleyn Girl*?

14. Which part of an abalone is edible?

15. What was Michael Jackson's third multi-platinum solo album?

16. Which African country has oil reserves that could rival those of the Middle East: Angola, Chad, Namibia or Nigeria?

The Bumper Family Quiz Book
Quiz 62

1. What common agricultural method is a large hazard in third world nations?

2. A Las Vegas hotel opened in 1999 with a theme built around which international city?

3. Which of the following is not an actual hair style: beehive, bob, mohawk or swirlie?

4. What two basic units make up the central processing unit or CPU?

5. What home console was introduced by Sony in 1994?

6. Which Cambridge college did Hugh Laurie attend?

7. Who searches for Mowgli in the jungle in *The Jungle Book 2*?

8. What is Tsavo infamous for in Kenya?

9. What word means to decompose naturally?

10. Buzz Lightyear is a main character in which series of films?

11. What's the alternative name of the San Siro stadium, home of Inter Milan and AC Milan?

12. What severely hampered the crews of Mark Antony's ships at the Battle of Actium?

13. What is the name for a place where you put your money to save it and collect interest?

14. What is the setting for Irving Berlin's 'White Christmas'?

15. John Watson and Rosalie Rayner's 'Little Albert' experiments proved that what emotion can be conditioned?

16. How many dumbbells are used in an exercise called the Dumbbell Fly?

The Bumper *Family* Quiz Book
Quiz 63

1. Garbanzo beans are also known as what?

2. Through what body of water does the International Dateline run?

3. Which of these is not a type of nut: almond, mocha, pecan or pistachio? 💡

4. In botany, what is an 'uva'?

5. Afrikaners were once known by what name?

6. In what year did Col. Muammar Qadafi seize power in the Arab country of Libya?

7. Who played the voice of young Simba in *The Lion King*? 💡

8. If I am 'supine', what am I doing?

9. What is the primary food source for coral reefs?

10. What year did the German military first use poison gas?

11. Who was the first person on the moon?

12. How do people enter the Kingdom of Terabithia in *Bridge to Terabithia*?

13. Which number appears opposite '20' on a dartboard?

14. What type of fruit grows in bunches on a tree: apple, banana or mango? 💡

15. How many life boats were on board the *Titanic*?

16. Who starred as the clown in Stephen King's *It*?

The Bumper Family Quiz Book
Quiz 64

1. Who played vampire Spike in *Buffy the Vampire Slayer*?

2. What is the name of the sombrero-sporting fast-moving cartoon mouse?

3. Cuba is located in what sea?

4. What colour are most taxicabs in London? 💡

5. What are the large masses of land containing most of the world's countries called?

6. Which country has Lilongwe as its capital?

7. In music, what does 'forte' mean?

8. What was the name of the Volkswagen in Disney's *The Love Bug*?

9. 'Muggy' means what? 💡

10. The repayment of a loan by instalments is termed what?

11. What is the main cause of caves?

12. How many points is a pink ball worth in snooker?

13. What does the US organization called PETA work to protect?

14. What colours are used on the iMessage app icon on the iPhone?

15. In what decade was the teddy bear invented?

16. Where was Magellan killed?

The Bumper Family Quiz Book
Quiz 65

1. Under Julius Caesar's rule, what did fathers of three or more children receive?

2. How many minutes are there in two hours?

3. What system was built to keep London from flooding?

4. What colour ball must be potted last in snooker?

5. Which 2005 film is about a woman's love life being reduced to a string of disastrous blind dates?

6. In what year did Napoleon capture Malta?

7. Which group has won the most Grammy Awards, as of 2014?

8. If you ordered 'akami' in a Japanese restaurant, what would you get served?

9. Somniphobia is the fear of what?

10. Which of these fruits has a seed which you shouldn't eat: kiwi, passion fruit or peach?

11. Tennis player Andy Roddick guest-starred on which magical sitcom?

12. What decade is the hit single *Getaway* by Earth, Wind & Fire from?

13. How many kilograms does one litre of water weigh?

14. How many paintings did Van Gogh sell during his lifetime?

15. What three colours are on the flag of Belgium?

16. Who once lived in the house now used for the Nelson Mandela National Museum?

Quiz 66

① Who directed the 1988 comedy *Dirty Rotten Scoundrels*?

② In photography, what type of space is used for processing or printing photographic materials?

③ What US President coined the phrase 'Good to the last drop', referring to coffee?

④ What character did Rupert Everett voice in *Shrek 2*? 💡

⑤ What country in Africa with Asmara as its capital uses nakfa as its currency?

⑥ Approximately how long was the Silk Road?

⑦ The May 5, 2007 crash of Kenya Airways Flight KQ 507 happened in which country?

⑧ What are the main functions of the spinal cord?

⑨ Who was named UEFA Club Defender of the Year in 2005, 2008 and 2009? 💡

⑩ Mary Anning was the first to discover complete fossils of which prehistoric marine reptile?

⑪ In anatomy, what is the 'velum'?

⑫ 'He's a real ham', means what?

⑬ What was a 'Dust Eater' in the Vietnam War?

⑭ Which conspirator was the first to strike Julius Caesar?

⑮ The European headquarters of the UN are located in which country?

⑯ Who beat Boris Becker to win the 1991 Wimbledon Singles Championship?

Quiz 67

1. Which part of Australia did Thomas Wingate's painting of a bushfire depict?

2. What metal is used in aeroplanes for its lightweight properties: gold, steel or aluminium?

3. Who became the first woman to head a Space Shuttle mission in 1999?

4. What was the first name of Sir Lipton, the creator of Lipton Tea?

5. What British force travels in 'panda cars'?

6. What aircraft was stolen by SPECTRE in *Thunderball*?

7. Which capital city was once the capital of a Spanish colony called New Granada?

8. In the *Mr Men* books, what colour is Mr Messy?

9. What year was Japan's Nikkei 225 started: 1933, 1943, 1949 or 1980?

10. What is the name of the young woman in *Hamlet*?

11. Who was the only England player selected for the 2006 World Cup all-star team?

12. What food group is milk in?

13. What is another name for the Neva Masquerade cat?

14. What do Google call their web-to-TV device?

15. In what year did Prince Albert, husband of Queen Victoria, die?

16. In *Doctor Who*, Weeping Angels can only move if a person looking at them looks away or does what?

The Bumper Family Quiz Book
Quiz 68

1. What two colours are on the flag of Denmark?

2. Which actor is the 2014 face of ice cream brand Häagen-Dazs?

3. In which popular sitcom did Billy Crystal and Robin Williams once make a cameo together?

4. Why is a rattlesnake so-called?

5. Which Middle Eastern country's highest elevation point is Mount Hermon?

6. What is Beth's profession in the 2006 film *Open Season*?

7. Which planet were the *Viking* spacecraft sent to study?

8. King George I could not speak English – true or false?

9. Which of these animals saves food for another meal time: bird, frog, leopard or lizard?

10. By what nickname is the 'Weimaraner' breed often called?

11. Which country is ruled by the Al-Sabah dynasty?

12. How did Anne Frank address her diary entries?

13. What plant's gel is often used in lotions and sunblocks?

14. What term is given to a new window that opens automatically while browsing?

15. What soccer team was David Beckham playing for when he first rose to stardom?

16. Where is the 'great dark spot' located: Jupiter, Mercury or Neptune?

The Bumper Family Quiz Book
Quiz 69

1. Who wrote *Dracula*?

2. Which comic superhero would you be most likely to meet if you were in Smallville?

3. What vegetable can turn your skin orange if you eat too much of it?

4. In which country will you find the cities Toledo and Granada?

5. What is the chemical element with symbol 'N' and atomic number 14?

6. Which Frenchman was the first 'ace' in the history of warfare?

7. Which is the sixth month of the year?

8. Which supermodel was Richard Gere once married to?

9. What is the name of the mountain range that runs through Scotland's centre?

10. Whose coronation took place at Westminster Abbey in 1553?

11. What song is played in *Flicka*?

12. What cooking term is used for a small amount of spice or seasoning?

13. In what year did Tiger Woods marry a Swedish model?

14. What is the 'sea parrot' more commonly known as?

15. Which elephant has the larger ears, African or Indian?

16. Who conducted the first complete stereo recording of Wagner's *Ring Cycle*?

The Bumper *Family* Quiz Book
Quiz 70

1. What type of element is radon?

2. Which 2010 golfing Major was won by Louis Oosthuizen?

3. Why is the standard computer keyboard layout called a 'QWERTY' keyboard? 💡

4. What are the names of Ella's stepsisters in the film *Ella Enchanted*?

5. Which African country's highest elevation point is Mont Nimba?

6. Where did 'pound cake' get its name?

7. Which of these is not a term for a room in a house: foyer, mausoleum, parlour or study? 💡

8. How many children did Nelson Mandela have?

9. What country in Africa with Accra as its capital uses cedi as its currency?

10. The Maldives' greatest source of income is from what industry?

11. Who founded the Leica Camera company?

12. Who remixed Elvis' *A Little Less Conversation* in 2002?

13. What gas makes up most of the atmosphere on Mars?

14. Kimchi is a common food of which country?

15. The ancient city of Petra was founded by what tribe?

16. What is the most plentiful mineral found in the human body?

The Bumper Family Quiz Book
Quiz 71

① In what year was the cash register invented: 1600, 1808, 1879 or 1934?

② The Communist Party of the government of which country resigned in June 1991: Albania, Greece, Lithuania or Serbia?

③ Where was the ghetto in *Schindler's List*?

④ How long is the average giraffe's tongue?

⑤ In what area is Sicily located in regards to the boot shape of Italy? 💡

⑥ Which Evanescence album first featured the song *Tourniquet*?

⑦ Which country hosted the FIFA World Cup in 1998?

⑧ What is chicken stuffed with garlic butter traditionally called?

⑨ What do the majority of the robots in the 2007 film *Transformers* turn into? 💡

⑩ Who portrays Jerry Seinfeld's neighbour Cosmo Kramer in comedy series *Seinfeld*?

⑪ In what continent is Mount Kilimanjaro located?

⑫ In which year was Edward VII crowned King of the United Kingdom?

⑬ Who is the Greek goddess of love?

⑭ Monarch butterflies migrate annually across how many North American countries?

⑮ On the Internet, what is the SMTP email protocol short for?

⑯ What nickname for the Asian black bear comes from the pattern of the white patch on their chests?

The Bumper *Family* Quiz Book
Quiz 72

1. Which of these is a 1996 album by the German group Scooter: *Deluxe*, *Maria* or *Our Happy Hardcore*?

2. What percentage of known volcanoes are subaerial, meaning they erupt into the atmosphere?

3. Who is captain of the 2014 Real Madrid squad?

4. How many red balls are used in a game of snooker? 💡

5. Who wrote the 1920 book titled *Main Street*?

6. What is the capital of the German State of Schleswig-Holstein?

7. What was the 'Steel Cow' in the Vietnam War?

8. What is the official language of the United Kingdom? 💡

9. Which Apollo mission launched on December 21, 1968, and spent Christmas in lunar orbit?

10. Which was the subtitle of the second Nintendo 64 *Zelda* game?

11. The Persian and what other Gulf borders the United Arab Emirates?

12. In geology, what is a 'col'?

13. What is the national flower of Bulgaria?

14. How do square dancers know which steps to perform?

15. What did Karl Marx say was 'the opium of the people'?

16. Who directed the 1973 French film *Day for Night*?

The Bumper Family Quiz Book
Quiz 73

1. What two countries fought over the Falkland Islands in 1982?

2. What colours are on the flag of Italy? 💡

3. What ancient Swedish tradition allows you to pass over any grounds, fields or woods?

4. In what year did *The Godfather* win the Academy Award for Best Picture?

5. What is the governing body for soccer in England?

6. Which port city was the first capital of Pakistan?

7. Which rapper was born Todd Anthony Shaw?

8. In genealogy, what is a 'stemma'?

9. Jef Raskin left due to a personality conflict with whom during the Macintosh Project?

10. What country first used tinsel as a tree decoration? 💡

11. Who established a Dublin brewery to produce stout in 1759?

12. Which former astronaut was the CEO of Eastern Airlines?

13. Which country has Copenhagen as its capital city?

14. In a mathematical problem, what is the name given to numbers that are added together?

15. A golden plover is which type of animal?

16. In physics, what is the name for the point around which a lever rotates, allowing it to amplify work?

The Bumper Family Quiz Book
Quiz 74

① During his time as President, Nelson Mandela was criticized for his relationship with what Indonesian leader?

② What is the official name of the F-22 aircraft?

③ *Coronation Street* takes place in what fictional town?

④ Who did Chelsea beat in the final of the 2010 FA Cup?

⑤ What element does hydrogen combine with to make water?

⑥ In the film *Pan's Labyrinth*, who is the main villain?

⑦ Who are 'small fry'?

⑧ Who won the Peloponnesian War?

⑨ What type of nut do squirrels most frequently bury?

⑩ What is the name for a virus that infects a bacteria?

⑪ What German chancellor was most responsible for the creation of the German Empire?

⑫ Elton John co-wrote the song *I Don't Feel Like Dancin'* with which rock group?

⑬ Who wrote *Wide Sargasso Sea*

⑭ South America includes how many sovereign states?

⑮ Near which organ of the body are the adrenal glands situated: bladder, heart, kidneys or liver?

⑯ Which US city is often likened to a large fruit?

The Bumper Family Quiz Book
Quiz 75

1. Which Central American country's highest elevation point is Montagne Pelee?

2. What is a mixture of gases that can be stored and transported like natural gas: biogas or biomass?

3. What city in Germany was first to manufacture glass ornaments: Berlin, Hamburg or Nuremburg?

4. Which animal eats the most: orca or penguin?

5. What was Edgar Allan Poe deathly afraid of?

6. In music, what does 'moderato' mean?

7. The history of coffee dates back how many years: 150 years, 500 years or more than 1000 years?

8. Which of these office supplies is a writing instrument: paper clip, pen, rubber band or stapler?

9. Which Madonna song features the lyric 'In the midnight hour I can feel your power'

10. Scolionophobia is the fear of what?

11. Which department store is central to *Miracle on 34th Street*?

12. In *Guardians of the Galaxy*, who voices Rocket?

13. Which country's highest elevation point is Mount Wuteve?

14. Which art movement is Salvador Dali associated with?

15. Who did Oscar Larios knock out in his first professional fight?

16. In what year did Richard II ascend the English throne?

The Bumper Family Quiz Book
Quiz 76

1. What two classification labels are used in the scientific name of an organism?

2. Floris Stempel founded which major European club?

3. Who succeeded Vespasian as Roman Emperor in 79AD?

4. On which continent is Slovakia located?

5. What is a 'sumpter'?

6. Lake Kariba in Africa is located on what river?

7. Which 1987 film starred Patrick Swayze and Jennifer Grey?

8. What year saw the death of Galileo and the birth of Isaac Newton?

9. On the Internet, what would you use an SMTP server for?

10. What is the name of the restaurant the students in *Glee* frequent?

11. In *The Twilight Saga: New Moon*, what attacked Bella?

12. What is a long skirt with a fluted, flared hem bottom called: flute skirt, trombone skirt or trumpet skirt?

13. What was the last country to be liberated from the Nazis?

14. If you feel sharp pain during exercise, what should you do?

15. What is liposculpture?

16. Documents relating to the Royal Family and British Monarchy are kept where?

The Bumper Family Quiz Book
Quiz 77

1. In which year did George VI ascend the British throne?

2. Which Shakespearean title character refers to himself as a shepherd?

3. What is the world's largest coral reef?

4. What city has the largest Polynesian population in the world?

5. The definition of 'free from mistakes' best fits which word: Accurate, awful, aware or amazing 💡

6. Which UK city was originally founded as the Roman settlement of Londinium?

7. Which sculptor's works include 'The Kiss' and 'The Thinker'?

8. What are mobile applications often called?

9. The word 'lunar' means something related to what? 💡

10. Which film won the 1997 Academy Award for Best Picture?

11. How do you say 'thank you' in Maltese?

12. Who wrote the book *Driver #8*?

13. Which monarch was the last of the Tudor dynasty?

14. What is the irregular and instantaneous motion of air called?

15. Which type of pasta is shaped like a corkscrew?

16. Much of Afghanistan's mountainous terrain is in which part of the country?

The Bumper *Family* Quiz Book
Quiz 78

1. Which country was formerly known as British Honduras?

2. What do you call a large body of salt water, usually connected to an ocean?

3. What is the highest navigable body of water in the world?

4. In which century were roller skates invented?

5. The 2005 animated film *Valiant* is set in what year?

6. In a circuit, what is the ratio of the voltage drop and current flow between two points?

7. What does 'jejune' mean?

8. What was Queen Victoria's favourite type of dog?

9. What is the first name of boxing's Mercer?

10. Which Disney animated feature is based on *The Snow Queen*?

11. What is the name of the character that constantly annoys Jerry Seinfeld?

12. What layer in the atmosphere is responsible for filtering out solar radiation?

13. In what year did Norway become an independent nation?

14. What was the working title of *EastEnders* before production started?

15. How long, approximately, did it take for the *Titanic* to sink?

16. Which German band sang *99 Red Balloons*?

The Bumper Family Quiz Book
Quiz 79

1. In MGM Studios, the MGM stands for what?

2. Which 'quiet' group in *Doctor Who* are a religious order bent on killing the Doctor?

3. What does the adjective 'otiose' mean?

4. What country hosted the 1996 UEFA European Football Championship?

5. What process carries minerals down into lower soil horizons: bleaching, leaching, leaving or mineralling?

6. Which ex-Yugoslavian country's highest point is peak Maglic?

7. What is the world's fastest dog?

8. What small Australian town suffered the most deaths in the 1875 sinking of the *Gothenburg*?

9. What is the most famous road in Auckland, New Zealand?

10. A Robbie Williams album title urges people to 'sing when' they're what?

11. What sauce is usually used on Peking Duck?

12. What does synoptic mean?

13. How many days are there in the month of January?

14. What is a manoeuvre used to eliminate the drift of an aircraft caused by wind?

15. What type of element is krypton?

16. The Latin word *finis* means what?

The Bumper Family Quiz Book
Quiz 80

1. Which of the following dances is called the 'fan dance': cha cha, jive, rumba or salsa?

2. Who was elected President of Poland in 2005?

3. What is another word for a person's signature?

4. Who plays Will Turner in *Pirates of the Caribbean*?

5. Which was the only German team to win the UEFA Champions League in the 1990s?

6. The 1934 book, *Appointment at Samarra*, was written by whom?

7. Medically, what is a loss of water called?

8. What is a 'mesa'?

9. What vegetable does Bugs Bunny most like to eat?

10. If you went to a party in Mexico, what would it be called?

11. Which dog is bred for its tracking skills?

12. What decade is the hit single *A Little In Love* by Cliff Richard from?

13. If someone speaks 'gnomically', how are they speaking?

14. Where is the oldest, still functional, brewery in the world?

15. What is the capital city of Vietnam?

16. What did Henry IV's Edict of Nantes guarantee citizens of France?

The Bumper Family Quiz Book
Quiz 81

1. East Bengal is now known as what country?

2. Which Disney animated feature centres on a lion family? 💡

3. What is 'myopathy'?

4. Who 'featured' with Duffy on a 2008 remix of the song *Mercy*?

5. In Scottish slang, what is a 'ned'?

6. What country does Alaska border?

7. Sudden non-draining ground water caused by heavy rain is called what?

8. Which English King was the son of Mary, Queen of Scots?

9. In what year was the Great Fire of London?

10. How many English *Little Miss* books are there in the series? 💡

11. For which James Bond film did Adele sing the title song?

12. When cooking, what must you avoid doing if you want to prepare a clear stock?

13. Which man hit a golf ball while he was on the moon?

14. Which word means to 'filter down through the soil horizons'?

15. In *Aliens*, which character used the shotgun for close encounters?

16. The book *The Door Into Summer* was written by whom?

The Bumper Family Quiz Book
Quiz 82

① Which element has the atomic number 5?

② What does 'a.k.a.' stand for?

③ What material do beaches consist mostly of? 💡

④ Rembrandt opened his first art studio at which age?

⑤ What was the name given to the government led by Nelson Mandela during his presidency?

⑥ An album by The Wombats is titled *A Guide to Love, Loss &* what?

⑦ Who voiced Woody in *Toy Story*?

⑧ Which *Glee* actor appeared in every single episode of the first four seasons? 💡

⑨ Which Christian King of East Africa had his people carve underground churches?

⑩ The world's tallest waterfall is located in which country?

⑪ Ladies singles events were first introduced at Wimbledon in what year?

⑫ Which Tudor monarch was born in October 1537?

⑬ What company bought YouTube for $1.65 billion in 2006?

⑭ Which word describes the effectiveness of something, in a medical context?

⑮ Dystychiphobia is the fear of what?

⑯ Which European country's highest point is Moldoveanu Peak?

The Bumper Family Quiz Book
Quiz 83

1. In *Oxford Comma*, Vampire Weekend urges listeners to 'know' their what?

2. For what film did Kevin Spacey win an Academy Award in 2000?

3. What celebration commemorates Mexico's defeat of the French?

4. What was British band S Club 7's debut single? 💡

5. The term 'sugar' is used generically to refer to which one of the following: fructose, glucose, lactose or sucrose?

6. Maria Sharapova comes from which country?

7. What is Adobe's photo-management software called?

8. Which child of Henry VIII became the next King of England?

9. What is 'Papercrete'?

10. What flag was adopted to unite the whole of the UK under a common banner? 💡

11. Who was the 'Master of Flemalle'?

12. What is the dominant religion of Cape Verde?

13. What would you call a long, snake-like fish that has circular gills?

14. Which of these nations borders Cambodia: China, Laos, Mongolia or Uzbekistan?

15. What is the name of the controlling party in North Korea?

16. In clothing, what is a 'rebozo'?

The Bumper Family Quiz Book
Quiz 84

1. What region makes up 75% of Russia?

2. Insulin was discovered by Banting and Best in 1921, but in which country?

3. Which DKNY designer worked for Anne Klein until 1984?

4. Artist, Mary Cassatt, was born in which city?

5. Which Disney animated feature is based on Rapunzel? 💡

6. What type of animal is a 'douroucouli'?

7. In the film, who did *Napoleon Dynamite* give one of his special drawings to?

8. In which country was the first commercial network of mobile phones set up?

9. What is the sixth book in the *Harry Potter* series called? 💡

10. What was the name of the first Canadian vessel to sink in the Mediterranean Sea during World War 2?

11. Which modernist author wrote *Mrs Dalloway*?

12. What is the capital of French Guiana, sandwiched between Suriname and Brazil?

13. Who performed the famous gold-foil experiment that first detected the existence of the atomic nucleus?

14. What do you add to milk, beaten eggs and sugar to make a 'Tom and Jerry'?

15. What shape is a stop sign?

16. In what year did Japan and South Korea share World Cup hosting responsibilities?

The Bumper Family Quiz Book
Quiz 85

1. What is the main land-form of the Federated States of Micronesia?

2. What country did the European Union agree to bail out at the cost of about 10 billion Euros: Cyprus or Sweden?

3. What colour is a 'yellow' traffic light?

4. The airport code JNB designates which international airport?

5. Where in Germany does Mercedes-Benz have its headquarters?

6. In what county is Blackpool Tower?

7. What item would you use to locate what the French call 'nord', 'sud', 'est' and 'ouest'?

8. What part of speech is the word 'quickly'?

9. The medical term 'thrombosis' is best defined as what?

10. Which actress played the lead role of *Buffy the Vampire Slayer* in the TV series?

11. Which film won the 2007 Academy Award for Best Picture?

12. Beach volleyball player Misty May tore what muscles in 2000?

13. What two colours are on the flag of Austria?

14. What is the name of the Nintendo handheld game system that was released in 1989?

15. Which Australian creature is the only mammal that doesn't seem to dream: Echidna, Koala or Tasmanian Devil?

16. If two graphed equations produce the same line, what do we call them?

The Bumper Family Quiz Book
Quiz 86

1. What year did Geronimo die?

2. Which country cut the natural gas supply to Ukraine in 2006 over a price dispute?

3. Where are 'anther' found?

4. What is Hercules' winged buddy called in the Disney film? 💡

5. What type of terrain makes up most of Cuba's?

6. Who developed the vaccine for polio?

7. What celebrated designer created Hillary Clinton's second inaugural gown?

8. What is a baby whale called? 💡

9. What is 'oca'?

10. What year saw the inception of the Formula One world championship at Silverstone?

11. Who is the actress in *Last Vegas* that played Diana?

12. What is a map that shows average temperature and rainfall called?

13. Which iPhone model superseded the iPhone 3G?

14. Which bodily organ makes urine?

15. During what month does the *Taurids* meteor shower take place?

16. You can get a fabulous view of what city from Mount Victoria?

The Bumper Family Quiz Book
Quiz 87

1. The Spanish holiday, National Day, celebrates whose arrival in America?

2. What do you call a word having the same spelling but a different sound and meaning?

3. In the book *Moonraker*, what game did James Bond beat Drax at?

4. What did Wegener call the main landmass that all the current ones came from?

5. In what country was the famous artist Leonardo da Vinci born?

6. Which is the largest type of rattlesnake?

7. Which type of pasta would be hardest to string onto a necklace: lasagna, macaroni or penne?

8. What is the English translation of the Indian dish 'murgh makhani'?

9. Because he liked writing, Paul Klee's paintings often included what?

10. Whose coronation took place at Westminster Abbey in 1559?

11. The airport code JFK designates which international airport?

12. When was the British Touring Car Championship established?

13. What online company was founded by Sergey Brin and Larry Page in 1998?

14. What do you traditionally give for a fifteenth anniversary?

15. Liechtenstein has which capital city?

16. Which Asian capital was formerly known as Batavia?

The Bumper Family Quiz Book
Quiz 88

1. Fiji is considered to be part of which continent?

2. What is on your tongue that allows you to taste differences in foods?

3. What was the mainstay rifle used by the French at the start of World War 1?

4. Amsterdam is the capital of what country?

5. Ana Ivanovic cited whom as her inspiration to play tennis?

6. Which of these cultures was conquered by Pizarro: Aztec, Incan or Tainoan?

7. In what year did Edward IV ascend the English throne?

8. What is the highest vocal part called?

9. Which country's highest elevation point is Sapitwa?

10. According to the code of chivalry, what did a knight have to do: fight fairly, joust weekly or marry a princess?

11. In *Happy Feet*, what kind of dancing does Mumble do?

12. Which detective fiction author wrote *The Big Sleep*?

13. Which iPhone model superseded the iPhone 5?

14. Where are carpal bones found?

15. What two countries lie on opposite sides of the Formosa Strait?

16. Which famous John Lennon song was covered by David Bowie's Tin Machine?

Quiz 89

① Why could it be dangerous to eat raw cookie dough?

② Which artist was not an Impressionist: Manet, Monet, Pisarro or Rembrandt?

③ Finish the lyric: 'You spin me right round, baby. Right round like...'?

④ What type of picture does an artist get when using a camera? 💡

⑤ What is the next number in the sequence 1, 1, 2, 3, 5, 8, 13, 21?

⑥ What number suffix did the recent Pope Benedict take?

⑦ A hedgehog's back has how many muscles?

⑧ What princess does Z meet in the 1998 animated feature *Antz*?

⑨ Which is the seventh month of the year? 💡

⑩ In Scotland, what does 'ava' mean?

⑪ Who won the 2013 International V8 Supercars Championship?

⑫ Which UK region is divided into Highlands and Lowlands?

⑬ What number, the root of 'tripod', 'trident' and 'triple', was 'tria' in Greek?

⑭ In Chinese, what does the name of China mean?

⑮ What is an acciaccatura?

⑯ Which actor did Tommy Hilfiger describe as the 'man with the best style'?

The Bumper Family Quiz Book
Quiz 90

1. What shape is in the centre of Switzerland's flag?

2. Which African country has a capital named after a US President?

3. What natural resource is drilled for in Iraq?

4. Which of the following fruits is usually red: cantaloupe, papaya or strawberry? 💡

5. What would you be served in a Japanese restaurant if you ordered 'unagi maki'?

6. In what year did Colombia become an independent country?

7. What shape of table did King Arthur and his knights famously use?

8. Daniel Craig leads a group of American cowboys in fighting off what threat in a 2011 sci-fi film?

9. The term 'assemblage' was coined by which artist?

10. Which compass direction is the opposite of West? 💡

11. How long can a queen termite live?

12. What does the vitamin B12 do for your body?

13. What must fossilize in order to form a coprolite?

14. Which Shakespeare play features Ferdinand, Prospero and Caliban?

15. How many international goals had soccer's Mia Hamm made when she retired?

16. The group of languages spoken in China, Tibet and Burma is of what language group?

The Bumper Family Quiz Book
Quiz 91

1. Who was a vice-captain along with Pepe of the 2014 Real Madrid squad?

2. Which country agreed to end nuclear testing in January of 1996?

3. What is the French term for a grilled cheese and ham sandwich?

4. In image terms, what is an 'avatar'?

5. In which country did the Christmas tree originate?

6. On what street do Anne Rice's *Mayfair Witches* live?

7. Who dies in the book *Jaws* but lives in the film?

8. The name of the Norte Grande region in Chile translates to which English phrase?

9. What material used in paint causes pigment particles to adhere to one another?

10. In what country might you expect to see people wearing sombreros?

11. How many dimples are on a regulation golf ball?

12. Which activity involves an air tank – snorkelling or scuba diving?

13. What was the family name of the dynasty that ruled Byzantium from 1081-1185 AD?

14. Which of these famous beaches is located in Brazil: Acapulco, Cancun, Copacabana or Ibiza?

15. What are black and white bears from China called?

16. What kind of bird is an 'ani'?

The Bumper *Family* Quiz Book
Quiz 92

1. Which Internet-related term comes from a Monty Python comedy sketch?

2. What is a polymer?

3. What Australian actor starred in the film *Nightclub* with Joan Bilceaux and Marjorie Harwood?

4. In what direction is sunrise?

5. What is the chemical symbol for silicon?

6. Which of the following nations do not speak a form of the Serbo-Croat Slavic language: Albania, Bosnia-Herzegovina, Croatia or Serbia?

7. Who invented both the fluorescent light and alternating current?

8. In both Ancient Greece and Rome, where did most of the farming take place?

9. The Key Tower, completed in 1991 at a height of 289m (947ft), is located where?

10. What title was given to Ancient Egyptian rulers?

11. What type of numbers means 'greater than zero'?

12. Who first played Batman in a full-length live-action film?

13. In what year did Felix Sturm debut as a professional boxer?

14. What makes Florida's Tampa Bay a unique aquatic environment?

15. What is the setting of Edward Hopper's 'Compartment C, Car 293'?

16. What special effects artist changed film-making with his 'Dynamation' method?

The Bumper Family Quiz Book
Quiz 93

1. When Edgar Degas' eyesight diminished, he turned to what art form?

2. What does the adjective 'thalassic' mean?

3. Teachers use chalk to write on which of these: blackboard, students, tables or windows?

4. How long did it take to build the Hagia Sophia in Constantinople?

5. How many years in prison was UK trader Nick Leeson sentenced to in 1995?

6. What do the initials stand for in author J.R.R. Tolkien's name?

7. Which scientist said 'In the centre rests the sun'?

8. What is a 'tea' or infusion made up of herbal medicines called?

9. What colour are holly berries?

10. In a set of data, what is the value in the very middle called?

11. What is a 'swami'?

12. Approximately how many mature trees can be saved by avoiding one ton of paper waste?

13. *Donburi* is a general term for what Japanese word?

14. What is the largest city in the Netherlands?

15. What is the middle name of Diego Maradona?

16. What is the name of the toy museum located on the Isle of Skye in Scotland?

The Bumper Family Quiz Book
Quiz 94

1. Who did Nathuram Godse assassinate in 1948?

2. By what nickname is the pepsid wasp known?

3. What are the seasonal rains that occur in south-east Asia called? 💡

4. What was Keanu Reeves character's name in the film *Speed*?

5. What was Mandela asked to do to receive early release in 1985?

6. In Roman times, what was a 'maniple'?

7. Cairo is located along the Nile River, along with which Sudanese capital?

8. What is the puffy skirt often worn by a ballet dancer called?

9. Which Weasley sibling unconsciously opens the Chamber of Secrets in the *Harry Potter* novel? 💡

10. Capable of diving at speeds of up to 200 mph, what is the fastest-flying bird in the world?

11. The FIFA award for 'Most Entertaining Team' went to France after which World Cup?

12. What is an 'ait'?

13. What four seas are named after colours?

14. In France, pigs are traditionally used to locate what delicacy?

15. Miley Cyrus's *Wrecking Ball* debuted on which of her albums?

16. What South American country took its name from the Inca word for 'cold winter'?

The Bumper Family Quiz Book
Quiz 95

1. What type of food is 'spelt'?

2. Victoria Falls is located in which two countries?

3. The tongue of what creature is used in the witches' brew from *Macbeth*?

4. In what year did the film *Girl, Interrupted* come out?

5. Grapes come in all but which colour: black, green or orange?

6. How many stars are there on the Australian flag?

7. What is the name of the land's ruler in the 1984 Anime film *Nausicaa Of The Valley Of The Wind*?

8. Nelson Mandela was charged with treason and eventually acquitted in March of what year?

9. Which regional animal is pictured on the Canadian $2 coin?

10. Which British boy band released as their debut single *Slam Dunk (Da Funk)*?

11. How many attempts did it take Mi Hyun Kim to qualify for the LPGA?

12. Which of these rivers flows north: Congo, Nile, Platte or Zaire?

13. What is Sam Sparro 'waiting for', according to a 2008 song title?

14. Kosher cooking requires keeping which types of food separate?

15. What was the yield of TNT in explosive force of the nuclear weapon dropped on Hiroshima, Japan?

16. What nationality of artists invented the futurism movement in 1909?

The Bumper Family Quiz Book
Quiz 96

1. What element is most important for oxygen and carbon dioxide transfer in blood?

2. Which iPhone models superseded the iPhone 5S and 5C?

3. What biblical character was said to have been created from the dust of the ground and the breath of God?

4. What were the names of the Hardy Boys? 💡

5. Which brand uses the slogan 'The best a man can get'?

6. What software protects client computers from malicious external connections?

7. When are the '12 Days of Christmas'? 💡

8. Which Australian town is situated closest to the centre of the continent?

9. Which is the lightest element?

10. In 1962, what label was FIFA using for the World Cup team groupings?

11. What is the first name of Emma Stone's character in *Easy A*?

12. What differentiates a Long Beach Tea from a Long Island Iced Tea?

13. When was the first Christmas card printed?

14. What is the capital of Australia's Northern Territory?

15. About how many seconds are there in 32 years: 1 thousand, 1 billion, 1 million, or 1 trillion?

16. Who was the first European to sail into New York Harbour?

The Bumper Family Quiz Book
Quiz 97

1. What is the primary ingredient of a Swiss fondue?

2. What country, to the north of the United States, uses the dollar as its currency?

3. What was Task Force Baum in World War 2?

4. What is Dorothy's dog called in *The Wizard of Oz*?

5. In music, who is a maestro?

6. Which city hosted the 1996 Olympic Games?

7. What colour is at the top of UK traffic lights?

8. What kind of animal is Ozzie in *Over the Hedge*?

9. What's the first name of the best-selling author, Bradbury?

10. What comet broke into fragments before crashing into Jupiter in the 1990s?

11. In heraldry, what do you call a shield divided into several horizontal stripes?

12. Who was the pilot of the plane, *Enola Gay*, which dropped the bomb on Hiroshima?

13. What was the name of the rebellion which attempted to overthrow Emperor Justinian?

14. In the fairy tale, who was the little wooden boy who came to life and whose nose grew when he lied?

15. The Taipei 101 building, at 509m (1670ft) tall, is found in which country?

16. What light-amplification device was first made operational in 1960, using a synthetic pink ruby?

The Bumper Family Quiz Book
Quiz 98

1. Which is not a type of neckline: boat neck, cowl, keyhole or kundan?

2. What is the main ingredient in the Malaysian dish, Nasi Lemak?

3. In Disney's *The Lion King*, what is Simba's playmate called?

4. 'Un chucho' is Spanish for what sort of dog?

5. The title of Chief Operating Officer is abbreviated to what?

6. Aer Lingus is the flag-carrier airline of which country?

7. How many degrees are there in a triangle?

8. What is the name of the computer in the 1957 film, *Desk Set*?

9. Which country does Maria Sharapova live in?

10. Which English monarch was born in September 1533?

11. Who were Stan Lee's first superhero team, launched in 1961?

12. For which song did Michael Jackson duet with sister Janet?

13. Most deaf people in England speak which official language?

14. Roughly how many geysers is Yellowstone National Park home to?

15. In the US, who created the first successful incandescent light bulb?

16. How many time zones are there in China?

The Bumper Family Quiz Book
Quiz 99

1. Which iPhone models superseded the iPhone 5?

2. In the 2007 film *Ratatouille*, what does Remy the rat secretly do?

3. Which of these characteristics allows an owl to see well at night: large eyes, silent wings or rotatable ears? 💡

4. Which bodily system includes the kidneys?

5. What would you call an animal with three main body parts and six legs?

6. Which Cambridge college did Stephen Fry attend?

7. In *Harry Potter and the Goblet of Fire*, who does Fleur go to the Yule Ball with?

8. In what year did Henry V ascend the English throne?

9. The Dead Sea is surrounded by what two countries? 💡

10. Which *Doctor Who* spin-off television show was set in Cardiff?

11. How many Formula One championship races did Michael Schumacher win in 2005?

12. Residents of Peru are referred to as what?

13. Which lake was created by a hydroelectric dam on the Zambezi River?

14. How many white stars are there on the Australian flag?

15. Who is the Patron Saint of England?

16. Roughly speaking, how much fat is needed to store 3500 calories?

The Bumper Family Quiz Book
Quiz 100

1. How long does it take Neptune to rotate on its axis?

2. A komodo dragon is what sort of animal?

3. What is the name of the device used to move the cursor around on the screen of a computer?

4. What musical instrument is often associated with Scotland?

5. What language is spoken in Spain?

6. If you 'flump', what do you do?

7. What are rabbit homes called?

8. Which country is closest to the South Pole?

9. Who is the month of January named after?

10. What was former British boxer Nigel Benn's nickname throughout his career?

11. What is the chemical name for salt?

12. What type of clothing is a 'taj'?

13. What were the little people called in the The Wizard of Oz?

14. In the Harry Potter books, where is the Slytherin common room located?

15. Which Ottoman ruler nearly captured Vienna in 1529?

16. Which Asian country's highest elevation point is Keokradong?

The Bumper Family Quiz Book
Quiz 101

1. In ice hockey, what is the name of the object the players hit around the playing field?

2. What was the name of Winston Churchill's cat during World War 2?

3. What is malt extract syrup for brewing made from?

4. Lionel Messi was the youngest player to play in La Liga. How old was he?

5. In the board game *Cluedo*, what is the green piece called?

6. Kiev is the capital of which European Country?

7. What element can be used as an antidote for arsenic poisoning?

8. What country do 'Birkenstock' sandals come from?

9. Which was the most decorated US unit in World War 2?

10. Which swimmer won BBC Young Sports Personality of the Year in 2012?

11. In mathematics, what is the most commonly used measure of spread in normal distribution?

12. In sailing, what is a 'burgee'?

13. Acetic acid gets its name from the Latin word for which condiment?

14. What is a front that does not advance called?

15. In *101 Dalmatians*, what colour is Pongo's leash?

16. Who discovered the island of Tierra del Fuego?

The Bumper Family Quiz Book
Quiz 102

1. Who is the UK Children's Laureate, as of 2014?

2. Who was the consort to King Edward VII?

3. Aubergine skin is mostly what colour?

4. In 2006, what British racer won the GP2 championship on his first attempt?

5. Who is the CEO of Twitter, as of 2014?

6. What were 'Dolmen' built to cover?

7. In what decade did The Gambia gain independence from the UK?

8. Which Disney villain sings *Poor Unfortunate Souls*?

9. Which of the following animals is nocturnal: dog, hedgehog or cow?

10. The island nation of Fiji is in what ocean?

11. What does 'malapropos' mean?

12. Which protein in monkeys is resistant to AIDS?

13. AMD was founded in 1969 by a group of former executives from which company?

14. In what year was Pope John Paul II wounded in an assassination attempt?

15. Which material do fossils make more attractive to an architect?

16. Who is Peter Parker in love with in the film *Spider-Man 2*?

The Bumper Family Quiz Book
Quiz 103

1. What meat is traditionally used in a cottage pie?

2. What type of single-celled organism doesn't have a membrane around its nuclear material?

3. In ancient times, what were professional writers called? 💡

4. What is the scientific term for an animal that walks on two feet?

5. American pioneer, John Chapman, was famous for planting which kind of tree?

6. Which is the longest river in Europe?

7. What was the period when machines took the place of hand tools called?

8. In tiddlywinks, what is the name of the counter that shoots a wink?

9. What country is famous for pasta? 💡

10. In which sea would you find the Cayman Islands?

11. Who wrote the best-selling *Vampire Chronicles*?

12. What do the initials 'CME' stand for in medical terms?

13. What sport takes place in a velodrome? 💡

14. What is the name of Woody's horse in *Toy Story 2*?

15. Which US boy band released the single *I Want It That Way*?

16. Enda Kenny is the leader of which Irish political party, as of 2014?

The Bumper Family Quiz Book
Quiz 104

1. Tajikistan, formerly part of the USSR, boasts which city as its capital?

2. The Transamerica Pyramid is found in which Californian city?

3. Cuba's climate is moderated by what type of wind pattern?

4. What is the major ingredient in Marmite? 💡

5. Hugh Jackman is from which country?

6. In primitive culture, what did dances typically commemorate?

7. Which of these is a North American rodent: beaver, chipmunk or both? 💡

8. What speed can a peregrine falcon reach during a dive?

9. Who became UK Poet Laureate in 2009?

10. Prior to the Euro, what currency was used in Germany?

11. Who won Argentina's 1999 Presidential election?

12. Dendrophobia is the fear of what?

13. What women-only sport was introduced to the Olympics in 1996?

14. What part of the world did the Vikings come from?

15. In philosophy, what is 'objectivism'?

16. Which woman was known to have had the admiration of Voltaire?

The Bumper Family Quiz Book
Quiz 105

1. What band sang the bluesy *New York City*?

2. As of 2014, who is the youngest player ever to play for the England football team? 💡

3. If I 'troop', what do I do?

4. Who played Wolfgang Amadeus Mozart in the film *Amadeus*?

5. What sort of object is a 'portmanteau'?

6. What was not one of the chief schools of Hellenistic philosophy: materialism, scepticism or stoicism?

7. A milk punch is made up of milk, sugar and which other ingredient?

8. In Disney's *Aladdin*, what is the name of Jasmine's pet tiger? 💡

9. When did Colin Montgomerie first meet Tiger Woods on the greens?

10. What is the name given to the Ancient Sumerian form of writing?

11. What does 'polyphonic ring tones' mean when referring to a cell phone?

12. Avarua, the capital of the Cook Islands, is located on which South Pacific atoll?

13. In which constellation does the vernal equinox appear?

14. What was the mantra of the 'minimalist movement', most popular between the 1950s and 1970s?

15. What is the very bottom soil horizon called?

16. What image can you find on the flag of Argentina?

The Bumper *Family* Quiz Book
Quiz 106

1. What are the main colours used in Jackson Pollock's 'Lavender Mist'?

2. In 1980, seven people were crushed to death in a Brazilian crowd while trying to meet which religious leader?

3. In database technology, what does 'SQL' stand for?

4. A person might go on safari in which of these countries: Iceland, Kenya or Mexico? 💡

5. What type of respiration uses glucose in the absence of oxygen?

6. What nationality are Dolce and Gabbana?

7. In *Frosty the Snowman*, what are Frosty's eyes made of? 💡

8. In *Doctor Who*, the 10th Doctor emerged after the Ninth Doctor was destroyed by what?

9. How many children did Queen Anne have?

10. Who composed the music for *Twilight: Breaking Dawn Pt. 1*?

11. What is a minim called in US music terminology?

12. In what year did Newfoundland become a Canadian province?

13. Fear of reptiles is known as what?

14. How many atomic tests did India conduct in 1998, despite worldwide disapproval?

15. Who was the top goal scorer during the 2014 World Cup?

16. What is the capital of Nigeria?

The Bumper Family Quiz Book
Quiz 107

1. New Delhi is the capital of which country?

2. Which of these is not a Mexican dish: enchiladas, sushi or tortillas?

3. Where was Checkpoint Charlie located?

4. In Greek mythology, who flew too close to the sun?

5. How do salmon find their way back to their home river to spawn every year?

6. Who was the author of *The Moonstone*?

7. Chimichangas are included in which cuisine?

8. In which James Bond film was Bond married?

9. What band recorded the songs *Piggy*, *March of the Pigs* and *Heresy*?

10. The three primary paint colours are red, yellow and what other colour?

11. Who was the commander of the German Army that was defeated in Stalingrad?

12. What is the national flower of Sicily?

13. In terms of written text, what is a 'saw'?

14. What does Hooke's Law describe?

15. What element was used inside the Hindenburg to keep it up in the air?

16. Early Formula One cars used steering wheels made of what material?

The Bumper *Family* Quiz Book
Quiz 108

1. Which is the largest city in Scotland, by population?

2. What film star directed *On Deadly Ground*, a pro-environmental action flick?

3. What type of clothing do people in the US refer to as 'pants'?

4. In terms of land size, where is Brazil ranked among countries of the world?

5. Top archer Lee Seung-Yun comes from which country?

6. What kind of muscle contraction is also referred to as 'static tension'?

7. Who wrote the 1969 novel *The Left Hand of Darkness*?

8. Who was the first West German chancellor during the 'German Miracle'?

9. 'Por favor' is the Spanish way of saying what polite word?

10. Who won the MTV Video Music Award for Best New Artist in 2014?

11. What happens to the pressure of water as depth under the water increases?

12. D-Day is associated with which war?

13. Iberia is the flag-carrier airline of which country?

14. On a boat, what is a 'skeg'?

15. Why do they call Johnny *The Human Torch* in *Fantastic Four*?

16. If you cook up some Mexican *frijoles*, what do you have in the pot?

The Bumper Family Quiz Book
Quiz 109

1. What meat is traditionally used in meatloaf?

2. In which US state does the golf tournament the Masters occur?

3. What product's processing method was used on potatoes to produce 'Pringles'?

4. Which London cathedral has the second largest dome in the world?

5. How fast do you need to travel on average to go 330 miles in 3 hours?

6. Petrarch is known as the father of what school of thought?

7. What is the largest city in Ivory Coast?

8. 'Genii' is the plural of 'genie', and which other word?

9. How many sizes too small was the Grinch's heart?

10. What 2004 English film made use of The Libertines' song *What a Waster*?

11. What is the oldest independent country in Africa?

12. Which artist painted 'Les Demoiselles d'Avignon'?

13. What country is the plot of *Quantum of Solace* mostly about?

14. Where would you find the Nazca Lines?

15. Which emperor was the child of Livia?

16. Which common garden bird has the Latin name *Troglodytes troglodytes*?

The Bumper Family Quiz Book
Quiz 110

1. In what year was the tattoo machine patented: 1875, 1896 or 1975?

2. In the film *Austin Powers*, what is Dr. Evil frozen in?

3. How many mascots were there for the 2004 Athens Summer Olympics?

4. Who ascended the English throne in July 1553?

5. How do you write 14 in Roman numerals?

6. The highest elevation point of what country is Mt. Shkhara?

7. Which Dan Brown novel is set within a Swiss physics lab in Vatican City?

8. Which noble gas has the lowest atomic number?

9. What object is Cogsworth in Disney's *Beauty and the Beast*?

10. In 2009, Apple released the fourth version of which web browser?

11. What was the name of the last great Mayan city to be destroyed by war?

12. In 1991, who became the first artist to refuse a Grammy award?

13. Which of Jewel's albums has 12x platinum status in the US alone?

14. What is the study of atmospheric conditions and climate called?

15. What is the name of the official residence of the monarch in Scotland?

16. In which year was the world's first heart transplant performed?

The Bumper *Family* Quiz Book
Quiz 111

1. Who starred in both *Phone Booth* and *Daredevil*?

2. Vietnam is located on which continent?

3. What is a group of whales called? 💡

4. In which Grand Slam event did Bjorn Borg never reach the finals?

5. Which Black Eyed Peas song won a 2005 Grammy?

6. What popular Japanese food features deep fried curry wrapped in a piece of dough?

7. What type of instrument is an 'erhu'?

8. Switzerland is located on which continent? 💡

9. Who wrote the 1900 book *Sister Carrie*?

10. In sleep, what does REM stand for?

11. What percentage of the human population is left-handed?

12. What is a similar group of animals that can breed with each other called?

13. What is the official language of Cuba?

14. What year were Queen Elizabeth II and Prince Philip married?

15. Which element has Na as its chemical symbol?

16. How was the Belgian Fort Eben Emael captured during World War 2?

The Bumper *Family* Quiz Book
Quiz 112

1. Where were the 1964 Winter Olympics held?

2. Which of these is part of an onion plant: heart, liver, root or stomach?

3. What car company is the sister company of the manufacturer of the Dornier 328 aircraft?

4. What symbol is on the flag of Liechtenstein?

5. Which south-east Asian country's highest point is Puncak Jaya?

6. Which film won the 1976 Academy Award for Best Picture?

7. Which two drummers played on Nirvana's first album, *Bleach*?

8. What farm animal does ham come from?

9. Which family of fish do largemouth bass belong to?

10. How long does the festival of Kwanzaa last?

11. How often does sunspot activity reach its lowest point: 10.6 years, 11.3 years, 11.9 years or 12.1 years?

12. What Hindu god is known as the creator of the universe?

13. Who wrote *The Hitchhiker's Guide to the Galaxy*?

14. In Easter celebrations in Germany, what do children decorate trees with?

15. What nation hosted the 2006 football World Cup?

16. Which country borders India to the East: Bangladesh, China, Nepal or Pakistan?

The Bumper Family Quiz Book
Quiz 113

1. What shape is the Swiss flag?

2. Which precious metal has the chemical symbol Au?

3. On which continent is Brunei located?

4. What was the code name for the invasion of Normandy by the Allies?

5. Who is Bert's roommate on *Sesame Street*?

6. What was British computer manufacturer Acorn's first product?

7. What is 'Fruit2O'?

8. Who plays the title character in *Ace Ventura: Pet Detective*?

9. Who won the MTV Video Music Award for Best New Artist in 2013?

10. Which element has the atomic number 11?

11. In what year did Edward III ascend the English throne?

12. Who was the first British rider to wear the yellow jersey in the Tour de France?

13. What is the national flower of Syria?

14. Situated between Italy and Hungary, what is the capital of Slovenia?

15. Which film is about a bored married couple surprised to learn that they are both assassins?

16. Which British computer was the first home computer from Sinclair?

The Bumper Family Quiz Book
Quiz 114

1. What street did William Shakespeare and his father live on?

2. In 1998, US cruise missiles hit suspected terrorist bases in what two places?

3. Which of the following dogs is not bred for speed: greyhound, saluki, husky or whippet?

4. How many primary teeth does a child have?

5. Which English monarch immediately preceded Elizabeth I?

6. In what film did Sting make his acting debut?

7. Who is often considered the world's first computer programmer?

8. What is 'seersucker'?

9. In text chat, what does WYWH mean?

10. What percentage of Bolivia is covered by rainforest?

11. In music, what is an aria?

12. In which gallery would you find Botticelli's 'The Birth of Venus'?

13. What is a 'farrago'?

14. Tennis pro Joachim Johansson comes from which country?

15. Which planet in our solar system is closest in size to the Earth?

16. In which French city was Joan of Arc burned at the stake?

The Bumper Family Quiz Book
Quiz 115

1. In botany, what is a 'seta'?

2. In what year did Captain Cook cross the Antarctic Circle?

3. What does the Latin phrase *de novo* mean?

4. Which Disney animated feature is based on an Arabian fairy tale?

5. Which company marketed the *Amiga 1000* personal computer?

6. What was David Beckham named as in the lead-up to the 2002 World Cup?

7. In the film *Star Trek: First Contact*, what holonovel chapter number did Captain Picard initially load?

8. How far can a porcupine throw its quills?

9. In which ocean would one find the Sargasso Sea?

10. The city of Irbid is located in the north of which Arab country?

11. Which continent is Benin on?

12. What type of hallucination is seen most in paranoid schizophrenic patients?

13. In which country is a dry cod traditionally eaten on Christmas morning?

14. Which element has the chemical symbol B?

15. What does 'holistic' mean in reference to holistic medicine?

16. Which Stuart King was crowned in April 1689?

The Bumper Family Quiz Book
Quiz 116

1. As the 20th century ended, what was the largest metropolitan area in Africa?

2. Who designed the DeTomaso Pantera?

3. What is the capital city of Cambodia, located on the river Mekong?

4. What do you call an instrument used for measuring temperatures?

5. Where was actor Michael Fassbender born?

6. What did Diego Maradona do after retiring from football?

7. What animals are reputed to have nine lives?

8. Which of the following is a secondary paint colour? Red, green, yellow or blue.

9. What is another name for vitamin B5?

10. Who introduced the potato as a staple part of the German diet?

11. What are the 'bangers' in the dish 'bangers and mash'?

12. What was the first ever film to win the Academy Award for Best Picture?

13. An eruption of which volcano buried the city of Pompeii?

14. Who was in charge of the German Luftwaffe during World War 2?

15. 'S'agapo' means 'I Love You' in which language?

16. What is the name for a powerful, rotating storm that forms over an ocean?

The Bumper Family Quiz Book
Quiz 117

1. Which of these has the most teeth: bear, opossum, shrew or tiger?

2. What does an ornithologist study?

3. Which *The Canyons* actress began her career as a child model at age 3?

4. In text chat, what does ROFL mean?

5. In what year was Australia's first bridge across the Murray River opened?

6. How many days of Christmas are there?

7. How many teams make the UEFA European Football Championship knockout phase?

8. Which world leader announced his resignation on May 10th, 2007?

9. Which country did Joan of Arc try to set free from English domination?

10. What kind of restaurant serves chow mein, fried rice, and moo goo gai pan?

11. In snooker, what is a spider?

12. What percentage of American adults exercise regularly and vigorously: 15%, 30%, 50% or 75%

13. What minimum security prison was Mandela transferred to in 1988?

14. In Shakespeare, who plans 'To set my brother Clarence and the king, in deadly hate, the one against the other'?

15. The poem that opens *Twilight: Breaking Dawn Pt. 1* is by which poet?

16. What is the term for pressing dough with your hands to make it smooth and elastic?

The Bumper *Family* Quiz Book
Quiz 118

1. What nickname was boxer Tony Thompson given?

2. What is the identifying feature of a cardigan?

3. The Galapagos Islands are located in which South American country?

4. Saddam Hussein was the President of which country?

5. Which fruit is related to a peach: apple, apricot, banana or watermelon?

6. What is royal jelly?

7. What term refers to the practice of trying to increase your vehicle's fuel efficiency?

8. If you are on the Spanish 'playa' enjoying the sun, where are you?

9. Which of the following is a non-renewable resource: air, natural gas, sun or water?

10. What is the capital of the nation with the largest area?

11. Where did *Skyfall* have its world premiere?

12. In heraldry, what do you call an animal that is lying down but awake?

13. Who recorded the hit single *Unbreak My Heart* in 1997?

14. Which insects lead to the most deaths?

15. Who is the Roman goddess of knowledge and war?

16. What type of headache is also known as a vascular headache?

The Bumper Family Quiz Book
Quiz 119

1. Who played Samantha Darko in *Donnie Darko*?

2. In what year did Egypt become an independent country?

3. The ancient practice of foot binding was popular in what country?

4. In *The Hunger Games*, how many people compete in each Games?

5. How many feet are in an imperial fathom?

6. Which Greek hero slew the Chimera?

7. Illumination of the night sky is also known as what?

8. Which Royal made a mistake when saying her wedding vows in 1981?

9. What is the name of the scientific tool used to zoom in on very small objects?

10. The 1959 book *Things Fall Apart* was written by whom?

11. What is the state flower of Hawaii?

12. Which band did Perry Farrell form in the early 1990s?

13. When launched in 1998, what was the longest narrow-body commercial passenger aircraft in service?

14. What is a marine biologist?

15. Which was the first professional fighter to beat Mike Tyson?

16. The yellow rice, Arroz Amarillo, is included in which cuisine?

The Bumper *Family* Quiz Book
Quiz 120

1. To which part of physics does the Archimedes' Principle refer?

2. To the nearest 5, how many venues were there for the 2002 World Cup?

3. Where does a sparrow make its nest? 💡

4. Which King of England had six wives?

5. A mixed number contains what two elements?

6. The Astronomical Unit (AU) is a unit of measurement based on the average distance between what two bodies?

7. In the Netherlands, what is Koningsdag?

8. Which of these is a term for slowly falling precipitation: drizzle or sleet? 💡

9. What names did the 'C.S.' in C.S. Lewis' name stand for?

10. Which German World War 2 aircraft was considered a total failure?

11. The Hague is the seat of government in what country?

12. What US soccer club did David Beckham play for?

13. Which *Wicked* Broadway singer did Taye Diggs marry in 2003?

14. What is it called when someone has low blood pressure?

15. Glucose, fructose and galactose are examples of what simplest form of sugar?

16. What character on the show *Wire in the Blood* is a psychologist?

The Bumper *Family* Quiz Book
Quiz 121

1. On April 22, 1996, nations pledged $1.23 billion in aid to rebuild which country?

2. Who played Tinkerbell in the 1991 film *Hook*?

3. What is a palindrome?

4. Which TV show followed the life of Beverly Hills plastic surgeons?

5. Which is the largest living mammal?

6. What flying creature is used in the witches' brew from *Macbeth*?

7. What comes from a cow and is used to make ice cream: eggs, milk or sugar?

8. What is the capital of Ukraine?

9. What does the name 'England' mean?

10. Brazilian legend Pele played for which US major league outfit in the 1970s?

11. The Bahamas has what capital city?

12. What gas makes up most of the atmosphere on Venus?

13. In 19th century Russia, what was a 'kulak'?

14. What is the name of the capital of East Timor?

15. How many fluid ounces make up one quart?

16. How many goals did Saudi Arabia score in the 2002 World Cup?

The Bumper *Family* Quiz Book
Quiz 122

1. The T-43 airborne navigator-trainer is a modified version of what commercial aircraft?

2. Which horse won the Grand National in 2008?

3. Which of these is a bird of prey: crow, jay or falcon? 💡

4. Valletta is the capital of which island nation?

5. In the *Twilight* book *New Moon*, what does Jacob discover he truly is?

6. Which mammal has the fewest teeth?

7. What was the first single released by Irish boy band, Westlife? 💡

8. Who plays Wolverine in the *X-Men* trilogy?

9. Which Queen video features band members vacuuming in drag?

10. Who was the first Chinese leader to use the term 'Emperor'?

11. Which California hotel is referred to as 'The Riot House' in the film *Almost Famous*?

12. What is caused when the Moon moves into the Earth's shadow?

13. In 1943, Rene Magritte adopted which new style of painting?

14. What are the names of the two fictional continents in *Game of Thrones*?

15. Legally, what is a 'plaint'?

16. From which country was Evita Peron?

The Bumper Family Quiz Book
Quiz 123

1. Who designed the flag of Italy?

2. What, in computing terms, is OCR?

3. What English King was known as 'Crookback'?

4. On which continent is Macedonia located?

5. Which colour is the amethyst birthstone?

6. Flying Fish Cove is the capital of which Australian territory?

7. Who scored the final goal of Euro 2000 when France beat Italy?

8. What destructive natural event can happen when it rains for a long period of time?

9. Which of the following describes a compound that prevents infection or decay: antiseptic, antipasti, antipathy?

10. How is the constellation *Lyra* known in English?

11. In what year was Aldwych tube station, London, permanently closed?

12. Where are the lines of longitude the farthest apart?

13. What Windows keyboard key is used to open top-level menus?

14. Which is the capital city of the Cayman Islands?

15. What car-racing film, starring Matt Schulze as Vince, was released in 2001?

16. How many colours are on the French flag?

The Bumper Family Quiz Book
Quiz 124

1. What are the first names of Dolce and Gabbana?

2. In which English city is the Lowry Centre, with a gallery of paintings by L. S. Lowry?

3. Which element has the atomic number 9?

4. Which American actor plays the monstrous *Hellboy*?

5. What angle is greater than 90 degrees, but less than 180 degrees: acute, obtuse, reflex or straight?

6. What word, derived from a Greek sea god, means 'able to change frequently'?

7. What do you call a tool used for drawing circles?

8. What ocean does the Amazon discharge into?

9. What country hosted the 1990 World Cup?

10. What vegetable looks like a tiny head of cabbage?

11. As it entered the 21st century, what was the leading cause of death in China?

12. Who has hosted all 35 annual UK *Children in Need* telethons, as of 2014?

13. What instrument does Caroline Corr usually play in The Corrs?

14. Which country does the kangaroo come from?

15. Most of the Ancient Egyptian art still extant was found in what?

16. 2011's *New Year's Eve* was director Gary Marshall's follow-up to what other holiday-themed film?

The Bumper Family Quiz Book
Quiz 125

1. What is the name for the Sun's outermost atmosphere?

2. What reusable spacecraft took astronauts into space?

3. 'I just need your body, baby, from dusk till dawn', is from which song?

4. In what UK city would you find the Abbey Road popularized by The Beatles?

5. Which of these instruments do Mexican mariachi bands use: cello, piano, trumpet or tuba?

6. What is the brightest star in the sky, other than the sun?

7. What band performed the song *London Calling*?

8. In the 19th century, what replaced fresh plums in Plum Pudding?

9. Who took Manchester United's number 7 shirt after David Beckham transferred to Real Madrid?

10. How often does a leap year generally occur?

11. In what year did Benin become an independent country?

12. Jute is an agricultural product of which of the following nations: Armenia, Bangladesh, Iraq or Jordan?

13. How does Dumbo first show up in the animated classic *Dumbo*?

14. In music, what is a coda?

15. Who became the first nominal leader of China's Kuomintang political party in 1912?

16. On 24 April 2013, an eight-storey commercial building collapsed in what country?

The Bumper Family Quiz Book
Quiz 126

1. How did British Labour Party leader John Smith die?

2. In text chat, what does THX mean? 💡

3. With 6 goals, Italy's Paolo Rossi was the World Cup's highest scorer in what year: 1982, 1988, 1992 or 1996?

4. The definition of 'changes that certain animals go through as they develop' best fits which science term?

5. Which 2005 sci-fi film based on a classic book had the tagline *They're already here*?

6. What are the Hindu holy books called?

7. What area of the arts is Australian artist Aida Tomescu associated with?

8. An animal that is active at night is called what? 💡

9. In *Doctor Who*, which character called the 10th Doctor 'the enemy of his own kind'?

10. What is 'purdah'?

11. Which mathematician founded the American Journal of Mathematics?

12. What type of shampoo is recommended for people with dry hair: moisturizing, normal or volumizing?

13. In which US state did the Three Mile Island nuclear plant experience a near-meltdown in 1979?

14. What is Al-Hayat?

15. Who were the judges in UK *MasterChef* in 2014?

16. Who is said to be the first great humanist?

The Bumper Family Quiz Book
Quiz 127

1. Who discovered pasteurization?

2. What natural features can the mnemonic HOMES help you recall?

3. In what year did King John sign the Magna Carta? 💡

4. Which *Apollo* flight was the first to orbit the moon?

5. What does 'tyro' mean?

6. Wiley and Dizzee Rascal collaborated on which compilation album?

7. Who succeeded Charles II as English King?

8. New York's Hudson river bridge has been named after which famous American?

9. Who is the female dame in the pantomime *Aladdin*? 💡

10. What was the name of Odin's hall in Norse mythology?

11. In the film *Nick of Time*, what does Johnny Depp have to do in order to keep his daughter safe?

12. Which element has the atomic number 6?

13. Which Renaissance painter is buried in Rome's Pantheon?

14. Which country has Nuku'alofa as its capital?

15. Who was the first successor of Muhammad?

16. Which rapper bought boxer Mike Tyson's Connecticut estate?

The Bumper Family Quiz Book
Quiz 128

1. What device transfers traffic from one network to another on the Internet?

2. What country has the last remaining language in the world to officially use Runic letters?

3. What is the largest island in the Indian Ocean?

4. The 'Mona Lisa' is a painting of what?

5. Which of these vegetables is least likely to be found in a Chinese recipe: artichokes, broccoli or water chestnuts? 💡

6. What Spanish-speaking nation is located just south of the United States?

7. What is the name for a building where aeroplanes are stored or fixed? 💡

8. The UN General Assembly declared 2013 as the 'International Year' of what food?

9. Fear of childbirth is known as what?

10. What, in Russia, was a 'muzhik'?

11. Who directed the 1993 thriller, *Jurassic Park*?

12. Which is the French term for 'very fashionable'?

13. Traditional Japanese robes are called what?

14. The amount of calcium in a given amount of bone is also known as what?

15. Which English actor is twice-knighted?

16. Which of the following players never played for Italian football club Inter Milan: Andrea Mazzantini or Giuseppe Signori?

The Bumper Family Quiz Book
Quiz 129

1. Yamoussoukro is the capital of which nation?

2. What type of animal is an 'eyra'?

3. What mythical creature is said to live in a Scottish lake? 💡

4. The 'Gamekeeper's Night Dog' is a nickname for which breed?

5. Which famous Australian landmark was opened in 1932?

6. In what year did British boxer Lloyd Honeyghan retire from the ring?

7. In medical terms, what is a 'neonate' child?

8. Which Portuguese explorer was the first to reach India?

9. What do men in Japan do more than men in any other country?

10. What pieces of jewellery are given in the song *The Twelve Days of Christmas*? 💡

11. Who plays Monica's millionaire boyfriend Pete Becker in *Friends*?

12. Piet Mondrian sometimes painted on a square canvas then hung it how?

13. What species makes the loudest noise made by a living creature?

14. What is a 'placebo'?

15. Who was President of Iraq from 2005-2014?

16. What animal is Indiana Jones afraid of?

The Bumper *Family* Quiz Book
Quiz 130

1. On which continent is Singapore located?

2. What tennis legend coached Novak Djokovic in his early life?

3. Madonna does not appear, except in animation, in the video for which one of her 1989 songs?

4. How many legs do scorpions have? 💡

5. Which children's brand uses the slogan 'Play. Laugh. Grow'?

6. What is Pablo Picasso's daughter's name?

7. Who wrote *The Red and the Black*?

8. Which golfer is nicknamed 'El Nino'?

9. What is the distance between New Orleans, Louisiana, and New York, New York?

10. To shed the hair, feathers, skin or shell is to do what? 💡

11. What is the fifth month of the year?

12. Which island country's national language is Malagasy?

13. How many ships made up the 'First Fleet' which colonized Australia?

14. Who directed the 1985 film *Ran*?

15. What devastated a Mongol fleet attempting to invade Japan in 1281?

16. Glossophobia is the fear of what?

The Bumper Family Quiz Book
Quiz 131

1. What is the name of the famous museum in London which houses realistic wax figures?

2. Which fictional organisation has their base on Tracy Island? 💡

3. What is meat from sheep called?

4. How many degrees equal one radian?

5. What does 'Hong Kong' mean in Chinese?

6. What type of worm is an earthworm?

7. In what direction were Sumerian tablets read?

8. Which 2009 Disney animated feature is partially based on a Brothers Grimm tale? 💡

9. Who is a former nurse and Malcolm's second wife in the 2014 film *Dawn of the Planet of the Apes*?

10. Henry VIII ascended the English throne in which year?

11. Jelena Jankovic was trained at whose American Tennis Academy?

12. Which vitamin is required for blood coagulation?

13. What did x-rays show exist underneath the final Mona Lisa?

14. PEZ sweets are native to which European country?

15. A particle of light is known as what?

16. Whose was the first face on Facebook?

The Bumper Family Quiz Book
Quiz 132

1. What is a semiquaver called in US music terminology?

2. Who discovered the effectiveness of using lithium to treat mental disorders in 1949?

3. With what book did Hilary Mantel win the 2009 Booker Prize?

4. Peter Paul Rubens' most famous works deal with religion and what else?

5. What are, respectively, the capital cities of England, Northern Ireland, Scotland and Wales? 💡

6. Which Afghan river shares its name with the country's capital city?

7. What illness caused Nelson Mandela to be hospitalized in 1988?

8. In what year did the Battle of Hastings occur? 💡

9. Which type of horse is named from the Spanish word meaning 'painted'?

10. Which actress was George Clooney first married to?

11. What is the main crop grown in Vietnam?

12. Who plays the role of Ducky in *Pretty in Pink*?

13. In what type of landscape would you most likely find an igloo?

14. Which city hosted the 2008 Olympic Games?

15. What is the capital of Ireland?

16. Who composed the opera 'Carmen'?

The Bumper Family Quiz Book
Quiz 133

1. Which Indian politician is known as Daughter of the East & Daughter of Destiny?

2. During the Babylonian Captivity, where did Pope Gregory XI hold court?

3. Who are the three friends in *Ice Age: The Meltdown*? 💡

4. How long did it take to build the Roman Colosseum?

5. How many towns are there on Stewart Island, New Zealand?

6. Who is credited with creating Nestlé's 'Toll House' Cookies?

7. If you make £11 per hour and work for 40 hours, how much do you make? 💡

8. Tennis player Patrick Rafter was known by which smelly nickname?

9. Which actor plays the lead role in the *Mission: Impossible* film series?

10. San Salvador is the capital of which country?

11. Which is the busiest British railway station?

12. Which of these foods is a typical Greek dish: gyro, hamburger or spaghetti?

13. What US President introduced the first Siamese Cat into the United States?

14. What kind of dog is Scooby Doo? 💡

15. Which element has the atomic number 3?

16. What is an 'attar'?

The Bumper Family Quiz Book
Quiz 134

① Which book did Nelson Mandela read that earned the nickname *Robben Island Bible*?

② Who were the Constructors' Champions in the 2013 Formula One season?

③ What is Steve Buscemi's middle name?

④ In the board game *Cluedo*, what is the white piece called? 💡

⑤ What is the name of the holy book of Islam?

⑥ Which South American country's highest elevation point is Cerro Catedral?

⑦ In *The Score*, what is Robert De Niro's character planning to steal?

⑧ What would you call a nautical unit of speed: feather or knot? 💡

⑨ What type of fish is a dangerous delicacy for sushi eaters if not correctly prepared?

⑩ Jack and Meg White are the White Stripes, but how are they related?

⑪ What colour is a polar bear's skin?

⑫ In the first *Harry Potter* book, what did Hagrid do to Dudley?

⑬ Which was the first Space Shuttle to enter orbit?

⑭ What modern artist sold invisible paintings?

⑮ What sort of boat is a 'curragh'?

⑯ Which country is due south of France?

The Bumper Family Quiz Book
Quiz 135

1. How long did it take Columbus to cross the Atlantic?

2. Which date only occurs during a leap year?

3. During the 20th century, Chile experienced 28 major instances of which natural disaster?

4. What will usually happen to matter that is cooled: it will expand or it will contract?

5. Who did Tanya marry in series three of the show *Footballers' Wives*?

6. Which 19th-century chemist has etched on his tombstone 'S=k log W'?

7. What is the distinguishing feature of a Manx cat?

8. Who starred as the titular drunken lout in the 2011 remake of *Arthur*?

9. Who was crowned as King of England in April 1661?

10. Who played vampire Drusilla in *Buffy the Vampire Slayer*?

11. Which of these is produced by a dairy farmer: apples, milk or wheat?

12. Who was the first post-independence President of Cameroon?

13. What country does tennis pro Lleyton Hewitt represent?

14. What, in the past, was a 'pettifogger'?

15. In *Doctor Who*, who played the Twelfth Doctor?

16. The Bank of America Plaza, completed in 1993 at a height of 1039 feet, is located in which US state capital?

The Bumper Family Quiz Book
Quiz 136

1. Who coached the England squad in the 2014 World Cup?

2. The first building on the site of Windsor Castle was built around 1070 by whom?

3. In what year was the first general-purpose computer made: 1812, 1884, 1944 or 2000?

4. Which Prince song is thought to be sung from the viewpoint of Jesus?

5. What is the most popular colour of rose?

6. What is another name for the vitamin riboflavin?

7. Which Canadian author wrote the acclaimed novel *I Heard the Owl Call My Name*?

8. What was the name of the large, elephant-like animal that lived during the last Ice Age?

9. What is the potential energy in the nucleus of an atom called?

10. Tortug' Air is the flag-carrier airline of which country?

11. What is the average salinity of seawater?

12. What year did Prince Rainier of Monaco marry Grace Kelly?

13. How does Horton carry Who-ville in *Dr. Seuss' Horton Hears A Who!*?

14. How many holes are there on a normal golf course?

15. In ancient times, the Roman Colosseum was used primarily for what?

16. What organization accredits top-level-domain registrars on the Internet?

The Bumper Family Quiz Book
Quiz 137

1. What do Apple call their application-download shop?

2. Who played the President of the United States in *The West Wing*?

3. What is a koala's favourite food?

4. Who was the dictator of Romania from 1965 to 1989?

5. What country does tennis pro Novak Djokovic represent?

6. The Portuguese man-of-war is also known by what colourful nickname?

7. The science term 'orbit' is defined how?

8. Which of these chocolates is Swiss: Creme Egg or Toblerone?

9. What nation was the only South American OPEC founder?

10. Which author wrote *The Glass Menagerie* and *Cat on a Hot Tin Roof*?

11. What large World War 2 battle cruiser is permanently docked on the south side of the River Thames?

12. What is the name of the rooster on boxes of Kellogg's 'Corn Flakes'?

13. Which core Church of England text was first introduced in 1549?

14. What did Marilyn Monroe famously say she wore to bed?

15. Which film won the Best Picture Oscar for 2002?

16. What is the capital of Niue, an island nation in the South Pacific administered by New Zealand?

The Bumper Family Quiz Book
Quiz 138

1. In financial terms, what is a CD?

2. Which English county is best known for producing fruit, hops, and garden produce?

3. On what date did the Australian colonies form the Commonwealth of Australia?

4. What does the Lion wish that he had in *The Wizard of Oz*?

5. In what year were Cabbage Patch dolls invented?

6. What does 'approbatory' mean?

7. In Formula One racing, what does a yellow and red striped flag indicate?

8. What is the top layer of the rain forest called?

9. Which country is colcannon associated with?

10. What is the biggest island in Canada?

11. What condition is characterized by a stiff neck and fever: meningitis or flu?

12. In which country did one-third of the population lose money in pyramid schemes in 1997: Albania, Greece, Poland or Sweden?

13. Which Scottish actor plays Filip 'Chibs' Telford in American series *Sons of Anarchy*?

14. What is a long, braided piece of hair at the nape of the neck called?

15. What holiday takes place in *E.T. The Extra Terrestrial*?

16. What is motion energy called?

The Bumper *Family* Quiz Book
Quiz 139

1. Which author taught at Harvard while working as an astrophysicist?

2. In what year was Queen Victoria's Golden Jubilee?

3. What product is Crayola most famous for? 💡

4. Where is the terror group Abu Sayyaf based?

5. An invertebrate of which phylum is a pseudocoelomate: chordata, nematoda or porifera?

6. Kim Clijsters was engaged to which other tennis player?

7. In Disney's *Aladdin*, what does Aladdin pretend his name is? 💡

8. In *The Big Lebowski*, who is Jesus' bowling partner?

9. Who is considered the Father of Modern China?

10. In medicine, what is the 'theca'?

11. A 2008 song by Wiley is called: *If You're Going Out, I'm* what?

12. What kind of meat is used to make buffalo wings?

13. Which element was the first ever artificially created?

14. What type of animal is a 'titi'?

15. Who was Peter the Hermit?

16. Tashkent is the capital of what country?

The Bumper Family Quiz Book
Quiz 140

1. On which mainstream social media website can you change your language to 'pirate'?

2. What do you call immature frogs or toads? 💡

3. What country has the greatest percentage of farmers: Bhutan, China or Columbia?

4. What was the name of the prototype Space Shuttle that never entered orbit?

5. What is the name of the ferryman into Hades?

6. In which country was the first Christmas card printed?

7. Which is the closest planet to the sun?

8. The cities of Cordoba and Mendoza are located in which country?

9. How do you calculate the volume of a cuboid? 💡

10. What is the daily disappearance of the sun below the western horizon called?

11. The medical term 'WBC' is short for what?

12. In what discipline did people try to convert base metals into gold?

13. Where did Zinedine Zidane transfer from to join Real Madrid in 2001?

14. Which Central American country's highest elevation point is Cerro El Pital?

15. What Windows keyboard shortcut will paste what is already in the clipboard?

16. What film is about the first American cargo ship to be hijacked in 200 years?

The Bumper Family Quiz Book
Quiz 141

1. Which actor played Zach in *An Officer and a Gentleman*?

2. Who ascended the English throne in November 1558?

3. What is the metric unit for measuring liquid volume? 💡

4. Avianca is the flag-carrier airline of which country?

5. Who directed the film *Million Dollar Baby*?

6. In 1762, Catherine the Great became Czarina of which country?

7. The Dual Towers 1, completed in 2006 at a height of 853 feet, is located where?

8. Which nation hosted and won the inaugural football World Cup?

9. In maths, what is 6001 – 4569? 💡

10. Which 13-letter term means 'an actor who appears in a non-speaking role'?

11. What type of fish is a rollmop?

12. Algeria gained independence in 1962 from which European country?

13. In which national park is Scafell Pike, England's highest peak, found?

14. Which metal band's 2012 tour was the first since the death of bassist Paul Gray?

15. Jacqueline Onassis popularized what style of woman's hat?

16. What visual impairment does a squirrel have?

The Bumper Family Quiz Book
Quiz 142

1. Which US island was the site of a lighthouse before it became a notorious prison?

2. How many planets out from the Sun is the Earth? 💡

3. What is the largest sesamoid bone in the body?

4. Who is the Greek goddess of marriage and women?

5. What are the tiny air sacs in the lungs called?

6. For how many years was Ferdinand Marcos the ruler of the Philippines?

7. Which animator created Wallace and Gromit? 💡

8. What device can track the number of steps a person takes?

9. In medical terms, what does the suffix '-penia' mean?

10. What is an 'odist'?

11. Who voiced Zazu in the film *Lion King*?

12. In what city is Citigroup headquartered?

13. What is the smallest country in mainland Africa? 💡

14. In what year did the US invade Panama to arrest General Noriega?

15. Who won the Pichichi Trophy for being the top scorer in the 2012-13 season of the Spanish La Liga?

16. Which Hindu goddess is depicted playing the sitar?

The Bumper Family Quiz Book
Quiz 143

1. Who directed the 1966 film *The Good, the Bad and the Ugly*?

2. Will.i.am was a founding member of which hip hop band? 💡

3. What is caviar?

4. Who dominated British Touring Car racing in the late 1980s?

5. Which US state's flower is the orange blossom?

6. In 1978, the moon Charon was discovered orbiting which Solar System object?

7. Who holds the most stock in Martha Stewart Living Omnimedia?

8. Which planet takes 29.5 Earth years to orbit the sun?

9. Which of the following foods is the best source of calcium: banana, chicken or yoghurt?

10. What is the name for a female fox? 💡

11. In the 1930s, what was 'The Dust Bowl'?

12. According to legend, how did Achilles die?

13. What was the capital city of the Heian Empire in Japan?

14. Who has had the most UK Singles Chart number ones?

15. Who was the first aviator to score an air victory for the US Air Service in World War 1?

16. Who became UK Poet Laureate in 1984?

The Bumper *Family* Quiz Book
Quiz 144

1. A burrito is included in which cuisine?

2. What is Apple's high-end video-editing software called?

3. Where is Logan International Airport located?

4. What kind of bird do you often see sitting on the back of a rhinoceros?

5. Who plays cheerleading coach Sue Sylvester in *Glee*? 💡

6. In 2011 what Premier League club was Andy Woodman the goalkeeping coach for?

7. Which of these measurements would be different on Mars than on Earth: length, mass, volume or weight? 💡

8. Which Pharaoh ordered the building of the temples at Abu Simbel?

9. What's the largest ocean in the world?

10. Which country is Alofi the capital of?

11. How do you say 'Merry Christmas' in French?

12. Who played Jackson Brodie in the television adaptation of *Case Histories*?

13. In the painting, 'American Gothic', what is the man holding?

14. The 2008 film *21* is based on what non-fiction book by Ben Mezrich?

15. What Yogic method did Indra Devi advocate above all other techniques?

16. Who was elected National Chairman of the Union at Poland's first Solidarity conference in 1981?

The Bumper *Family* Quiz Book
Quiz 145

① The island of Cuba is approximately what length?

② In what town was David Beckham born?

③ What colour do ripe tomatoes usually turn?

④ Who invented the seed drill, making it possible to plant crops in regular rows?

⑤ Who came up with the name 'Nazis' prior to World War 2?

⑥ How long after Germany's invasion of Poland did France and Britain declare war?

⑦ In what year did FIFA first allow 23-member teams to play in the World Cup?

⑧ In *Happy Feet*, how do the penguins find a mate?

⑨ In the Anne Rice novels, who is the first Mayfair that Lasher goes to?

⑩ Which Disney animated feature is set in China?

⑪ What is the official language of Uganda?

⑫ What is Charlie's surname in *Charlie and the Chocolate Factory*?

⑬ What was a 'stater'?

⑭ What band was Dave Grohl in before Nirvana?

⑮ What is the Japanese word for 'dog'?

⑯ Which scientist oversaw Hitler's rocket program?

The Bumper Family Quiz Book
Quiz 146

1. In Japanese cooking, what utensil is required to prepare a Nabe dish?

2. Which is the busiest airport in the UK?

3. What is the physics term for a fundamental constituent of matter?

4. What comes next in this series: 2, 3, 5, 7, 11, 13, 17?

5. What city is the setting for the 2006 film *The Good German*?

6. What was the name of the world's first electronic computer?

7. What is best-selling author Rushdie's first name?

8. In the *Mr Men* books, what colour is Mr Greedy?

9. What is the word for drawing blueprints?

10. What type of organism is a 'neem'?

11. Ireland is bounded by which ocean?

12. What is a bathymeter?

13. Who is Australia's official head of state?

14. In music, what does 'sforzando' mean?

15. Sweden took which place at the 2010 IIHF Hockey World Championship?

16. Which country had to surrender Korean rule after World War 2?

The Bumper Family Quiz Book
Quiz 147

1. What do Hermione's parents do for a living in *Harry Potter*?

2. Out of the following list, which is not a strong acid: bromic, oxalic, perbromic or selenic?

3. What colour are Dorothy's slippers in *The Wizard of Oz*?

4. Historically, what was 'demesne'?

5. What online company did David Filo and Jerry Yang create in 1994?

6. How many people perform the Quadrille at a time?

7. Astraphobia is the fear of what?

8. What does Dorothy follow on her journey through Oz?

9. What kind of oil was used to light the first menorah?

10. Maromokotro is the tallest mountain on which African island country?

11. Who played Judge Doom in *Who Framed Roger Rabbit*?

12. What other band besides Ratt has Stephen Pearcy been a part of: Arcade, Desperado or Imagika?

13. What was Che Guevara known as?

14. Who directed the film *Argo*?

15. Boxer Samuel Peter is known by what nickname?

16. The Ryugyong Hotel, at 330m (1083gt) tall, is found in what restrictive country?

The Bumper Family Quiz Book
Quiz 148

1. How is a horse's coffin bone also known?

2. What is the term for rain that contains chemical pollutants?

3. Which country's highest elevation point is Benara?

4. As of 2016, how many teams will play in the UEFA European Football Championship? 💡

5. Where was Caesar salad invented?

6. What horse did Bruce Davidson ride in the 1996 Olympics?

7. What are 'ados'?

8. What would you expect if you ordered 'surf and turf' in a restaurant?

9. What were trade associations formed in medieval towns called?

10. Which band was singer Justin Timberlake originally a member of? 💡

11. Which of these is 'the visual impression that remains after the initial stimulus is removed': afterimage, preimage or subimage?

12. In what film did Daniel Stern play Hal Petersham?

13. The AMRAAM missile was designed to replace what other missile?

14. What is the upper house of the German Parliament called?

15. For which religion is the Tibetan Book of the Dead a holy text?

16. Three-fifths of Duran Duran formed Arcadia. What was the name of their sole album?

The Bumper *Family* Quiz Book
Quiz 149

1. Who directed the 2004 movie *Hellboy*?

2. What Roman military battle ended the Dacian Wars?

3. What are the three primary ink colours for printing?

4. What geometric shape has eight sides?

5. The Washington Irving character Ichabod Crane had feet shaped like what?

6. Who commanded the British forces in the Battles of Talavera and Ciudad Rodrigo?

7. In what year did Nero's reign end?

8. In which country in the United Kingdom is the town of Usk located?

9. What is the repeated sound when sound waves bounce off other objects called?

10. What is a 'putsch'?

11. Who beat Marat Safin to win the 2004 Australian Open Singles Championship?

12. Which European country's highest elevation point is Carrauntoohil?

13. What is the name of the light-sensitive layer inside the eyeball?

14. In which 2002 film did Chris Klein play the character Jonathan Cross?

15. What kind of seeds are roasted and salted at Halloween in the US?

16. Who recorded the hit single *You Mean The World To Me* in 1994?

Quiz 150

① Who captained the remarkable 2012 European Ryder Cup team?

② What releases the flavour of maple syrup?

③ For which film did Colin Firth receive his first Academy Award notification?

④ Champagne is what type of wine?

⑤ What is a normal systolic blood pressure?

⑥ In India, what class of people used to be called 'ryots'?

⑦ In *The Hunger Games*, how often do the Hunger Games occur?

⑧ How would one describe Tierra del Fuego?

⑨ What would you call an orange, green, yellow and blue brush-tongued parrot from Australia?

⑩ Medically, 'congenital' means what?

⑪ In botany, what are 'vela'?

⑫ Who was Zeus' brother?

⑬ Who won the 2013 Booker Prize with the novel *The Luminaries*?

⑭ While Nelson Mandela was President of South Africa, the country hosted what sport's World Cup?

⑮ Which river flows by Windsor Castle?

⑯ In the song 'Fast Car' you've got a fast car, but what does Tracy Chapman have?

The Bumper Family Quiz Book
Quiz 151

① What is the name of Celine Dion's own-brand perfume?

② Which African country's highest elevation point is Monte Binga at 2,436 metres?

③ Which ceremonial object of African tribal art might also be worn at Halloween: cape, hat, mask or sword? 💡

④ In *Happy Feet*, who is the penguin who can't sing?

⑤ Over 99% of the population in Afghanistan belong to which religion?

⑥ What is the most popular first name in the world?

⑦ What term is defined as 'sharpness', most often relating to the senses or wit: acuity or sarcoma?

⑧ What were Carrot, Goat, and Onion in World War 2?

⑨ Where was Andy Murray's position in the ATP tour ranking at the end of 2013? 💡

⑩ Which poem by Lord Byron popularized vampire mythology?

⑪ Colin Montgomerie played amateur golf in which country?

⑫ What is another name for a butter bean?

⑬ Prague is the capital of what country?

⑭ What name is used specifically to describe the region around the South Pole?

⑮ What is the spinal column found in vertebrate animals called?

⑯ In music, what does the instruction 'da capo' mean?

The Bumper Family Quiz Book
Quiz 152

① Which European microstate's highest point is Monte Titano?

② What is the biggest-selling UK Christmas single of all time? 💡

③ On what part of the body is hair growth the fastest?

④ Formula One tyres are normally filled primarily with which gas?

⑤ The film *Reality Bites* features which touching U2 song?

⑥ What is traditionally found in *croissants aux amandes*?

⑦ What warning do children traditionally call out during pantomime? 💡

⑧ Who co-starred with Jackie Chan in *Rush Hour 2*?

⑨ Which was the subtitle of the second *Zelda* game?

⑩ In zoology, what is a 'mya'?

⑪ Where was the only air attack against the continental US during World War 2?

⑫ Which nation in Southern Asia gained its independence on August 15, 1947 from the UK?

⑬ After 1904, Piet Mondrian decided to stop painting what he liked and paint for whom?

⑭ In what year did Napoleon annex the Papal States?

⑮ What is a *Canis lupus*?

⑯ Which author wrote *David Copperfield*?

The Bumper Family Quiz Book
Quiz 153

1. What does 'Iran' translate to in English?

2. Which bread ingredient is made from wheat?

3. What US President created the US Environmental Protection Agency?

4. The name of the Italian dessert 'tiramisu' means what?

5. You can find Plymouth Rock in which US state?

6. Which pairs of minerals are almost always found together: Azurite and Malachite or Quartz and Pyrite?

7. What country's four official languages are German, French, Italian and Romansh?

8. Which film won the 1999 Academy Award for Best Picture?

9. Which of these is a traditional food of Germany: rice, pizza, sauerkraut or spaghetti?

10. What honorary position did John Betjeman hold from 1972?

11. What is a viola?

12. What is the first name of golf's Palmer?

13. What underlying operating system is Mac OS based upon?

14. What type of creature is a 'jerboa'?

15. What is the primary cause of scurvy?

16. Who became Iran's supreme religious leader in 1989?

The Bumper Family Quiz Book
Quiz 154

1. Andy Murray won his first ATP singles title in which US tournament?

2. What kind of animal is Aslan in *The Chronicles of Narnia*? 💡

3. Which city was Poland's capital in the 14th century?

4. Which land animal can run up to 75mph (120km/h)?

5. Which Cumbrian museum documents the history of writing with graphite?

6. The coccyx is commonly known as what?

7. Who plays cheerleader Quinn Fabray in *Glee*? 💡

8. Which German city was home to the first large brewing industry?

9. Rembrandt van Rijn is known for being what?

10. What process did the Ancient Egyptians use to preserve the human body?

11. In *Lord Of The Rings*, who first named Frodo an 'Elf Friend'?

12. Which planet was pummelled by pieces of the comet Shoemaker-Levy in 1994?

13. Which UK supermarket uses the slogan 'Every little helps'?

14. In what year did IBM sell its first personal computer?

15. What did Kim Kardashian and Kanye West name their 2013 baby?

16. What Latin title did the Poet Laureate hold in Medieval England?

The Bumper Family Quiz Book
Quiz 155

1. Which was the first modern country in the world not to have a rectangular or square flag?

2. What decade is the hit single *Too Many Rivers* by Brenda Lee from?

3. Which country is famous for paella?

4. St. Patrick's Day celebrates what cultural heritage?

5. What country has Washington, DC as its capital and uses the dollar as its currency? 💡

6. Who became Pope on April 24th, 2005?

7. What word refers to 'the exchange of money for goods and/or services'?

8. How many letters are there in the nonsense word in *Mary Poppins*?

9. What is dietary fibre made up of?

10. Which of these meats does not come from a pig: bacon, ham, pork chops or sirloin steak? 💡

11. In which 2002 film did Jack Black play the character Zeke?

12. What Australian band was fronted by future AC/DC lead singer Bon Scott in 1966?

13. Robert Louis Stevenson is famous for writing which pirate novel?

14. Which element is a poisonous gas that combines with sodium to form table salt?

15. What was Floyd Mayweather Jr.'s nickname as an amateur boxer?

16. During what month does the *Quadrantids* meteor shower take place?

The Bumper Family Quiz Book
Quiz 156

1. Approximately what percentage of eligible people voted in the Iraqi elections of 2005?

2. What feature of a camera eliminates parallax error?

3. In what year did Blur win four Brit Awards in one night?

4. What pseudonym was the *Hardy Boys* series published under?

5. What type of computer document is a 'PNG' file?

6. Who were the only two astronauts who both flew to the Moon and also flew the space shuttle?

7. What is the name of the award bestowed on the best player in a World Cup?

8. What is the modern birthstone for the month of May?

9. What fish can smell one drop of blood in a million drops of water?

10. *Multiplicity* and *Pacific Heights* featured which actor?

11. What was *Microsoft Frontpage* designed for?

12. How many enemy aircraft was the Sopwith Camel credited with destroying in World War 1?

13. What strategic body of water does Singapore overlook?

14. What is a 'mud puppy'?

15. What is the largest island in the Mediterranean Sea?

16. Who is the Patron Saint of children?

The Bumper Family Quiz Book
Quiz 157

1. In 1917, Jewish artist Marc Chagall was named a provincial commissar for what?

2. What event is caused by radiation hitting the Earth's atmosphere: cloud cover, the northern lights or a rainbow?

3. How many pockets are there on a snooker table?

4. Which English King ascended the throne in August 1485?

5. Which of these is not a type of bacteria: bacillus, coccus, heteroccus or spirillus?

6. What was the main ingredient in the UK Ministry of Food's 'mock duck' recipe?

7. Which characters do the majority of the singing in Disney's *Hercules*?

8. What is the reciprocal to the sine function?

9. What is the central region of a star, planet, or galaxy called?

10. Sculptures of which animals lie at the base of Nelson's column in Trafalgar Square, London?

11. In 2013, which flavour of Ben & Jerry's became America's top-seller?

12. The Q1 building, completed in 2005 at a height of 1058 feet, is located in which southern country?

13. What do you call the weakening of a material caused by repeated or alternating loads?

14. What country is the setting for the 2009 film *3 Idiots*?

15. Which US state had the longest period of Prohibition?

16. The mountain ranges of Chile are known for an abundance of which violent geographical feature?

The Bumper Family Quiz Book
Quiz 158

1. How many ships did Ferdinand Magellan take on his trip around the world?

2. Which animal is called the ship of the desert?

3. Which month is the first month of the year? 💡

4. Where in Europe is the River Una?

5. Who took a shower in the dishwasher in *Alvin and the Chipmunks*?

6. Which Greek philosopher invented the way of thinking called 'logic'?

7. Winter in Brazil occurs during which months?

8. Who co-wrote *Lifeguard* with James Patterson?

9. Which country has Monaco as its capital? 💡

10. Which Australian island is named after one of the days of the week?

11. Who had a huge hit in 2013 with *What Does the Fox Say*?

12. What is the bus width of the main CPU in the Sony PlayStation 2?

13. How long does a typical house fly live?

14. Which is the largest rodent in North America?

15. At a Japanese restaurant, if you order 'yakizakana' what will arrive on your plate?

16. In what year did Diego Maradona captain Argentina to the World Cup?

The Bumper Family Quiz Book
Quiz 159

1. Which person is best known for leading the Iranian Revolution?

2. In the game of chess, how does the knight move?

3. Which Grand Slam did Kim Clijsters win in 2005?

4. Who became the first Poet Laureate of the US in 1986?

5. Which of the following is a type of cloud: marshmallow, cotton, circus or cirrus? 💡

6. Who played Marty McFly's father in *Back to the Future*?

7. In which fairy tale would you find the Big Bad Wolf? 💡

8. What Greek city hosted the 2004 Olympic Games?

9. What is the name of the plane that flew around the world without refuelling in 1986?

10. What is the longest bone in the human body?

11. Where did the Vikings first attack England?

12. Who starred as Eddie Wilson in *Eddie and the Cruisers*?

13. What city was the last imperial capital of Vietnam under the Nguyen dynasty?

14. What school is featured in the show *Hex*?

15. What is the sum of the interior angles of a pentagon?

16. What is another name for vitamin C?

The Bumper Family Quiz Book
Quiz 160

1. Where did India's first civilization arise?

2. What colourful cheese is often crumbled over salads: blue cheese or red cheese? 💡

3. What did Gail Borden invent?

4. Who was the Greek God of Love?

5. In what year was the South Korean boxer In-Jin Chi born?

6. What was the name of the Hong Kong hotel featured in *The Man with the Golden Gun*?

7. Which cat breed combines the features of a tiger and the size of a domestic shorthair?

8. What does 'usury' refer to?

9. Who is Angelina Jolie's famous father?

10. In Disney's *The Lion King*, what do Pumbaa and Timon say means 'no worries'? 💡

11. Which union did Arthur Scargill lead from 1992 to 2002?

12. What snake is also known as a 'water moccasin'?

13. What is poi made from?

14. What modern country was previously known as Anatolia?

15. When painting in watercolours, what is granulation?

16. What was Velvet Underground's second studio album?

The Bumper Family Quiz Book
Quiz 161

1. What sports brand uses the slogan 'Impossible is nothing'?

2. Who is the supreme governor of the Church of England?

3. What instrument uses sound waves to help get a picture of the ocean's bottom?

4. What anagram of the word 'melon' is also a fruit?

5. Who won the 1974 World Cup, hosted by West Germany?

6. In heraldry, what metal is 'argent'?

7. What is molten rock beneath the surface of the earth called?

8. Which leader of the Soviet Union resigned on December 25th, 1991?

9. What would you be served in a Japanese restaurant if you ordered 'udon'?

10. Who wrote *To Kill a Mockingbird*?

11. What is the place where an air mass forms called?

12. Intermittent windscreen wipers were first introduced by which company?

13. Who was inaugurated as Afghanistan's first popularly elected President in 2004?

14. Who was the ultra-cool star of the 1968 film *Bullitt*?

15. Which of these countries lies partly inside the tropics: Argentina, Lebanon, Tunisia or Uruguay?

16. The medical term 'perforation' is best defined as what?

The Bumper Family Quiz Book
Quiz 162

1. What is Adobe's video-editing software called?

2. In what year did Joseph Stalin die?

3. Al-Azhar, the oldest University in the Arab world, is located in which country?

4. Which character does Lena Headey play in *Game of Thrones*?

5. In text chat, what does TTYL mean?

6. What kind of vehicle was the 'ARV' in World War 2?

7. What are the three primary colours of light?

8. What makes up most of an elephant's trunk: bone, cartilage, muscle or nerves?

9. What type of creature is a seahorse classified as?

10. What is the chemical symbol for iodine?

11. What sea does the Yangtze discharge into?

12. What fighter had more professional fight knockouts than anyone in history?

13. In what US state is the Cape Canaveral spaceship launch site?

14. What was a 'jerkin'?

15. Which Chinese fruit is white on the inside and bumpy and reddish on the outside?

16. Who wrote the music score for *Cars*?

The Bumper Family Quiz Book
Quiz 163

1. Who was the Parthenon in Greece built to honour?

2. What is a 'redoubt'?

3. What does 'bedaub' mean?

4. What does the symbol '<' mean in maths? 💡

5. With which Beatle did Michael Jackson duet to sing *The Girl Is Mine*?

6. Which wizard is looking for someone to share an adventure with in *The Hobbit*?

7. What exact title did Edvard Munch give to 'The Scream'?

8. On what day do Americans celebrate the Battle of Puebla by eating Mexican food?

9. What do you call turf cut out by the club when a golf shot is taken?

10. How many UK Chart Number Ones did Westlife have when they split? 💡

11. Which mapping projection distorts the most at the Earth's poles: Conic, Equilateral, Mercator or Robinson?

12. Which scientist proposed that the Sun was the centre of the solar system?

13. What is the name of the building housing the UK Houses of Parliament?

14. What occupation does Ryan Reynolds' character hold down before becoming a superhero in *Green Lantern*?

15. In May 1960, the first underwater circumnavigation of the earth was completed by what submarine?

16. Which was the first retail *Zelda* game released for the 3DS?

The Bumper *Family* Quiz Book
Quiz 164

① What is 'dysphoria'?

② What do we call a physical substance that occupies space and has mass?

③ What is the weather phenomenon known as a 'tsunami'? 💡

④ What painter painted the famous black and white 'Guernica'?

⑤ Which Asian country's highest mountain is Kanchenjunga?

⑥ To which boxer did Sugar Ray Robinson lose his last professional fight?

⑦ Beirut is the capital of what nation?

⑧ Skippers Canyon is near which New Zealand town?

⑨ What is the up and down movement of ocean water caused by wind called? 💡

⑩ Which Pope set the day of Christmas as December 25th?

⑪ What is the most common eye colour in the world?

⑫ What type of dog is Queen Elizabeth II's favourite?

⑬ Who starred with Bernie Mac in the 2005 film *Guess Who*?

⑭ In what year did Edoardo Fendi marry Adele?

⑮ What beverage did Galileo call 'light held together by water'?

⑯ On which sea of the moon did *Apollo 11* touch down?

The Bumper Family Quiz Book
Quiz 165

(1) What was the occupation of karaoke-loving Dennis van der Horst in the 2006 Dutch film *Nightrun*?

(2) Which of the following is the total chemical activity of processing food: metabolism, metaforce or metatags? 💡

(3) Who discovered quaternions?

(4) What are the names of the only two egg-laying mammals in existence?

(5) Which sea borders north-west Colombia?

(6) What is the capital of Greenland?

(7) In which film did Richard Gere and Julia Roberts reunite after *Pretty Woman*?

(8) Who was Mike's best man when he married Alma on *Coronation Street*?

(9) What fish species was threatened due to the Cajun style of cooking it?

(10) The equator sits on what latitude, in degrees? 💡

(11) Golfer Ernie Els is from which country?

(12) Which US comedy-drama did Adele appear in in 2009?

(13) How many voyages did Columbus make to the New World?

(14) Which planet is thought to have the tallest mountain in the solar system?

(15) What 1960s activist/performer sang at Mandela's 90th birthday tribute?

(16) Relative to symptoms appearing, when can adults start to pass the flu virus to others?

The Bumper Family Quiz Book
Quiz 166

1. Elizabeth II is the eldest daughter of whom?

2. In Hawaii, what is a 'luau'?

3. Clomiphene, introduced in 1967 to increase fertility, also resulted in what?

4. What currency was reintroduced into Lithuania in 1993?

5. What do black bears do during the winter? 💡

6. What is a map that shows an area's shape and elevations called?

7. From which language did English borrow the word 'golf'?

8. What is the name of the town in Ireland whose name means 'the little field' and is home to a legendary stone?

9. Which boxer retired in 1938 at the incredible age of 60?

10. What is Mulan's dragon friend called in the Disney film? 💡

11. What shape is a baguette?

12. What is a normal diastolic blood pressure number?

13. Which character in *The Other Boleyn Girl* suffers a miscarriage?

14. The necropolis of Saqqara is closest to which ancient city near Cairo?

15. In what year did McDonald's introduce the McChicken sandwich?

16. Pablo Picasso's 'Guernica' was painted using only what three colours?

The Bumper Family Quiz Book
Quiz 167

1. Which country uses the real for currency?

2. What type of water fowl has the greatest number of vertebrae in its neck?

3. Which film won the Best Picture Oscar for 2012?

4. What is the capital of the Philippines?

5. Which Disney animated feature is based on a Greek myth?

6. In folklore, who was Mab?

7. What could the Egyptian god Osiris grant?

8. Tachophobia is the fear of what?

9. A mink coat is made from the fur of which kind of animal?

10. Complete the saying: 'A dog is a man's best ___'

11. What is the first thing you do on any golf hole?

12. In Hindu mythology, who is the god of destruction?

13. What sort of animal is a 'kelpie'?

14. What was the name of the Internet browser licensed by Spyglass Inc that then became the basis for Internet Explorer?

15. Who was the Angevin dynasty, begun with Henry II in 1154, named after?

16. How tall was the Berlin Wall?

The Bumper Family Quiz Book
Quiz 168

1. Which city is nicknamed Tinseltown?

2. Which Ancient Mexican civilization developed the symbol for 'zero': Aztec, Incan or Mayan?

3. What do scientists use to help organize the elements?

4. Who plays Spider-Man in the film *Spider-Man 3*?

5. What do you have when you are served *gazpacho* in southern Spain?

6. On which continent is Bangladesh located?

7. What is the name of the Kent castle which has an aviary, a maze, a grotto and a golf course?

8. Which pair sang the duet on the *Quantum of Solace* soundtrack?

9. What value is 10 squared equal to?

10. Who are the three kings mentioned in the biblical account of Jesus' birth?

11. Which term describes flying at six times the speed of sound?

12. Which of these fictional characters is honoured by a statue in Kensington Gardens: Oliver Twist, Paddington Bear or Peter Pan?

13. What is Microsoft's spreadsheet application called?

14. Which Australian Prime Minister held office for the shortest term in the 20th century?

15. In a Formula One race what does a green flag indicate?

16. If an object 'skirrs', what does it do?

The Bumper *Family* Quiz Book
Quiz 169

1. Kevin Spacey played Eugene Simonet in which film?

2. During his tenure as President of South Africa, Nelson Mandela's office was in what city?

3. How many wheels does a tricycle have? 💡

4. What are chemicals processed from oil called?

5. What was the world's first electronic digital watch called?

6. Baguettes and croissants are examples of breads from what country?

7. What year was the Marshall Plan announced?

8. In what year did David Beckham first play in a World Cup?

9. What colour is a giraffe's tongue? 💡

10. The leg of what creature is used in the witches' brew from *Macbeth*?

11. What are you hearing when you put a seashell to your ear?

12. Dr J. J. C. Bradfield was the architect of which world-famous bridge?

13. If you ordered 'niika' in a Japanese restaurant, what would you get served?

14. As of 2014, how many BRIT awards has Leona Lewis won?

15. What was Marilyn Monroe's real name?

16. What UK brand uses the slogan 'It's got our name on it'?

The Bumper Family Quiz Book
Quiz 170

1. Where is the Grolsch brewery located?

2. Which of the following is traditional garb worn by Scottish men: kilt, ponchos or purple shoes?

3. Which film won the 1998 Academy Award for Best Picture?

4. The 1929 book, *A High Wind in Jamaica*, was written by whom?

5. What is a series of lines drawn on a map called?

6. What is the formula to convert Fahrenheit to Celsius?

7. Which singer was sampled in the song *Stan* by rapper Eminem?

8. In medicine, what does the adjective 'crural' mean?

9. Which precious metal has the chemical symbol Pt?

10. What is the most expensive square on a standard UK Monopoly board?

11. Who wrote the 1881 account, *Incidents in the Life of a Slave Girl*?

12. If you lived in medieval times you'd wear 'hose' on your ...?

13. Which English monarch was born in February 1516?

14. British fans threatened a riot in 1976 if who was not allowed a grand prix restart?

15. What broke up after President Gorbachev's resignation in 1991?

16. Which of these is an official language of Chile: Brazilian, Chilean, Peruvian or Spanish?

The Bumper Family Quiz Book
Quiz 171

1. What type of computer document is an 'RTF' file?

2. How many hours behind Paris is New York City, usually?

3. What was the nickname fans gave the pony-tailed Roberto Baggio?

4. In the board game *Cluedo*, what is the purple piece called? 💡

5. Who starred as Molly Brown in *Titanic*?

6. In maths, what is a 'minuend'?

7. Roughly how long can a cockroach live without its head? 💡

8. What is the International System of Units also known as?

9. As of 2014, how tall is the world's shortest living woman?

10. In which mountain range is Ben Nevis?

11. Which British comedian starred in *The Idiot's Weekly*, an Australian comedy program?

12. What was impressive about the city planning of early Indus Valley civilizations?

13. What is another term for funded debt?

14. What artistic style involves paintings made up of thousands of tiny dots?

15. What are the dark spots on the Sun that appear in 11-year cycles called?

16. What name did Jacques Cousteau give his main research vessel?

The Bumper Family Quiz Book
Quiz 172

1. Which of the following is not a type of Irish folk dance: waltz, jig, reel, half set?

2. Citrus fruits are a great source of which vitamin?

3. Who played Harry Gordon Selfridge in the series *Mr Selfridge*?

4. Where was Swedish footballer Henrik Larsson's father born?

5. J Allard oversaw which Microsoft games project? 💡

6. Who is the Roman goddess of the hearth?

7. In the animal kingdom, what is a jungle pouch?

8. What was unusual about HMS *Sirius*, Arthur Philip's flagship in the First Fleet?

9. Which monarch built the Tower of London?

10. A whisk would be most appropriate for which of these cooking tasks: mashing potatoes, mixing batter or cooking chips? 💡

11. Which Greek god wears winged sandals?

12. In medical terms, what does the suffix '-genic' mean?

13. What do Microsoft call their cloud version of *Office*?

14. Which insurance brand uses the catchphrase 'Simples'?

15. Why was production of *Skyfall* suspended throughout 2010?

16. In what year did the British scientist William Herschel discover Uranus?

The Bumper Family Quiz Book
Quiz 173

1. What was Adrian's maiden name, as mentioned in the film *Rocky II*?

2. What is the tenth month of the year?

3. What is the smallest country in Africa?

4. Who recorded *Pretzel Logic*?

5. What is the name of the UK's central bank? 💡

6. Who was the first US President?

7. What mineral makes both sapphires and rubies when cut and polished?

8. What do the letters 'ATM' stand for?

9. How long did the series of conflicts known as the Hundred Years' War really last?

10. Who was named Chelsea manager in June 2013? 💡

11. Near which Australian city can you find Mount Coot-tha?

12. What did a German pilot named Mathias Rust infamously do in 1987?

13. What is the O'Hara family plantation called in *Gone with the Wind*?

14. Why is Leonardo da Vinci considered a prime example of a 'Renaissance man'?

15. What is boxer Mario Santiago's nickname?

16. How many volts are in a kilovolt (kV)?

The Bumper Family Quiz Book
Quiz 174

1. In microbiology, what is a 'nostoc'?

2. How many destinations are served by Heathrow Airport, as of 2014?

3. Which film won the Best Picture Oscar for 2013?

4. Up to how many gallons of water can an African elephant drink a day? 10, 25 or 50 gallons?

5. What does Amy Macdonald call Pete Doherty in a 2007 song?

6. Which hotel is sometimes described as an extension of Buckingham Palace?

7. What determines a shareholder's equity: assets minus liabilities, total funds in bank or weighted capital?

8. What fruit was often in the Bible: banana, fig, grapefruit or watermelon?

9. What element is a diamond composed of?

10. What year were women first allowed to compete in the Olympic Games?

11. In computer terms, what does 'USB' stand for?

12. Which English King married Elizabeth of York, daughter of Edward IV?

13. What Canadian province joined seven years after confederation?

14. What was the capital of the Ancient Mauryan Empire?

15. How wide is the opening to an anteater's mouth?

16. Which middle-eastern country's highest elevation point is Jabal ad Dukhan?

The Bumper *Family* Quiz Book
Quiz 175

① Which of the following animals gives birth underwater: giraffe, hippopotamus or zebra?

② How long did the 18th-century impeachment and trial of Warren Hastings last?

③ Princess Diana attended whose funeral as her first official state visit abroad?

④ What does #FF on Twitter stand for? 💡

⑤ In what year did Kuwait achieve independence?

⑥ In the film *Corpse Bride*, where does Victor's new bride take him?

⑦ What flavour is Grand Marnier?

⑧ Which of these fruits has an inedible outer covering: peach, pear or pineapple? 💡

⑨ What are scientists that study the ocean called?

⑩ What did the British government present to Malta on April 16th, 1942?

⑪ Who wrote the 1952 book *Wise Blood*?

⑫ In World War 2, in what city did the French government surrender to Germany?

⑬ What does 'a priori' mean?

⑭ In which year was boxer Ricky Hatton's debut fight?

⑮ What is a quaver called in US music terminology?

⑯ What is the capital city of Italy?

The Bumper Family Quiz Book
Quiz 176

1. What was Michael Jackson's second multi-platinum solo album?

2. How many consonants are there in the English alphabet?

3. In what country are you expected to say 'kampai!' instead of 'cheers!'?

4. What is an espresso macchiato?

5. What British headland is known in Cornish as *Penn an Wlas*?

6. Which monarch ascended the English throne in February 1689?

7. Who was the author of *Old Goriot*?

8. What does Planet Earth do to cause night and day?

9. Nelson Mandela opened his first law office in which year?

10. Where was the Fauvism art movement first introduced?

11. What is the most easterly city in all of North America?

12. The juice of what plant is commonly applied to burnt or damaged skin?

13. Which country is Abu Dhabi the capital of?

14. Which horse won the Grand National in 2011?

15. Because of its widespread habitat and potent venom, which African snake causes more fatalities than any other?

16. In *All About Steve*, how did Mary meet Steve?

The Bumper Family Quiz Book
Quiz 177

1. What name did Nelson Mandela give the Presidential residence during his tenure?

2. Which kind of dog has a rounded, long body and short legs: dachshund or golden retriever? 💡

3. What was Wassily Kandinsky's work *Yellow Sound*?

4. What is the world's tallest land mammal?

5. What is the capital city of the province of Saskatchewan, Canada?

6. Who is the author of the book *The Exorcist*?

7. Type I diabetes results from the destruction of which organ?

8. What term means the space taken up by a surface: area, array, base or volume? 💡

9. What type of car was featured in the 1977 film *Smokey and the Bandit*?

10. How many crew of the German battleship *Bismarck* survived its sinking?

11. What is the southernmost part of India called?

12. Who was Andre Agassi married to from 1997 to 1999?

13. In music, what speed is 'prestissimo'?

14. How many kinds of fat/fatty acids are there?

15. What is a compote?

16. In what year did the Space Shuttle first launch?

The Bumper Family Quiz Book
Quiz 178

1. Which author wrote the book *A Prayer for Owen Meany*?

2. In medicine, what is a 'haematoma'?

3. Where are you when you sunbathe at the Phuket Island beaches?

4. What city does *The Hangover* take place in?

5. By what process do plants use chlorophyll to make glucose?

6. Which golfer is nicknamed 'Cinderella'?

7. What sort of crockery is 'raku'?

8. What is 3,291 rounded to the nearest 100?

9. What is the name of the ship's computer on *Red Dwarf*?

10. Which artist released the album *Lovehatetragedy*?

11. The Tour de France bicycle race was first run in which year?

12. What shape are a camel's blood cells?

13. What was the very first British ship sunk in action in World War 2?

14. Which polygon has eight sides?

15. Rhinoplasty is the medical name of which type of plastic surgery?

16. What country in South America has Quito as its capital?

The Bumper Family Quiz Book
Quiz 179

1. After the PLO's military wing the PLA was defeated in Jordan, where did the PLO relocate?

2. Bolivia shares its shortest border with which country?

3. What does the US slang term 'crib' mean, as used on MTV? 💡

4. Who did Christopher Walken play in a *Batman* film?

5. What type of brandy is usually included in recipes for lobster bisque?

6. What is a baby sea lion called?

7. Which city has an underground train network with stations called Town Hall, Wynyard and Central?

8. Who voiced Rapunzel in Disney's *Tangled*? 💡

9. What word can you make by unscrambling 'acdeeent'?

10. In ballet, 'first position' has the feet together in what shape?

11. Lufthansa is the flag-carrier airline of which country?

12. The Sugababes were nominated for a BRIT Award for which of these singles: *Look At Me*, *Overload* or *Real Thing*?

13. Hanukkah lasts for how many nights?

14. What is the estimate of the true age of a mineral or rock called?

15. Which English football team are nicknamed the 'Pilgrims'?

16. In what year did Winston Churchill give his earliest warnings about Nazi Germany?

The Bumper *Family* Quiz Book
Quiz 180

1. In Greek mythology, who was the father of Zeus?

2. In which ballet are seasons represented by individual dancers?

3. What is the official name of Angola's legislative body?

4. In the *Little Miss* books, what colour is Little Miss Naughty? 💡

5. Which big cat is bred with a tiger to make the tigon?

6. Who was Cleopatra in love with?

7. Which IEEE 802.11 network standard directly preceded 802.11g?

8. On the Internet, what is a DNS?

9. What is the name of Dudley's best friend in the *Harry Potter* books? 💡

10. What flowery word is another name for a leopard's spots?

11. Which Western African nation gained its independence on January 1, 1960?

12. What company once labelled every box of tea with 'blessed by a certified tea shaman'?

13. What was the name of the Ewok chief in *Return of the Jedi*?

14. Which country hosted the FIFA World Cup in 1990?

15. Cvitan Galic had what distinction during World War 2?

16. What year was Yitzhak Rabin awarded the Nobel Peace Prize?

The Bumper Family Quiz Book
Quiz 181

① Which monarch ordered the death of Mary, Queen of Scots?

② What vegetable is traditionally carved at Halloween? 💡

③ Giant squid and swordfish can grow to the same size, but how much larger are a squid's eyeballs?

④ What sound is created at sea level at 761mph (1225km/h) at a temperature of 20°C (68°F)?

⑤ What constant is referred to as 'The Universe's Clock'?

⑥ How much taller is the new One World Trade Center than the Empire State Building, to the nearest 100 feet?

⑦ In Australia, 'chewie' is not a Star Wars Wookiee, but what sweet treat? 💡

⑧ Which raw material is used to make plastic?

⑨ What colour ball must be struck first in snooker?

⑩ What does 'basal' mean?

⑪ The airport code YTO designates which international airport?

⑫ Who supplied the voice of Timon in Disney's *The Lion King*?

⑬ Marsala is a form of Italian what?

⑭ Which river is Windsor Castle on the banks of?

⑮ What is the term for the amount of money a government owes?

⑯ In 1983, a terrorist explosion killed 237 US Marines in what country?

The Bumper Family Quiz Book
Quiz 182

1. Who painted the 'Blue Boy'?

2. Which Disney animated feature is based on a Victor Hugo story?

3. Which TV sitcom featured the character Joey Tribiani?

4. What is the deepest spot in the world?

5. In what language is the 2009 film *3 Idiots* filmed?

6. What does the adjective 'pseudo' mean?

7. To which food groups do a hot dog and a bun belong?

8. Which of the following means 'impenetrable by light': opaque, translucent or transparent?

9. Who beat Jimmy Connors to win the 1978 Wimbledon Singles Championship?

10. Who wrote the *95 Theses* against the Catholic Church?

11. What is the middle name of English rocker and songwriter Robert Plant?

12. How is the constellation *Ursa Major* known in English?

13. Who succeeded Nelson Mandela as President of South Africa in 1999?

14. Who is allowed to edit most pages at Wikipedia.org?

15. In which country will you find most of the Kalahari Desert?

16. What *Harry Potter* creature turns into a person's worst fear?

The Bumper Family Quiz Book
Quiz 183

1. Who is the only English Poet Laureate to have been dismissed from the position?

2. What type of material attracts iron and some other metals? 💡

3. Which is the busiest airport in the world, as of 2014?

4. Nelson Mandela became President of South Africa in 1994 as the leader of which party?

5. What is the feeding structure found in sea urchins: Archimedes' Flashlight or Aristotle's Lantern?

6. What do the Monsters in *Monsters, Inc.* use to generate power?

7. Lima is the capital of which country?

8. Who lives at the top of Enid Blyton's *Faraway Tree*? 💡

9. What is the last name of the Italian family who set up a multinational company selling whirlpools?

10. What is the half-life of Potassium 40 as it decays to Argon?

11. In what year were the *Gibson Explorer*, *Flying V*, and *Modern* guitars patented?

12. What did Lloyd Honeyghan try but fail to become after retiring from boxing?

13. What step in 'methode champenoise' results in the carbonation of champagne?

14. Which country had free parliamentary elections for the first time in 47 years in 2005?

15. How many zeros in a trillion?

16. Mary Tudor married Philip II of what country?

The Bumper Family Quiz Book
Quiz 184

1. What stick-like vegetable's name comes from the Greek word for 'sprout' or 'shoot'?

2. In the film *Mona Lisa Smile*, who did Julia Stiles play?

3. Who wrote Johnny Cash's classic *A Boy Named Sue*?

4. What was the name of the New York rock festival headlined by Peter Gabriel in 1994?

5. In what season do the leaves of some trees start falling to the ground?

6. Gustavus Adolphus, led Sweden in which war?

7. Enchiladas, burritos, and tacos are examples of what nation's food?

8. What do you call a baby frog?

9. What is the process of turning used products into new products called?

10. Which battle was fought on August 22, 1485?

11. What is the name of British businessman Richard Branson's space-travel company?

12. The medical term 'refractory' is best defined as what?

13. Where was boxer Oleg Maskaev born?

14. What are chemicals that reduce or prevent oxidation called?

15. In a religious building, what is an 'aumbry'?

16. Myanmar is the world's second-leading producer of what illicit drug?

The Bumper Family Quiz Book
Quiz 185

1. The Matamata turtle is found on which continent?

2. What vegetable is a fungus: broccoli, carrot, mushroom or onion? 💡

3. How low, in feet below sea level, is the lowest point of Lake Eyre, Australia?

4. Which organ produces oxytocin to control childbirth contractions?

5. Who won the 2010 FIFA World Cup?

6. The Argentinian region of Patagonia is partly located in which other country?

7. What colours are on the German flag?

8. In which country was Vlad the Impaler born? 💡

9. Which nationality does Caldo de Queso belong to?

10. In zoology, what is a 'chela'?

11. How many *Indiana Jones* films were released in the eighties?

12. What are underwater mountains called?

13. Which country was the last to join the 'nuclear club'?

14. Which English King was nicknamed 'The Unready'?

15. How many days did it take to complete the first non-stop balloon flight around the world in 1999?

16. What famous prize did the novel *The Good Earth* win?

The Bumper Family Quiz Book
Quiz 186

1. What year did the nuclear-related accident at Three Mile Island occur?

2. Which arch-villain is finally destroyed at the end of *The Deathly Hallows*?

3. Which Roman emperor succeeded Augustus in 14AD?

4. Which animal provides most of the milk that we drink?

5. Where were the 1936 Olympics held?

6. How many seasons of US show *Frasier* were made?

7. Which member of the X-Men is bound to a wheelchair?

8. A painter generally uses what to hold up his canvas?

9. What is the name of the giant Ferris wheel on the South Bank in London?

10. What sort of lighting increases the likelihood of overindulgence in food: bright lighting or dim lighting?

11. What are the huge storms that the sun produces called?

12. Which precious metal has the chemical symbol Ag?

13. If I stick up my thumb at the side of the road, what am I doing?

14. A song title by The Libertines asks 'what became of the' what?

15. In maths, what is 6 to the power of 0?

16. The 'czardas' is a national dance in which European country?

The Bumper Family Quiz Book
Quiz 187

1. In India, what is a 'sadhu'?

2. On which African island can lemurs be found?

3. Which city is due to host the 2018 Winter Olympic Games?

4. What season is between winter and summer? 💡

5. Melbourne's China Town is located on which street?

6. In what year was the US Vietnam War Memorial dedicated?

7. Korsakoff's syndrome occurs when what vitamin is lacking in the body?

8. The 2001 Bonn Conference addressed the government of what nation?

9. When looking at an ocean, which of these is the colour it mostly appears to be: blue, orange or white? 💡

10. What is the most common contaminant found in fish?

11. In *Much Ado About Nothing*, Beatrice has a battle of wits with whom?

12. In heraldry, what do you call an animal standing on all fours?

13. Which 1970s fashion movement featured spiked hair?

14. Which of these varieties of pasta is the tiniest: Acini di pepe, buctani, pipette rigate or rocchetti?

15. Finish the Mandela quote, 'A good head and a ___ are always a formidable combination'.

16. Which group had a 1965 hit with *Anyway, Anyhow, Anywhere*?

The Bumper *Family* Quiz Book
Quiz 188

1. Aeroflot is the flag-carrier airline of which country?

2. Who was the author of *On the Road*?

3. In what city is Buckingham Palace located? 💡

4. San Marino is totally surrounded by which country?

5. Which was the world's first broadcast colour TV system?

6. Who won the 1986 FIFA World Cup?

7. What country is made up of over 6,000 islands, the largest being Honshu?

8. Mandela was given 'phuzamandla' for lunch while in prison, which means what?

9. How many English *Mr Men* books are there in the series? 💡

10. Which is the scientific term for feeding on blood?

11. What 19th-century composer revived interest in the music of J.S. Bach?

12. What was the emblem of the Caesarian Legions?

13. In which film did Joaquin Phoenix portray Lucius Hunt?

14. As of 2014, how many Academy Award nominations has Tom Cruise had?

15. What type of food do most Brazilians refrain from eating during Lent?

16. What do human adults usually have 32 of?

The Bumper Family Quiz Book
Quiz 189

(1) How were Silvio Berlusconi's decadent parties better known?

(2) What writer worked for British Naval Intelligence and used his experiences in his writing?

(3) Who wasn't a band member of Nirvana: Dan Peters, Nate Mendel or Pat Smear?

(4) What is a pilchard?

(5) What is a 'culm'?

(6) What sea contains the world's largest supply of caviar?

(7) In which room would you expect to find a sofa?

(8) What is the name of the playing area in which boxing matches are held?

(9) Who was the first UK Prime Minister of the 20th century?

(10) Which device is used by a computer to display graphics and information: modem or monitor?

(11) How long is the Panama Canal?

(12) What is the formal name for climate studies?

(13) Who is the director of Disney's live-action film of *Cinderella*?

(14) A crocodile is what type of animal?

(15) When selling items, what does the acronym 'ONO' short for?

(16) What was Saddam Hussein sentenced to after being found guilty of crimes against humanity?

The Bumper Family Quiz Book
Quiz 190

1. Who plays Magneto in the *X-Men* trilogy?

2. Which kind of clock is accurate to within one second in 1.7 million years?

3. What feature film did Michael Jackson play a scarecrow in? 💡

4. Bolivia shares its northernmost border with which country?

5. In heraldry, what colour is 'sanguine'?

6. In what year did Mussolini's dictatorship in Italy collapse?

7. What is amber made from?

8. What are the names of Peter Rabbit's siblings? 💡

9. Who wrote the play that the film *About Last Night* was based upon?

10. In *Seinfeld*, who is George Costanza's architect alter ego?

11. Who succeeded Otho as Roman Emperor in the Year of the Four Emperors?

12. When was the first time the World Cup was not held in Europe or the Americas?

13. Raisins are made by drying which fruit?

14. What flower is the drug *digitalis* prepared from?

15. Circuitry that electronically separates the colour from the picture signal is called what?

16. What was Josef Stalin's nationality?

The Bumper Family Quiz Book
Quiz 191

1. What was Kim Jong Il's honorary title while his father, Kim Il Sung, was in power?

2. What is the name of Google's webmail service?

3. What does the adjective 'echt' mean?

4. What was Neo's real name in the 1999 film *The Matrix*?

5. Which of these animals is closely related to sharks: blue gill, manta ray, octopus or trout?

6. 'Gris', 'grau' and 'plata' are all foreign words for what English colour?

7. Which version of Microsoft *Windows* was released in 1990?

8. Which country's highest mountain is K2?

9. If a recipe asked you to 'sauté' a chopped onion, what would you do?

10. In the *Harry Potter* series, what colour is Harry's scar?

11. What is a scientist who specializes in the study of cells called?

12. Where is the birthplace of Charles Dickens?

13. Who participated in the 'triangular slave trade'?

14. What slithering creature is used in the witches' brew from *Macbeth*?

15. Who was the first rider to win the Tour de France five times in a row?

16. Which Somalian actor made his screen debut in *Captain Phillips*?

The Bumper Family Quiz Book
Quiz 192

① Among the Pacific nations, Colombia consistently records which statistic: heaviest snowfall, highest rainfall or longest drought?

② Which artist painted 'The School of Athens'?

③ Which is the smallest species of deer?

④ What is an 'aerolite'?

⑤ How many separate World Cups has David Beckham scored in? 💡

⑥ The definition, 'an experiment on patients', best fits which medical term?

⑦ Who released the comical one-hit wonder *Because I Got High* in 2001?

⑧ What was the first indigenous people wiped out by Conquistadors?

⑨ Which event marked Phil Mickelson's first major golf championship?

⑩ What is a homophone? 💡

⑪ Phobos is one of Mars's moons – which is the other?

⑫ What did Heian noblemen wear to distinguish themselves from ordinary citizens?

⑬ What is 'aune' an old French measure of?

⑭ What settlement granted Lutherans the right to practise their religion?

⑮ In the Marvel franchise, what does SHIELD stand for?

⑯ How many fluid ounces make up a half-gallon?

The Bumper Family Quiz Book
Quiz 193

1. Who wrote the thriller *The Partner*?

2. Which country is associated with haggis? 💡

3. The film *A Perfect Murder* was directed by whom?

4. Which island nation lies 1200m (1800km) off the east coast of Africa?

5. How does sunscreen work?

6. What do you traditionally give for a sixtieth anniversary?

7. Which city hosted the 2002 Winter Olympic Games?

8. Which 1980s cartoon series with tiny blue creatures was made into a feature film in 2011? 💡

9. During what war in 1899-1902 did Britain gain territory abroad?

10. What unusual profession does Danny DeVito have in his cameo in *Friends*?

11. In what year did Gordon Brown become UK Prime Minister?

12. What is a general name for a living thing?

13. Focaccia al Rosmarino is a food item of what type of cuisine?

14. What British chef initiated a program of healthy eating in UK schools?

15. What is the name of Tom Cruise and Katie Holmes' daughter?

16. In World War 2, what emblem was painted on the conning tower of the German U-Boat U-201?

The Bumper *Family* Quiz Book
Quiz 194

1. What sort of muscle is located near the front of the body: anterior, inferior or posterior?

2. Other than the platypus, what is the only other egg-laying mammal?

3. Leona Lewis' first single was a soulful cover of what song?

4. What did Romans call the Colosseum?

5. Which US President was known as 'Abe'?

6. How old was Bill Gates when he became a billionaire?

7. Which of these weapons did the British use in the trenches of France during World War 1: Mills Bomb, Skunk Grenade or Taffy Explosives?

8. At which age was Tiger Woods first seen on TV playing golf?

9. Who voices Wyldstyle in *The Lego Movie*?

10. Nigeria is located on which continent?

11. How is the constellation *Gemini* known in English?

12. What is a 'kaon'?

13. What is the state flower of New Jersey?

14. Who acted in *Roxanne*, *LA Story*, and *The Jerk*?

15. When a horseshoe bend in a river is cut off, what is formed?

16. Which nationality does carne asada belong to?

The Bumper Family Quiz Book
Quiz 195

1. In what year did the first person land on the moon?

2. In *Twilight*, what does Bella's stepfather do for a living?

3. Basseterre is the capital of what country?

4. Which type of jewellery is traditionally given on a 30th anniversary?

5. What film franchise is Robert Pattinson best known for?

6. Who did most of Tom Cruise's stunt driving in the film *Days of Thunder*?

7. What colour is Jessie's hat in *Toy Story 2*?

8. Geographically, what is a 'mete'?

9. What function does a 'scale' serve on a map?

10. What was the name of the first space station?

11. What is the capital of the Faroe Islands?

12. The country now known as Belgium was once known as what?

13. Which European country was occupied by Britain from 1814 until 1964?

14. Which food item is a potato-based pasta?

15. What is the name of Microsoft's web search site?

16. How many facial muscles does it take to produce a smile?

Quiz 196

1. Who designed the Guggenheim Museum?

2. Who voices Unikitty in *The Lego Movie*? 💡

3. What famous chef created the world-renowned Spago's restaurant?

4. What country produced the largest bomber of World War 1?

5. Who wrote *Brighton Rock*?

6. How many different airlines fly from Heathrow, as of 2014?

7. What paint colour is formed when yellow and red are mixed? 💡

8. Who was nicknamed the 'Maid of Orleans' in the 15th century?

9. Which film won the 2000 Academy Award for Best Picture?

10. What kind of punishment was called 'castigatio' in the Roman army?

11. Near what Vietnamese city will you find Truc Bach Lake?

12. The '#' symbol on a telephone goes by what name?

13. Which Chelsea FC manager held the job for the longest?

14. *Mariner 4* sent the first close-up pictures of which planet back to earth?

15. Who painted 'The Scream' in 1893?

16. What symbol appeared on the left shoulder of an Apollo astronaut's spacesuit?

The Bumper Family Quiz Book
Quiz 197

1. The film *In the Bedroom* was directed by whom?

2. In which Australian state were the 'Sara' quadruplets born in 1950?

3. Which Caribbean country did the US agree to ease restrictions on in 1999?

4. Who handled lead vocals and guitar for Nirvana?

5. Which country did Napoleon Bonaparte lead?

6. In weather, what is a 'bora'?

7. When tea leaves unfold as they steep it is sometimes called what?

8. Which southern Australian island is named after a marsupial?

9. Which of the following awards did Matt Kuchar win in 2010: Arnold Palmer Award or Jack Nicklaus Trophy?

10. What type of creature was the megalodon?

11. What year did King Hussein of Jordan die of cancer?

12. Who headbutted Marco Materazzi in the chest during the 2006 World Cup?

13. What is fast food chain Subway's slogan?

14. Which snake will roll over and fake a gruesome death to confuse its attacker: Eastern hognose, European adder or parrot snake?

15. What is the name for the narrow part in the middle of an hourglass?

16. What famous structure can be found on Salisbury Plain, England?

The Bumper Family Quiz Book
Quiz 198

1. In what year was pop star, Madonna, born?

2. *War Horse* is set during which war?

3. In Hinduism, what is the representation of a god or goddess in human or animal form called?

4. In *The Godfather*, who played the hit man Luca Brasi?

5. Who ascended the English throne in March 1625?

6. On the Internet, what is the POP email protocol short for?

7. Which Disney animated feature has a famous computer-animated ballroom?

8. Where in Chile is the Atacama Desert situated?

9. Which insect carried the Bubonic Plague to Europe?

10. Which designer is the star of the film *Unzipped*?

11. What was Britney Spears' debut single called?

12. If you were hungry for a 'Wiener schnitzel', what would you be craving?

13. What size is a full-size snooker table?

14. What is a body of water surrounded by land called?

15. Who is the Roman King of the Gods?

16. Who established the nematode *C. Elegans* as an experimental organism?

The Bumper Family Quiz Book
Quiz 199

1. Which country has Asunción as its capital city?

2. In *Cars*, what kind of car is Sally?

3. What are Indian pastries stuffed with potatoes called?

4. How many points is a brown ball worth in snooker?

5. What are young beavers called?

6. What is the clear gel extracted from aloe vera leaves used for medically?

7. How many keys are there on a standard Microsoft keyboard?

8. In what century did Ethelred the Unready become King of England?

9. What is the nickname given to the Huang He River?

10. In what direction does the sun set?

11. What was the 'mother culture' of Mesoamerica?

12. What is the point of a pyramid called?

13. What is the average approximate lifespan of a grizzly bear?

14. The liner notes for Nirvana's *From the Muddy Banks of the Wishkah* were written by whom?

15. Which *Friendship 7* astronaut, later a US senator, has the middle name Herschel?

16. What is a 'smorgasbord'?

The Bumper Family Quiz Book
Quiz 200

1. In *The Haunting*, who called the girl to the house?

2. Capitol Hill (Saipan) is the capital of which US island territory?

3. What fruit has a fuzzy, brown skin and green flesh?

4. As of 2014, how many *Fast and the Furious* feature films have there been?

5. What sort of lines did Robin Thicke sing about in 2014?

6. What were the 'Four Olds' Mao wanted to replace during China's cultural revolution?

7. In 2014 what Premier League club was Paul Ince the manager of?

8. How many countries border North Korea?

9. In which city would you find Buckingham Palace?

10. The famous collection of children's fantasy books called *The Chronicles of Narnia* were created by whom?

11. In what year did David Cameron become UK Prime Minister?

12. Which god was the patron deity of the city of Babylon?

13. What term is used for military use of harmful biological agents?

14. What type of material is 'organza'?

15. Which variety of snake is feared for its fast-acting venom: black mamba or python?

16. Australia, the Bahamas, Singapore and the United States all use what form of currency?

The Bumper Family Quiz Book
Quiz 201

1. The film *Jagged Edge* was released in which year?

2. Which American animal has mask-like markings on its face and a ringed tail?

3. What colour is Vegemite, the Australian 'Marmite'?

4. Which Disney animated feature is about a dog who thinks he has super powers?

5. Which country ranks first in cereal consumption per capita?

6. Which Ancient Greek is considered to be the founder of the practice of medicine?

7. Which word describes a long poem describing heroes and great events, such as 'The Odyssey'?

8. Cuba is less than a hundred miles away from what US state?

9. Who wrote *In Search of Lost Time*?

10. Which cell part is responsible for controlling most of the activity inside a cell?

11. Who was the second US President?

12. 'NiCad' is a brand name of what product?

13. Who won the women's singles at the 1999 French Open?

14. In legal terms, what is 'abrogation'?

15. As an illustrator, Marc Chagall provided drawings for what book?

16. Which of the following is not the name of an official language group: Altaic, Indo-European, Romano-Italic or Semitic?

The Bumper *Family* Quiz Book
Quiz 202

1. Where did German sailors land during World War 2: Alaska, Florida, Maine or New York?

2. In 2002, Xanana Gusmao was elected to be the first President of what new nation?

3. Where is the Colin Montgomerie Golf Academy?

4. What musical fantasy was Disney's third animated feature?

5. What type of element is neon?

6. In what year did Soviet troops defeat the German army at Stalingrad?

7. What is used for flavouring schnapps made from potatoes in Germany?

8. Which key part of a map allows you to calculate the distance between two places?

9. What is the smallest independent nation in South America?

10. Who did Giancarlo Giannini play in *Quantum of Solace*?

11. What is the capital of Slovakia?

12. What is the record duration for the World's Longest Kiss, as of 2014?

13. During World War 1, Malta became known as the what?

14. What 2003 Dizzee Rascal song features vocals by Wiley?

15. What physical constant did Henry Cavendish first determine using two weights and a cantilever?

16. Copenhagen is the capital of what country?

The Bumper Family Quiz Book
Quiz 203

1. Which horse won the Grand National in 2012?

2. What was the name of Hitler's private train?

3. About how many days does it take for the moon to pass through all phases? 💡

4. With complete bed rest, studies show a muscle might lose what percentage of its strength per day?

5. Who did King George III appoint as the first President of the Royal Academy in 1768?

6. What is behaviour taught by the parent or other adults of a species called?

7. The Marshall Islands has which capital city?

8. In Israel, what is a 'moshav'?

9. What are the maids doing in the song *The Twelve Days of Christmas*? 💡

10. Which international soccer striker of the 1980s was known as 'The Vulture'?

11. The first non-Axis jet plane to see combat during World War 2 was the what?

12. Who does Guy Pearce play in the 2006 film *Factory Girl*?

13. Who was the founder of Cartier?

14. In *Lord of the Flies*, what do the boys hold when they want to speak?

15. On which continent is Kazakhstan located?

16. Who recorded the hit single *Because You Loved Me*, from *Up Close & Personal*?

The Bumper Family Quiz Book
Quiz 204

1. How many PGA tour events did Phil Mickelson win in 2003?

2. What country hosted the 2004 UEFA European Football Championship?

3. Who plays Cedric Diggory in the *Harry Potter* films? 💡

4. Who directed the 2006 film *Pan's Labyrinth*?

5. What is papaphobia?

6. Bolivia is landlocked by which of these countries: Chile, Columbia, Ecuador or Venezuela?

7. Who created *Buffy the Vampire Slayer*? 💡

8. Which is the closest star to Earth, after the sun?

9. In what year was Adele awarded a Grammy for Song of the Year?

10. Who painted 'The Almond Tree in Flower'?

11. In anatomy, what is 'medulla'?

12. Which country is known by its inhabitants as Suomi?

13. Who was the leader of the 'War Hawks' during the War of 1812?

14. What will happen to a bowl of ice cream left in the sun? 💡

15. Which designer launched 'Intrusion', a fragrance for women?

16. Which dog was considered sacred among Chinese royalty?

The Bumper Family Quiz Book
Quiz 205

1. Which of the following cities never served as capital of independent Pakistan: Islamabad, Karachi or Rawalpindi?

2. In which year was George II crowned King of the United Kingdom?

3. What song did Paul McCartney write about the civil rights turmoil in America?

4. What is the name of the female steam engine in *Thomas and Friends*? 💡

5. What popular US holiday beverage is made from sugar, milk and eggs?

6. Which art movement started in France during the 1860s?

7. Which film won the 2008 Academy Award for Best Picture?

8. In heraldry, what metal is 'or'?

9. How many goals did Germany score in the 2010 World Cup? 💡

10. In the days of the Roman Empire, which luxurious fabric was sold for its weight in gold?

11. Who was the author of *Dr Zhivago*?

12. Where was golf's British Open played in 2014?

13. How is the constellation *Libra* known in English?

14. Which spice is used to flavour cevapcici?

15. What is the major religion of India?

16. The Binturong comes from what part of the world?

The Bumper Family Quiz Book
Quiz 206

1. What is designer Prada's first name?

2. In what year did Jamaica gain full independence?

3. Plato thought the lost island of Atlantis was linked to which ancient culture?

4. Which species of animal can fly, and usually lives in caves?

5. When you bump your 'funny bone', what nerve are you actually hitting?

6. In what decade is *Raiders of the Lost Ark* set?

7. Which philosopher wrote *The Elements*?

8. In 2005, the IRA announced that it was ending its violent campaign for what?

9. What did pirates believe that earrings could improve?

10. What was the name of Robin Thicke's debut single?

11. In religion, what is a 'stupa'?

12. On the London underground, what colour is the Piccadilly line?

13. Which treaty brought an end to the Eighty Years' War?

14. Which German won six gold medals for swimming at the 1988 Summer Olympics?

15. Which landlocked country is bordered by Russia, Ukraine, Poland, Lithuania and Latvia?

16. How many principles of holistic medicine are there?

The Bumper Family Quiz Book
Quiz 207

1. Which rhinoceros has only one horn?

2. Who is the CEO of Facebook?

3. Who resigned as President of Haiti in 2004?

4. In 2006, Damon Hill succeeded which legend as President of the British Racing Drivers' Club?

5. Which of these is not a tool usually used by painters: brush, canvas or chisel?

6. What type of creature might leave 'frass' lying about?

7. Who is the Roman goddess of the harvest?

8. Which rapper made an extended music video in 2013 featuring artists and art in New York City?

9. What is the medical name for a face lift?

10. In which country was Cheddar cheese first produced?

11. How many World Music Awards did Mika win in 2007?

12. Which designer produced the fragrances 'One' and 'Be'?

13. How old was Juan Lazcano when he started boxing?

14. Which nation in the Middle East gained independence from the UK on June 19, 1961?

15. 2010's *Clash of the Titans* is a remake of a film of the same name from what year?

16. Which famous architect designed a home in Bear Run, Pennsylvania?

The Bumper Family Quiz Book
Quiz 208

1. In how many European countries did the physical Euro currency debut in January, 2002?

2. Who wrote the 1853 novel *Cranford*?

3. How many eggs does the average chicken lay in a year?

4. Which 2001 film featured Heath Ledger and Paul Bettany?

5. How do you write five hundredths as a decimal number? 💡

6. What is the common name of the star *Alpha Canis Majoris*?

7. When Christopher Columbus first landed in Jamaica in 1494, who claimed it as a territory?

8. What are Nancy Drew's two best friends called? 💡

9. Which English monarch married Philip II of Spain?

10. What country decorates banana and mango trees for Christmas?

11. What disability did World War 2 squadron leader Douglas Bader have?

12. How many balls are used in a game of snooker?

13. In the film *The Lives of Others*, what job does playwright Georg Dreymana's girlfriend have?

14. Who played Lindy Chamberlain in the film *Evil Angels*?

15. What is the name of the depression under the nose?

16. What season is it in Australia during December?

The Bumper Family Quiz Book
Quiz 209

1. Who is Ian Fleming's cousin who starred in 1974's *The Man With the Golden Gun* as Scaramanga?

2. For what period of years was Margaret Thatcher UK Prime Minister?

3. Who was the first *Mr Men* character created by Roger Hargreaves? 💡

4. What is the impossibly small point in a black hole where all matter converges called?

5. Where in England was the *Magna Carta* signed in 1215?

6. What character was played by Jena Malone in the 2004 film *Saved!*?

7. The Tigris and the Euphrates rivers flow through what Middle-Eastern country?

8. Who was the author of *The Stranger*?

9. Originally, how many *Raggy Dolls* lived in the Reject Bin? 💡

10. TAME is the flag-carrier airline of which country?

11. Thimphu is the capital of which country?

12. Who scored the most goals in the 1986 World Cup in Mexico?

13. What is the substance that cell walls in green plants are made of?

14. Picasso's first name was what? 💡

15. When did UNICEF produce the first charity Christmas card?

16. What is used to thicken gazpacho?

The Bumper Family Quiz Book
Quiz 210

1. Who was known as the 'Angel of the Mountains' in Tour de France circles?

2. Which organ regulates the amount of sodium kept in the body?

3. Approximately how much air does a human breathe per minute?

4. Which band did Robbie Williams once belong to? 💡

5. What type of clouds are thick and puffy and can sometimes turn into thunderstorms?

6. Henri Matisse began drawing after what happened?

7. In what year did Egypt become an independent country?

8. In heraldry, what do you call an animal in a walking pose?

9. What couldn't Kylie Minogue 'get out of her head' in 2001?

10. On a map, what is a 'legend'? 💡

11. Who directed the 1982 thriller, *Poltergeist*?

12. What did German ships start doing in Australian coastal waters in October 1940?

13. Whose coronation took place at Westminster Abbey in 1626?

14. What enzyme is responsible for breaking down starches?

15. Mauritania borders which ocean?

16. What was Maroon 5's debut single called?

The Bumper Family Quiz Book
Quiz 211

1. What year was the atom split for the first time?

2. Which Andrew Lloyd Webber musical features songs *Memory* and *Mr Mistoffelees*?

3. What is a sudden violent explosion on the sun called?

4. What is 'kosher' food?

5. Which country is Skopje the capital of?

6. Which is the longest muscle in the human body?

7. Who roamed around Sherwood Forest with his merry men?

8. What is Baby's real name in the film *Dirty Dancing*?

9. What odds did bookmakers give for Cameroon to win the 1990 World Cup?

10. Who is in love with the fictional character Irene Adler?

11. For what film did Maggie Smith win an Academy Award in 1970?

12. What unit is defined as the average distance from the Earth to the Sun?

13. What is the region between the first and second cataracts of the Nile known as?

14. What art form is Andy Warhol known for?

15. Which of Socrates' students is best known for making others aware of his tutor's ideas?

16. Which ingredients are used for making 'ants on a log'?

The Bumper *Family* Quiz Book
Quiz 212

1. Which South American mammal resembles a small llama?

2. Which North American country's highest elevation point is Mount Logan?

3. What is the national flower of Ukraine?

4. In the Dr Seuss book, who 'stole Christmas'?

5. How many legs does an earwig have?

6. Which of these countries has the largest population: Egypt, Iraq, Jordan or Kuwait?

7. What year did Pasteur produce the first anti-rabies vaccine?

8. Who wrote *Middlemarch*?

9. What does Guido tell Giosue the prize is if he wins the game in the 1997 film *Life is Beautiful*?

10. What geometric shape has six sides?

11. How many zeros are there in the number ten thousand?

12. What is the capital of Nepal?

13. Whose ad tagline was 'Where Do You Want To Go Today?'

14. Who won the inaugural Daytona 500 race?

15. Which database program is included with *Microsoft Office Professional*?

16. Which Canadian artist designed the flag for Newfoundland and Labrador?

The Bumper Family Quiz Book
Quiz 213

① Which medical abbreviation describes coronary heart disease?

② The 1979 book titled *The Burger's Daughter* was written by whom?

③ Frederic Chopin is famous as what?

④ What does 'dim sum' literally mean?

⑤ Leonardo da Vinci was well known for making paintings on what theme?

⑥ The Bering Strait lies between which two continents?

⑦ Who directed the 2003 Marvel film, *Hulk*?

⑧ In text chat, what does BFF mean?

⑨ Who was the top British 'Ace' of World War 1 despite being practically blind in one eye?

⑩ What US city surprisingly ranked 41 of 50 in a 2010 list of America's fittest cities: Cleveland, Las Vegas or Los Angeles?

⑪ Which golfer won the 2012 HSBC Women's Champions Tournament?

⑫ How many children did William Shakespeare have?

⑬ In what year did Sony introduce the 'Walkman'?

⑭ Which river does not empty into the Gulf of Mexico: Mississippi, Colorado or Rio Grande?

⑮ What does the Canadian Motto *A mari usque ad mare* mean?

⑯ What type of animal is a 'cob'?

Quiz 214

① In the 'Twilight' book 'Eclipse', what city is experiencing a string of unsolved murders?

② Which painter is known for 'The Hay Wain'?

③ Which of these is the heaviest unit of weight: kilogram, ounce, pound or ton? 💡

④ In cooking, if you 'pare' a carrot, what do you do to it?

⑤ Which film tells the story of a man who has fathered 533 children through a sperm bank?

⑥ Where in the UK is the River Eea?

⑦ In a square-based pyramid, what shape is the base? 💡

⑧ Which planet has a day that lasts 41 minutes longer than Earth's?

⑨ During his Presidency, Nelson Mandela was known for doing what multiple times a day?

⑩ How many rubber ducks are included in the world's largest collection, as of 2014?

⑪ In tiddlywinks, what is the target receptacle called?

⑫ What Egyptian monster feasts on the heart of someone unworthy of eternal life?

⑬ What is the name of Britain's national museum of modern art in London?

⑭ Which country has the capital Warsaw?

⑮ What colour flame does tin burn with?

⑯ Who played the lead break in The Rolling Stones song *One Hit to the Body*?

The Bumper Family Quiz Book
Quiz 215

1. Which golfer documented his fight against cancer in his book *Zinger*?

2. Which of the following animals is not found in Australia: dingo, kookaburra or hyrax?

3. Which of Australia's states or territories was created in 1901?

4. What is the person who writes or compiles dictionaries called? 💡

5. The medical term 'stupor' is best defined as what?

6. Brown peas and bacon are traditionally cooked in which Eastern European country on Christmas morning?

7. The wing of what creature is used in the witches' brew from *Macbeth*?

8. What do you call a sudden collapse of ice and rocks on a mountainside? 💡

9. What do Amazon call their TV set-top box?

10. What was the name of the first British Royal Navy ship sunk in action during World War 2?

11. Who has won the most Brit Awards, as of 2014?

12. Which constellation represents a hunter with weapons?

13. Which Caribbean country's highest elevation point is Cerro de Punta?

14. In terms of EU transport, what is the ERA?

15. In what year did the United States and Canada agree on borders?

16. In what film did Alan Rickman play Metatron?

The Bumper Family Quiz Book
Quiz 216

① What part of the body is also known as the 'wandering nerve'?

② What does an adult human have an estimated 75 trillion of?

③ What is the calm centre of a hurricane called?

④ Which football team does boxer Ricky Hatton support?

⑤ Which Dutch artist was famous for painting sunflowers?

⑥ How is the constellation *Taurus* known in English?

⑦ Why was the Cornish Pasty invented?

⑧ Which Middle-Eastern country's highest elevation point is Haji Ibrahim?

⑨ What prince does Ella fall in love with in the film *Ella Enchanted*?

⑩ The 'Mona Lisa' was painted during what artistic time period?

⑪ If a US worker has a 401k, what are they planning for?

⑫ Who first developed the military formation of the phalanx?

⑬ What are the names of Harry Potter's parents?

⑭ In the film *Lilo & Stitch*, what does the name Lilo mean?

⑮ Who was the Roman guardian of entrances and exits?

⑯ Who became UK Leader of the House of Commons in 2014?

The Bumper Family Quiz Book
Quiz 217

① What country does tennis pro Xavier Malisse represent?

② In the board game *Cluedo*, what is the yellow piece called? 💡

③ Architecturally, what is a 'stoa'?

④ Who is the Greek god of sleep?

⑤ Which group inducted into the Rock & Roll Hall of Fame in 2012 currently tours without founding member Slash?

⑥ What prestigious award was established by a Swedish scientist and inventor of dynamite?

⑦ By what nickname is supermodel Elle Macpherson known?

⑧ Which state of matter has molecules packed together the most tightly? 💡

⑨ Fear of blood is known as what?

⑩ What does Raja Yoga advocate?

⑪ Which nation has the most indigenous languages?

⑫ What is a multi-grid Sudoku puzzle usually called?

⑬ Which food commonly considered a staple of German cuisine is actually Chinese?

⑭ Which film won the 2009 Academy Award for Best Picture?

⑮ What was the name of the young shepherd who became King of Israel?

⑯ What feature does a cat have in common with sharks?

The Bumper *Family* Quiz Book
Quiz 218

1. What year did Crayola crayons debut: 1902, 1903, 1907 or 1908?

2. Who is an 'amah'?

3. Foods high in saturated fats tend to raise: blood cholesterol, blood sugar or heart rate?

4. In which 2002 film did Ray Romano play the character Manfred? 💡

5. What was the name of the character featured in the *Dude, you're gettin' a Dell* adverts?

6. What is a nybble?

7. Who was the voice of Mrs Potts in Disney's *Beauty and the Beast*?

8. Bhutan is a nation in which continent?

9. Which fraction is greater than 1/2: 1/3, 3/7, 5/12, 5/8? 💡

10. What battlefield weapon debuted on September 15th, 1916?

11. In what year did Henry IV ascend the English throne?

12. What colour flame does boron burn with?

13. The Leyden jar was an early example of what device, used for storing electrical charge?

14. How many stomachs does a pig have?

15. Belize is located on which continent?

16. Which British athlete was banned for life from the Olympics in 2004?

The Bumper Family Quiz Book
Quiz 219

1. What is the largest city in Italy?

2. The John Hancock Center skyscraper, completed in 1969, is located where?

3. In online writing, what does TL;DR mean?

4. Who played the villain, The Penguin, in *Batman Returns*?

5. Who wrote *On the Pulse of the Morning* for Clinton's Inauguration?

6. What is the free-to-air digital TV service in the UK called?

7. What was Beyonce's debut solo single called?

8. In which country was revolutionary Che Guevara killed?

9. Gho and kira are traditional dresses from which country?

10. Of which drug did Sigmund Freud talk of the virtues and also use?

11. Who invented HTML?

12. What type of student is a 'medico'?

13. Which of the following is a monotreme: caribou, hyena, cobra or platypus?

14. After retiring from tennis, Ivan Lendl focused on which sport?

15. What is the top speed of a roadrunner: 8-10 mph, 15-17 mph or 30-40 mph?

16. What airline had the world's first partially biofuel commercial flight?

The Bumper Family Quiz Book
Quiz 220

1. In what year did the Irish Parliament vote to join the United Kingdom of Great Britain and Ireland?

2. Five of which shape make up the Olympic symbol? 💡

3. Falstaff fits readily in which comic tradition: Miles Gloriosus, Miser or Pantaloon?

4. Approximately how long is the border that Chile shares with Peru?

5. What was the fictional address of the house in *Amityville Horror*?

6. Which Roman general fathered the emperor Caligula?

7. What is the name for a building on a farm where the animals live? 💡

8. In what Chinese city did the 2008 Summer Olympics take place?

9. What substance carries the code for making proteins from the nucleus to the cytoplasm?

10. Who was US President immediately prior to Ronald Reagan?

11. South Tarawa is the capital of which country?

12. Which of these is not a type of multiple intelligence as theorized by Howard Gardner: musical, verbal or visual-spatial?

13. Where in the body would you find an 'incus'?

14. Who painted 'Persistence of Memory' in 1931?

15. What does fibre help to prevent?

16. What was Lady Gaga's debut single release?

The Bumper Family Quiz Book
Quiz 221

1. What is an automatic response that doesn't involve the brain called?

2. What is the meaning of the word 'sesquipedalian'?

3. How many sides does a hexagon have? 💡

4. Between which planets is the asteroid belt located?

5. Which Australian state capital city is located on the Swan River?

6. Which three English players joined the English Football Hall of Fame in 2014?

7. What would you most likely find at French *boulangeries*?

8. What type of children's toy is a 'peewee'?

9. What is a triangle with a 90-degree angle called? 💡

10. In what country did the Shopping Mall Attack of the 21st of September 2013 take place?

11. Norway, Sweden, Finland, Denmark and Iceland are also known as what?

12. Which English King was known as the 'Mad Monarch'?

13. Jean Renoir is known for being which one of the following: film director or opera singer?

14. The 2008 French film *The Colonel* was set during what African nation's war for independence?

15. What honorary position did Andrew Motion hold from 1999?

16. Which river is The Gambia centred along?

The Bumper Family Quiz Book
Quiz 222

1. In which year did Allied forces defeat Rommel in North Africa?

2. True or false: Wolverines are a member of the canine family?

3. In Scots English, what is a 'stob'?

4. What is the only country that shares a border with Qatar?

5. Which singer and actress previously dated American tennis player Andy Roddick?

6. In technology, what does 'PC' stand for?

7. Most of India's Thar Desert is situated in which state?

8. What is the French word for bread?

9. What time is equal to twelve o'clock at night: six o'clock, midday or midnight?

10. The dependence of a plant on the proper day-length to flower is called what?

11. A nun would call what home?

12. In which US state is Hearst Castle?

13. Momentum is to force as angular momentum is to what?

14. What was the name of Dave Matthews Bands' first self-released album?

15. In what year did most of the southern counties in Ireland become independent from the UK?

16. In *The Golden Compass*, Lyra bands together with what witch?

The Bumper Family Quiz Book
Quiz 223

① Who recorded the hit single *Nuthin' But A 'G' Thang* in 1993?

② Who co-starred with Jennifer Lopez in *The Wedding Planner*?

③ What is Apple's music store called?

④ What unit of measure does the kilometre represent? 💡

⑤ The name for what large yellow or pink citrus fruit is the same in German and English?

⑥ Point Pelee is the southernmost point on the mainland of what country?

⑦ Which company created *Jabulani*, the match ball for the 2010 World Cup?

⑧ The cord draped over the frame of a soccer goal is called what? 💡

⑨ Chronomentrophobia is the fear of what?

⑩ What is the closest living relative to the Tyrannosaurus Rex?

⑪ Despite its name, the Arctic country once known as Greenland is covered mostly in what?

⑫ What number is also the same as proton number and the number of electrons of a neutral atom?

⑬ In 1934, John O'Hara wrote which classic book?

⑭ On what was the Italian economy based before the advent of World War 2?

⑮ What is the name of the top soccer league in Germany?

⑯ Who wrote the novel series *Vampire Academy*?

The Bumper Family Quiz Book
Quiz 224

1. Who arranged for Goldie's murder in the film *Sin City*?

2. What kind of cheese is usually found on pizza?

3. With what book did Aravind Adiga win the 2008 Booker Prize?

4. In what game are there 'Chance' and 'Community Chest' cards?

5. Which paper format is wider than it is tall: landscape or portrait?

6. The airport code TYO designates which international airport?

7. When it's 9pm in New York on Tuesday, what time is it in London, UK?

8. What type of weapon is a 'kris'?

9. In what year did Lenin lead the Bolshevik revolution?

10. Mozambique is the only nation besides South Africa to border what nation?

11. How many of Queen Victoria's nine children sat on thrones?

12. Which golf star is known as 'The Golden Bear' with 6 Masters victories?

13. What is information collected about people or things?

14. What does *Pax Romana* mean?

15. What is hyperglycemia?

16. Which London memorial is located on Park Lane near Hyde Park?

The Bumper Family Quiz Book
Quiz 225

1. Jamaica is nearest to which US state?

2. What property helps determine what state of matter a substance is in?

3. Who voices Emmet Brickowoski in *The Lego Movie*? 💡

4. Where are the Pampas located?

5. In *Lord of the Rings*, what is the name of Elrond's daughter, who eventually marries Aragorn?

6. When did Benjamin Netanyahu resign in protest against the Plan for Disengagement?

7. Which horse has spots on its body: Appaloosa, Arabian or Brumby?

8. Which Disney animated feature is based on a novel by Burroughs? 💡

9. Which actress played Viola in the film *Shakespeare in Love*?

10. King William III of England suffered from asthma – true or false?

11. Naturalist artist John James Audubon painted images of what?

12. Earl Grey tea is blended with oil extracted from what fruit?

13. What is pop star Prince's full name?

14. What was the name of the first emperor of China's Yuan Dynasty, in 1279?

15. What Russian produce is 'kvass'?

16. Which horse won the Grand National in 2009?

The Bumper Family Quiz Book
Quiz 226

1. In what year did the Brit Awards relocate their show to the Royal Albert Hall?

2. Which famous actor voiced Disney's animated dog, *Bolt*? 💡

3. What is the typical length of an adult African rock python?

4. Who wrote *The Great Gatsby*?

5. What is the FIFA code for Argentina?

6. On July 1, 2004, Saddam Hussein's first legal hearing since his capture was held before what panel?

7. In clothing, what is 'ecru'?

8. Mauritania lies in what continent?

9. You can find the Eiffel Tower in which city? 💡

10. Who designed the famous sunglasses worn by the agents in *Men in Black*?

11. UK rock group The Wolfmen released a 2011 album titled *Married to* what landmark?

12. Which country's name is derived from the element silver?

13. In the film *The TV Set*, what is the profession of the character played by Sigourney Weaver?

14. Who was King during the Great Fire of London in 1666?

15. What would you call a 'low blood calcium level'?

16. The small Persian Gulf nation of Bahrain uses what form of currency?

The Bumper Family Quiz Book
Quiz 227

1. What former province of Mali became an empire on its own?

2. What ocean is off the east coast of the United States?

3. Which Disney animated feature is named after a native American?

4. The airport code LGW designates which European airport?

5. West Island is the capital of which Australian territory?

6. In England, what is 'The Naze'?

7. Instead of putting out stockings at Christmas, what do Dutch children use?

8. Which is a popular children's book by Madeleine L'Engle: *A Wrinkle In Time* or *Island Of The Blue Dolphins*?

9. In Greek mythology, who murdered Pelops?

10. In what 1997 film did Jeff Bridges play 'The Dude'?

11. Which African capital city was known during colonial times as Leopoldville?

12. How many feet are there in one furlong?

13. In text chat, what does GR8 mean?

14. The figures in Rembrandt's 'The Night Watch' worked as what?

15. What is the name of Superman's home planet?

16. How many Grand Slam events did Steffi Graf win in her tennis career?

The Bumper *Family* Quiz Book
Quiz 228

1. Vermicelli is included in which cuisine?

2. What does wind cause on the surface of the ocean?

3. What might be put on a tall building to prevent damage from lightning strikes?

4. Amman is the capital of which country?

5. What was the first product sold by IBM?

6. Which of these is a river basin located partly in Colombia: Amazon basin, Argentina basin or Hudson basin?

7. What was Radiohead's first hit?

8. What number base is the scientific measurement system based on?

9. What type of government did the USSR have until 1991?

10. Which colour is in the middle of a rainbow?

11. Who played Peggy Bundy in American series *Married With Children*?

12. What British aircraft was used to shoot down V-1 buzz-bombs during World War 2?

13. Which of Andy Murray's brothers also plays professional tennis?

14. In what year was the Danish toy company Lego formed?

15. Who first vulcanized rubber?

16. What does the 'R' stand for on an R18 film?

The Bumper Family Quiz Book
Quiz 229

① What did a shepherd boy discover at Qumran, Jordan, in 1947?

② In text chat, what does TYVM mean? 💡

③ The 126th FA Challenge Cup Final was the first to be held at which stadium?

④ Which dictator organized Italians into the Fascist Party in 1919?

⑤ In U2's *Beautiful Day* lyrics, what came out 'after the flood'?

⑥ English borrowed the word 'tsunami' from what language?

⑦ Which of the following is not a member of the mollusc family: clam, lobster, mussel or oyster?

⑧ Which Disney animated feature is based on stories by A.A. Milne? 💡

⑨ In what country is 'Sri' a title of respect?

⑩ Who ascended the English throne in July 1603?

⑪ What is a 'dibble'?

⑫ Out of the five Academy Award nominations received, how many Oscars did the 2001 film *Amelie* win?

⑬ Which leaf used for making a popular beverage was first discovered by the Chinese?

⑭ Which landlocked European principality is bordered by Switzerland and Austria?

⑮ Which city hosted the 2010 Winter Olympic Games?

⑯ Which dog breed name means curly toy dog: Bichon Frise, Poodle or Shiatsu?

The Bumper *Family* Quiz Book
Quiz 230

① In *Harry Potter*, why is Remus Lupin also known as Moony?

② Which South American country is Iguazú National Park located in?

③ Which art form interested Wassily Kandinsky as much as painting?

④ What city in Asia was designated by Spain as a royal and loyal city?

⑤ What is the title of the third *Hunger Games* book?

⑥ What is the name of the cricket in Disney's *Mulan*?

⑦ The term 'precipitation' often refers to which weather condition?

⑧ What type of lens has a thin middle and makes objects appear smaller?

⑨ In which country is Lake Como located?

⑩ In which type of food does an anteater specialize, besides ants?

⑪ What sort of plant is a 'weigela'?

⑫ Who was Golda Meir?

⑬ In what decade was the first artificial heart-lung machine created?

⑭ How many goals did Frank Lampard score for Chelsea in the 2010-11 season?

⑮ Who recorded the hit single *Rhythm Is A Dancer* in 1993?

⑯ In currency, what is one hundredth of a Romanian leu?

The Bumper Family Quiz Book
Quiz 231

1. What Mel Gibson film told the story of the Scottish war for independence?

2. Avril Lavigne was born and raised in what country?

3. How many World Cup tournaments has soccer player Chris Albright played in?

4. Which nutrient group is used to help grow and repair cells?

5. A large type of North American deer is what: duck, moose or roadrunner? 💡

6. What country was artist Jan van Eyck from?

7. The Chinese chu-ko-nu is a variety of which weapon?

8. Which of the following is a macronutrient: minerals, protein, vitamins or water?

9. Tartan is a traditional fabric of what country? 💡

10. Which two fruits get fatter instead of sweeter as they ripen?

11. Which woman received a proposal in the final-ever episode of *Coupling*?

12. Who was the first British Hanoverian sovereign?

13. Which Shakespearean character said 'My kingdom for a horse'?

14. What is the capital of Eritrea, itself once a province of Ethiopia?

15. What name appears on Fogell's fake ID in the 2007 film *Superbad*?

16. What kind of animal is a chukar?

The Bumper Family Quiz Book
Quiz 232

1. The 1968 film *Bullitt* involves a spectacular car chase in which city?

2. What song did Lea Michele sing for her audition for *Glee*?

3. What was the name of the US B-29 Bomber which dropped the atom bomb on Nagasaki, Japan?

4. Who plays the brilliant title role in the British series *Luther*?

5. In what year did Tony Blair become UK Prime Minister?

6. A 2007 Robyn song begs the question 'who's that' what?

7. In text chat, what does XOXO mean?

8. What is the largest snake in the world?

9. What is the name of the oldest museum in England, founded in 1683 in Oxford?

10. Which horse won the Grand National in 2006?

11. Which Stuart monarch died in March 1702, after falling from his horse?

12. How long after birth do the eyes of young kittens open?

13. Which capital city was destroyed by an earthquake and volcanic eruption in 1917?

14. A coffee tree produces its first full crop when it is how old?

15. Kiribati is located in what continent of the world?

16. Berlin is the capital of what country?

The Bumper Family Quiz Book
Quiz 233

1. How many points are scored for a field goal in American football?

2. On what Australian peninsula is the city of Victor Harbour located?

3. What decade is the hit single *What's My Name?* by Snoop Dogg from?

4. What is the first priority in dealing with a medical trauma: airway, chest, events or blood?

5. What feature film did Michael Jackson play 'Agent M' in? 💡

6. Which *Phantom of the Opera* song was a chart hit for Sarah Brightman and Michael Crawford?

7. How many pleats are in a traditional chef's hat?

8. Which British royal was born on Christmas Day in 1936?

9. Which studio is Mickey Mouse most associated with? 💡

10. Which two organs does Wilson's disease primarily affect?

11. Pope Francis's election was first announced from the balcony of St Peter's Basilica in what language?

12. What former TV star directed *The Da Vinci Code*?

13. What is a 'romaji' used for?

14. On which Maltese Island can you find Calypso's Cove?

15. You can find the Nile River in which continent?

16. What is soft brown coal that has lost all of its moisture called?

The Bumper *Family* Quiz Book
Quiz 234

1. Who led a slave revolt in 73 BC?

2. Ankara is the capital of what country?

3. What did the UK Ministry of Food tell children were just as tasty as ice-creams?

4. What holiday is celebrated by wearing green?

5. What vegetable is added to some types of pasta to make them green?

6. What is the number one French export product?

7. As a young girl, what did athlete Denise Lewis dream of being when she grew up?

8. What is the hard, dark substance found in the ground that is mined for fuel?

9. In the film *Braveheart* Robert the Bruce is which Earl of Bruce?

10. Which country's highest mountain is Pico da Neblina?

11. Which child actor played Nathan in *The Full Monty*?

12. Which planet travels through space at 66,700mph?

13. What is the largest country in Africa?

14. Which of the following cannot be found in the brain: astrocyte, glial cells or stereocyte?

15. What computer system ran the RISC OS operating system?

16. In what year did the Intel 80486 chipset first come out?

The Bumper *Family* Quiz Book
Quiz 235

① In what country was Monterey Jack cheese invented?

② Where did the Blitz of World War 2 take place?

③ What is the most common chemical element found in the Earth's atmosphere?

④ Nelson Mandela helped bring about the end of what hated system? 💡

⑤ Which animal almost exclusively eats bamboo?

⑥ In *Flowers for Algernon*, who is Algernon?

⑦ What is the name of Harry Potter's owl? 💡

⑧ At which golf club does the Masters occur each year?

⑨ There is an animal called the 'aardwolf' – true or false? 💡

⑩ Prior to Pope Francis, in what year did a Pope from outside Europe last reign?

⑪ Who is the Greek god of the sea?

⑫ What Serbian Prime Minister was assassinated on March 12th, 2003?

⑬ In text chat, what does STBY mean? 💡

⑭ What is the fate of the commandant in *Schindler's List*?

⑮ Phoenix Park and St. Stephen's Green are located in what national capital?

⑯ Which footballer wrote an autobiography titled 'A Goal in the Sky'?

The Bumper Family Quiz Book
Quiz 236

1. Who wrote *The Strange Case of Dr Jekyll and Mr Hyde*?

2. Which fast-food brand uses the slogan 'I'm lovin' it'?

3. What US state is Indiana Jones said to be from?

4. Iran generally has less than 30cm (12 inches) of what each year? 💡

5. How many of her children had Queen Mary outlived by her death in 1953?

6. Which of these items will float in a glass of water: ice cube or sugar cube?

7. In what year did Sinclair launch the ZX Spectrum?

8. What is a substance that your body needs for energy and growth: melanin, nutrient or virus? 💡

9. MEA is the flag-carrier airline of which country?

10. What type of clock is Germany famous for producing?

11. Which dinosaur did O.C. Marsh discover in 1871?

12. What was the birth name of Royal Ballet founder Ninette de Valois?

13. How old was England's Peter Shilton, the oldest player in the 1990 World Cup?

14. Which two colours make up the English flag?

15. What is the name of a polygon with seven sides? 💡

16. Which monarch ascended the English throne in March 1702?

The Bumper Family Quiz Book
Quiz 237

1. 'Ghost fishing' refers to what?

2. Which direction do you need to travel to get from Antarctica to the Arctic?

3. Who was awarded the Nobel Prize for Literature in 1954?

4. In which European city would you find the Tagus River?

5. What ocean borders the west of South America?

6. What American football club did Franz Beckenbauer play with for four seasons?

7. In Ancient Greece, what was the 'agora'?

8. Which film won the Best Picture Oscar for 1999?

9. Where were the first Olympic Games held?

10. What is a tree whose leaves never turn brown called?

11. What does 'dachshund' mean in German?

12. U2 covered which Patti Smith classic song featured on the *Threesome* film soundtrack?

13. What cargo was the British ship *Arandora Star* carrying when it was sunk by a U-Boat in World War 2?

14. What is most hay used for?

15. What is the capital city of Tanzania?

16. What is xanthaphobia?

The Bumper Family Quiz Book
Quiz 238

1. What is Christophe Lollichon's job for Chelsea FC during the 2013-14 season?

2. How is the constellation *Canis Major* known in English?

3. Spain is the world's leading producer of which of these: bananas, coconuts or olive oil? 💡

4. What country, home of the world's highest mountain, is Kathmandu the capital of?

5. What is phalacrophobia?

6. According to the Athenian ideal, what developed the mind and emotions?

7. In what year did George V adopt the name Windsor for his dynasty?

8. In the first *Harry Potter* book, what kind of dragon is Norbert?

9. What country is the koala from? 💡

10. Botanically speaking, which of the following is not a nut: chestnut, hazelnut or peanut?

11. Where is the landmark 'Big Ben' located?

12. Formerly known as Titograd, which city is the capital of Montenegro?

13. Who is the genius inventor in the 2005 film *Robots*?

14. What Windows keyboard shortcut will let you open a file?

15. Which body system helps your body keep its shape?

16. Which is the first letter of the Greek alphabet?

The Bumper *Family* Quiz Book
Quiz 239

1. In which year did the 14th Dalai Lama flee Chinese-occupied Tibet for exile in India?

2. What is the St. Louis Gateway Arch?

3. Finish the Britney Spears lyric: 'Oh baby, baby. How was I supposed to know that...'?

4. After being sentenced to life imprisonment, where did Galileo serve his sentence?

5. What do you call a male sheep? 💡

6. Which of these animals has the highest blood pressure: elephant, giraffe or hummingbird?

7. Bolivia is approximately twice the size of which country: Greece, Italy, Serbia or Spain?

8. What are software options to supervise what children can surf on the web called?

9. Which country first built the *Soyuz* space launch vehicles?

10. What piece of polished, cut glass reveals the spectrum of visible light? 💡

11. Who wrote the novel *High Rise*?

12. Who was Henry VIII's first wife?

13. Who became the first amateur in 31 years to win a PGA Tour event?

14. Which English monarch died in 1553, at the age of 15?

15. If you 'abjure' something, what do you do?

16. In *Akeelah and the Bee*, in what city does Akeelah live?

Quiz 240

1. In snooker, what is the first shot of the game called?

2. Bathmophobia is the fear of what?

3. In what year did Nazi troops invade Soviet Russia?

4. What flavour is a bourbon biscuit? 💡

5. Where might you find a 'p-trap'?

6. Which city was Australia's temporary capital before Canberra was proclaimed as capital?

7. Which luxury fabric was first used by the Chinese in the 27th century BC?

8. What part of the body does scoliosis affect?

9. Where do lobsters live? 💡

10. A 'sawbuck' is how many US dollars?

11. What is a 'punty'?

12. Which shortcut in Windows allows you to cut?

13. Which historical figure were the Enterprise-E crew trying to assist in *Star Trek: First Contact*?

14. What is in the US dish 'succotash'?

15. What is the name of the seaside resort known as the Queen of the Yorkshire Coast?

16. What year was Mahmoud Ahmadinejad elected President of Iran?

The Bumper Family Quiz Book
Quiz 241

1. What is the medical term for a slow heartbeat?

2. Which model married Calvin Klein model Donovan Leitch: Claudia Schiffer, Heidi Klum or Kirsty Hume?

3. Which country has Banjul as its capital city?

4. What are mounds of windblown sand called?

5. What ape raises the title character in the 1999 animated film *Tarzan*?

6. What does 'w/' generally stand for?

7. Who shot Andy Warhol?

8. In text chat, what does TMI mean?

9. Which Australian marsupial is often mistaken for a monkey?

10. How many men survived the sinking of the *Hood* by the *Bismarck* in World War 2?

11. Where was golfer Trevor Immelman born?

12. Which creature is deaf: butterfly, swallow or skunk?

13. In which city in Britain is the Henry Moore Institute, devoted to sculpture of all periods and nationalities?

14. What happens to tofu if you freeze it: it goes bad or it gets chewier?

15. Which US President first signed an executive order authorizing bin Laden's assassination?

16. Which book won the Pulitzer Prize for fiction in 1961?

Quiz 242

1. In what year was the John Lewis Partnership founded?

2. Historically, Iraq was known as what ancient region, meaning 'between the rivers'?

3. How many goals were scored in the 1958 World Cup final?

4. In geography, what is 'elevation'?

5. In Paul Bowles' *A Distant Episode*, what is the occupation of the main character before he is kidnapped?

6. What was the prison cell number on Robben Island which held Mandela?

7. What does calcium do for the body?

8. What is the name for a vertical passageway for smoke from a fireplace?

9. Which African country was partially occupied by Spain: Egypt or Morocco?

10. 1980s hairstyles can best be described by which word: big, braided or short?

11. The science term 'biological warfare' is best defined as?

12. Which chipmunk is the brainy one in the film *Alvin and the Chipmunks*?

13. Fish take in oxygen through their gills; what do insects take in oxygen through?

14. What Manga series was not created by Rumiko Takahashi?

15. Which two countries in Europe have square flags?

16. What is the capital of St. Lucia, one of the Windward Islands in the West Indies?

The Bumper Family Quiz Book
Quiz 243

① Musician Mike Shinoda is from which group?

② What is a rotating neutron star that gives off sharp regular pulses of radio waves called?

③ Which Disney villain sings *Be Prepared*? 💡

④ What did Louis Braille invent?

⑤ In which country is the Acropolis located?

⑥ What is the medical term for a nose job?

⑦ Which author wrote the line 'A woman must have money and a room of her own if she is to write fiction'?

⑧ Who voiced Elsa in Disney's *Frozen*? 💡

⑨ Which Tudor monarch reigned for 44 years?

⑩ The Tropic of Capricorn runs closest to which part of Chile? North or south?

⑪ What are 'pomodori secchi' more commonly referred to as?

⑫ How many snooker World Championships did Stephen Hendry win?

⑬ Which city is the capital of Rwanda?

⑭ What former NFL player plays Tripp's dad in *Failure to Launch*?

⑮ What does 'syllogistic' refer to?

⑯ The airport code STO designates which European airport?

The Bumper Family Quiz Book
Quiz 244

1. In the 1997 film, *Batman And Robin*, who unplugs Mrs. Freeze?

2. Who voiced the Genie in Disney's *Aladdin*? 💡

3. What do we call data sent from a spacecraft to ground stations?

4. What is the principle function of subcutaneous tissue?

5. What is the capital city of American Samoa, a group of islands in the South Pacific?

6. Which island of Malta was used for target practice by the Royal Navy?

7. Mark, the potential adoptive father in *Juno*, does what for a living?

8. Who was Michael Jackson's pop-star date for the 1990 Grammy Awards?

9. The process of going to the polls and casting a ballot for a candidate is what? 💡

10. Bern is the capital of what country?

11. For what period of time did the Industrial Revolution last?

12. What is the national flower of the United Kingdom?

13. Which hotel was built on the site of the former London residence of the Dukes of Westminster?

14. Who won the World Snooker Championship in 2013?

15. To which Greek god was the oak tree sacred?

16. What item did British ace Albert Ball always carry with him during air combat in World War 1?

The Bumper Family Quiz Book
Quiz 245

① Which country depends almost totally on wood for fuel: China, India, Nepal or Tunisia?

② Wildebeest and rhinoceros inhabit which country: Italy, Kenya or Portugal?

③ Which element has the chemical symbol Na?

④ Paul Klee claimed that, as a painter, he was one with what?

⑤ Bolivia has what length of coastline?

⑥ Who was the King of France when Cartier sailed to North America?

⑦ Which Welsh city has the suburb of Ely?

⑧ Who was the author of *The Trial*?

⑨ In the *Mr Men* books, what colour is Mr Happy?

⑩ What space satellite series had a name meaning 'fellow traveller'?

⑪ What did Chinese astronomers discover 1600 years before European astronomers?

⑫ Who escaped from MI6 custody in the film *Quantum of Solace*?

⑬ What do you call a crossword puzzle where all letter squares have both across and down clues?

⑭ Why are The Pet Shop Boys so-called?

⑮ Which British driver won the Formula One and Indy Car titles in consecutive years?

⑯ In what year did Henry I become King of England?

The Bumper Family Quiz Book
Quiz 246

① What is the currency of Sweden?

② What year was Mexican President Madero killed?

③ Which state of matter is an ice cube?

④ Which of these rivers forms part of the border between Colombia and Ecuador: Putumayo, Rio Mayo or Rio Negro?

⑤ What makes flamingos pink?

⑥ What dangerous element was in the claimed *Radithor* 'elixir'?

⑦ Which planet in our solar system has the highest average surface temperature?

⑧ Which Disney animated feature is a remake of their original third feature?

⑨ Who provided the voice of Aslan in the 2008 film *Prince Caspian*?

⑩ What man set a Decathlon world record in 2012 with a 9,039 point score?

⑪ What is a 'cote'?

⑫ What was the title of a 2006 EP from Babyshambles: *The Blinding* or *The Shouting*?

⑬ The big, white bean sprouts used in Chinese cooking come from which kind of bean?

⑭ What does 'Lux' soap translate as in Latin?

⑮ How many years was Mandela sentenced to in 1962 for incitement and leaving the country illegally?

⑯ Which Spanish King retired in 1556 and divided his kingdom among members of his family?

The Bumper Family Quiz Book
Quiz 247

1. What is a line segment going from one side of a circle to the other through the centre called?

2. List these cities in order from northernmost to southernmost: Minsk, Montevideo, Moscow.

3. In what year did the Nazis discover Anne Frank and family?

4. What word can you get by unscrambling 'ocaoscni'?

5. Mexico's Independence Day, Cinco de Mayo, is celebrated on what day?

6. Which highly acclaimed English architect lived from 1632 to 1723?

7. Whose goal against England in 1986's World Cup was voted the Goal of the Century?

8. Why did artist Georgia O'Keeffe say flowers were better than models?

9. What country is the homeland of the Danish people?

10. Who wrote the book *Childhood's End*?

11. Which basketball player won the Associated Press 2013 Athlete of the Year award?

12. Which South American country's highest elevation point is Mount Roraima?

13. Who was President of the US when the Hawley-Smoot Tariff Act was passed?

14. What is an 'oenophile'?

15. In what type of container is heroin smuggled into the US in 2007's *American Gangster*?

16. What are the lower chambers of the human heart called?

The Bumper Family Quiz Book
Quiz 248

① Where does the X in 'Xmas' come from?

② Which of these famous philosophers was Greek: Hume, Marx, Freud or Socrates? 💡

③ How many candles are on a Hanukkah Menorah?

④ What is *Frumenty*?

⑤ Which famous author owned Joan Miro's painting 'The Farm'?

⑥ What do we call things that directly affect all activities of cells?

⑦ Which of the following animals lives in a shell: octopus, salmon or scallop? 💡

⑧ Which country has Bucharest as its capital city?

⑨ Rice, soy sauce and fish sauce are traditional ingredients in which cuisine: Argentinean or Vietnamese?

⑩ Who does Dakota Fanning play in *The Twilight Saga: New Moon*?

⑪ What is a young swan known as?

⑫ What was the last year the World Cup used the 'final pool' format?

⑬ Which empire was a major trader on the Mediterranean Sea around the time of Christ?

⑭ Who was the only Egyptian Pharaoh known to be killed in battle?

⑮ Which three colours make up the Welsh flag?

⑯ Your heart beats about how many times per day: 2000, 10000, 15000 or 25000?

The Bumper *Family* Quiz Book
Quiz 249

① Who succeeded Tony Blair as UK Prime Minister?

② Which Sesame Street character lives in a bin?

③ What is the national flower of Venezuela?

④ What Tour de France rider was nicknamed 'Campionissimo' (Champion of Champions)?

⑤ Who described the rings of Saturn as the 'ears of a teacup'?

⑥ What are the units of torque?

⑦ In the *Harry Potter* books, what is Hagrid's first name?

⑧ A gale is a strong what?

⑨ Who wrote the soundtracks to the first three *Indiana Jones* films?

⑩ What is a second, lower ceiling used to hide pipes and wires?

⑪ What does Duffy pair syrup with in a 2008 song title?

⑫ On what date did Italy declare war on Britain during World War 2?

⑬ Which plains are large floodplains of the Indus and the Ganga-Brahmaputra river systems: Indian-Ganga or Indo-Gangetic?

⑭ What, technically speaking, does vitamin C do for your body?

⑮ What body of water lies between Texas and Mexico?

⑯ What is the most poisonous fish in the world?

The Bumper *Family* Quiz Book
Quiz 250

1. Which stage musical was written by *South Park* creators Trey Parker and Matt Stone?

2. What do you call the line segment where two faces of a solid figure meet?

3. What was the main intent of the Dutch colonial effort?

4. Which is the process of placing plants in a certain way in an area called: bottling, hilling or landscaping? 💡

5. Which of the following is a well-known Japanese condiment: hot sauce, ketchup, mustard or soy sauce?

6. What Duffy album hit the number one spot in the UK album charts in March 2008?

7. Which of these countries was in Europe's Eastern Bloc: Panama, Poland or Portugal? 💡

8. How do archaeologists believe early humans started fires?

9. In what year did Louis XIV revoke the Edict of Nantes?

10. What course played host to the 2006 British Open?

11. Which scientific term is defined as the solid surface layer of a planet or moon?

12. Stretching after a workout helps to accomplish what?

13. Where did Joan of Arc take charge of French forces during the Hundred Years' War?

14. Which film won the 2013 Academy Award for Best Picture?

15. In what year was the designer Stefano Gabbana born?

16. Shtriga is the name of a vampire witch from which country's folklore?

The Bumper Family Quiz Book
Quiz 251

1. Which Shakespearean play refers to jealousy as a 'green-eyed monster'?

2. Orange-seller Nell Gwyn was the mistress of which Stuart King?

3. Which company provides the tennis balls for Wimbledon? 💡

4. Who did Hadouken! tour with in February 2007?

5. Which horse won the Grand National in 2005?

6. Many of Francisco Goya's paintings detailed the horrors of what event?

7. What country in Europe uses the zloty as its currency?

8. *Unorthodox Jukebox* was recorded and released by whom?

9. What is the central colour of a rainbow? 💡

10. The Bernoulli Effect concerns what physical system?

11. Which creature can use one eye to hunt and the other eye to watch for predators?

12. What was Operation Clarion in World War 2?

13. What river flows through Oxford, UK?

14. Blarney Castle can be found in which country?

15. What sweet comes in refillable dispensers with characters on top?

16. Which desert covers the country of Turkmenistan?

The Bumper Family Quiz Book
Quiz 252

1. Who wrote the book *Desperation*?

2. What type of plant is a 'spiraea'?

3. Which curved fruit is picked while green because it continues to ripen after picking?

4. In golf, what is the name of the employee who is responsible for course maintenance?

5. How many storeys high is the Leaning Tower of Pisa?

6. What language is spoken most widely in Saudi Arabia?

7. In the *James Bond* films, what does SPECTRE stand for?

8. Which English monarch was born in May 1630?

9. Which Disney animated feature is based on a picture book by William Joyce?

10. How many essential amino acids are there?

11. How long is the average single thread unwound from a silkworm cocoon?

12. The Waitemata Harbor is part of which New Zealand city?

13. What is Australia's most easterly mainland town?

14. Which fruit is the largest in the world, weighing as much as 45kg (100lb)?

15. Money problems led Rembrandt to declare what in 1656?

16. In a lead storage battery, what strong acid is consumed in a reaction which produces the voltage?

The Bumper Family Quiz Book
Quiz 253

① What is the energy of moving parts called?

② Who approached the Air Ministry about converting Silverstone into a race circuit?

③ What was Joey's chat-up line in *Friends*?

④ In text chat, what does OMG mean?

⑤ What Ancient Israeli item was an 'ephod'?

⑥ Which Irish writer wrote *Ulysses*?

⑦ What is the study of plant life called?

⑧ Which river is not in France: Ebro, Loire, Rhone or Seine?

⑨ Paella and chorizo are typical foods of which country?

⑩ Peru's national flag, like Japan's, consists of what two colours?

⑪ In what year was the answering phone machine invented?

⑫ Chisels and hammers are the tools of what kind of artist?

⑬ What pseudonym was the *Nancy Drew* series published under?

⑭ Which US President succeeded Lyndon B. Johnson?

⑮ Which purple vegetable is used a lot in Italian cooking?

⑯ What is the name of the school in the 2007 film *Stomp the Yard*?

The Bumper Family Quiz Book
Quiz 254

1. What is the marshy region in Gujarat which borders the Sindh region of Pakistan called?

2. Wool generally comes from which animal? 💡

3. What are the strips of tissue which connect bones together called?

4. The 1938 book, *The Death of the Heart*, was written by whom?

5. What type of bird is a 'marabou'?

6. What is the process of a river washing away its riverbanks called?

7. Which is the app that snaps a photo or video you can send that then disappears? 💡

8. What is the charity which was founded by Mandela to raise awareness about the impact of AIDS?

9. Which Italian goalkeeper captained his country to World Cup success in 1982?

10. What is a Red Savina?

11. Robert Frost is known for writing what?

12. In which 2001 war film did Tom Sizemore play the character Earl Sistern?

13. In music, what does 'pianissimo' mean?

14. 'Kindergarten', from the German, translates as what?

15. Which of these is the longest river located completely within Brazil: Amazon, Parana or Sao Francisco?

16. In 2003, Offspring's Ron Welty left the band and started what new band?

The Bumper Family Quiz Book
Quiz 255

1. Who won the Best Actress Academy Award for the title role in *Julia*?

2. In the Edwardian Age, what sturdy shoe was typically worn during the day?

3. What is an earthquake's epicentre? 💡

4. Which former Beatle appeared alongside Adele on *Later with Jools Holland*?

5. What was Socrates' motto?

6. Rembrandt's most famous work, 'The Night Watch', is also his what?

7. In what year was the supersonic Concorde jet first put into service?

8. Moving in a circle around an axis is called what?

9. In the UK version of *Cluedo*, who has been murdered? 💡

10. Tennis star Caroline Wozniacki represents which country?

11. Which author wrote the classic vampire novelette *Carmilla* in 1872?

12. How much water can an elephant's trunk hold?

13. Which Oceanic country's highest elevation point is Mount Cook?

14. Which natural landmark is partly located in Bolivia: Amazon rainforest, Patagonian mountains or Victoria Falls?

15. In London, the Emirates Air Line connects Greenwich Peninsula with what Docklands Light Railway station?

16. What colour is the star on the flag of Chile?

The Bumper Family Quiz Book
Quiz 256

1. What is the common name for the country officially called the Swiss Confederation?

2. What sort of nutrient is cholesterol?

3. Which Queen was crowned at Westminster Abbey in 1702?

4. What is Adobe's market-leading painting software?

5. What is space which is entirely devoid of matter called?

6. In *Shrek*, what vegetable does Shrek say ogres are like?

7. Corsewall Lighthouse, a converted four-star hotel, can be found in which country?

8. What are the swans doing in the song *The Twelve Days of Christmas*?

9. The Atlantic Ocean separates Brazil from which continent: Africa, Asia, Australia or Europe?

10. If an Australian becomes the proud owner of a bitzer, what has he or she got?

11. Which 2004 Morgan Spurlock documentary focused on a thirty-day extreme diet?

12. The book *Double Star* was written by whom?

13. What did Salvador Dali say was his greatest joy?

14. Who was the first golfer to successfully defend his Masters title?

15. Which element has the chemical symbol He?

16. In England, what is 'Brown Willy'?

The Bumper Family Quiz Book
Quiz 257

① Which artist named a urinal 'Fountain' and exhibited it in 1917?

② What is traditionally used in China in place of a knife and fork?

③ What lobster part is made into a delicacy known as 'tomalley'?

④ How old was John Conteh when he first began to box?

⑤ How many top ten hits had Westlife had when they announced their split? 💡

⑥ Bridges first linked Cairo to which Nile Islands?

⑦ What do ship captains use to help them know when water levels allow them to dock? 💡

⑧ Who played the very first Doctor Who?

⑨ Which country covers the smallest total area: Algeria, Australia, Brazil or China?

⑩ Which of the following human traits can be used for visual ID, like fingerprints: hair, fingernails or veins in the eye?

⑪ Who was the Greek goddess of wisdom?

⑫ Who wrote the 1929 book *Look Homeward, Angel*?

⑬ How many gallons of crude oil did the *Exxon Valdez* spill: 1 million, 10 million or 100 million?

⑭ What was the name of the French Huguenot settlement in Florida?

⑮ How far back can Wolverine remember in the *X-Men* films?

⑯ Johnny Lydon had some hits in the 1980s with which New Wave band he fronted?

The Bumper Family Quiz Book
Quiz 258

1. Which nation in Southern Asia gained its independence on August 8th, 1949?

2. What is the inverse function of the exponential function?

3. Which two colours are most associated with Christmas? 💡

4. Who is at the top of the famous column in Trafalgar Square?

5. In what year did *Driving Miss Daisy* win the Best Picture Oscar?

6. Whose book *Baby and Child Care* sold over 50 million copies in their lifetime?

7. Which Brontë sister wrote *Wuthering Heights*?

8. What Bob Dylan song does Adele cover on her album '19'?

9. What was Disney's 50th in-house animated feature? 💡

10. Which member of the X-Men has adamantium bonded to his skeleton?

11. What do Adobe call their vector-drawing software?

12. When was 'Bloody Sunday' in Northern Ireland?

13. What is the name of the French flag?

14. What purpose is served by a Native American 'coup stick'?

15. In what country was the first human face transplant performed in 2005?

16. Which PGA golfer was given the Payne Stewart Award in 2011?

The Bumper Family Quiz Book
Quiz 259

1. What kind of flower does golfer Tony Jacklin have named after him?

2. What German company in 1998 purchased and took over Chrysler Motors?

3. In folklore, what is an 'auf'?

4. Which was the last province to enter confederation in Canada?

5. In the film, what colour were *E.T.*'s eyes?

6. How is niacin better-known?

7. In the 2005 *The Dukes of Hazzard* film, what CB handle does Bo use?

8. Peleus and Thetis were the parents of what famed warrior?

9. Which band was singer Beyonce a member of before going solo?

10. What activity takes place in a French home's 'cuisine'?

11. Into which body of water does the River Danube empty?

12. Who wrote the book *Rainbow Six*?

13. How many pounds are in a US ton?

14. Agliophobia is the fear of what?

15. Which country's highest elevation point is Buurgplaatz?

16. Which of these did Galileo popularize: calculus, microscopes or telescopes?

The Bumper Family Quiz Book
Quiz 260

1. In the early days of slot machines, illegal machines were often disguised as what?

2. Where is designer Ana Abdul from?

3. In which English county is Arundel Castle?

4. What are the specialists who guide ships to port docking areas called?

5. Which *Fight Club* actor turned down the role of Private Ryan in *Saving Private Ryan*?

6. What is a Herkimer diamond?

7. In what year was Chanel No.5 first released?

8. Which wild cat has a spotted coat: cougar, leopard, lion or tiger?

9. What do you call a word spelled the same both backwards and forwards?

10. In which year did Churchill coin the term 'iron curtain'?

11. What is the capital city of Saint Helena?

12. What is the black tea used in Turkey?

13. On what celestial object is the largest known mountain in our solar system?

14. Who won the Pichichi Trophy for being the top scorer in the 2010-11 season of the Spanish La Liga?

15. What was Christina Aguilera's debut single called?

16. Who released the album, *Songs About Jane*?

The Bumper Family Quiz Book
Quiz 261

1. Who was the first Pharaoh of Egypt?

2. What is the opposite art style of realism?

3. What is 'tahini' made from?

4. Where is the official London residence of Queen Elizabeth II? 💡

5. Popular styles of dress in what country include the sari for women and the dhoti for men?

6. In the film *Shrek 2*, where do Princess Fiona's parents live?

7. What is the state flower of New York?

8. On the first day of Christmas, what did my true love give me? 💡

9. What type of clothing is a 'caftan'?

10. Which European country's highest elevation point is Coma Pedrosa?

11. What is the term used for a biofilm that builds up on the teeth?

12. What unit of measurement is equal to 43,650 square feet?

13. What was the first network-supporting operating system?

14. Which two flags does Taylor Dent have tattooed on his right shoulder?

15. In his early years while living in Johannesburg, Nelson Mandela worked as what?

16. What brand of drums did Ringo Starr play?

The Bumper Family Quiz Book
Quiz 262

1. Which country has the world's two largest dams?

2. What is the first letter on the bottom row of a computer keyboard?

3. What kind of animal is the Disney film *Bolt* about?

4. What country touches the Mediterranean Sea, the Bay of Biscay and the Atlantic Ocean?

5. How many Tony Awards does Stephen Sondheim hold?

6. What word describes a material which maintains a magnetic field after an external field is removed?

7. What are the lords doing in the song *The Twelve Days of Christmas*?

8. Who was the top goal scorer in the 2008 UEFA European Football Championship?

9. On which continent is Iraq located?

10. What flower, also the name of a song, is often considered the national flower of Austria?

11. Who was the author of *The Savage Detectives*?

12. In which year was George V crowned King of the United Kingdom?

13. Which two players won the FIFA Player of the Century Award?

14. Which of these was not one of Christopher Columbus' ships: Nina, Pinta, Santa Fe or Santa Maria?

15. Which cell part contains instructions and determines organism characteristics?

16. Which art type was very dominant in Germany during the early 1900s?

The Bumper Family Quiz Book
Quiz 263

1. Where is the Oval cricket ground?

2. Which city in France has the second-highest population?

3. What name is given to water in the gaseous state? 💡

4. What was the name of the biblical child found in a basket by a pharaoh's daughter?

5. Which English golfer won the 2010 BMW PGA Championship by one stroke?

6. In what year did Bulgaria declare independence?

7. What is the driest state in the driest country in the world?

8. What structures hold plants in the ground? 💡

9. Colombia's hot climate is because of its proximity to which geographical feature?

10. In which parts of the world do vampire bats live?

11. Orchestral Manoeuvres In The Dark had their biggest US hit with which song?

12. Enchilada is included in which cuisine?

13. What book did Ian McEwan win the Booker Prize for in 1998?

14. What substance, found in food, helps move waste through the body?

15. What type of animal is a 'titi'?

16. In the 2014 film *Dawn of the Planet of the Apes*, what species is the majority of the ape population?

The Bumper Family Quiz Book
Quiz 264

1. How is the constellation *Sagittarius* known in English?

2. What Italian dessert is made from sweetened ricotta stuffed into crispy pastry tubes?

3. Who was Margaret Thatcher?

4. What is the capital city of Cape Verde, a tiny grouping of islands off the west coast of Africa?

5. How many recessions hit Japan in the decade leading up to September 2002?

6. What is the name of Spider-Man's alter ego?

7. Edouard Manet's painting 'The Fifer' is of a boy playing what?

8. What was *Calamity Jane* to the golf world?

9. What American commonwealth's Spanish name translates to 'rich port'?

10. Who is the author of *The Very Hungry Caterpillar*?

11. What part of kelp holds it to the ocean floor beneath it?

12. Which major US river is called 'Rio Bravo' in Mexico?

13. What is your 'paunch'?

14. In *The Aeneid*, who is Aeneas' chief antagonist?

15. What root spice is said to help with nausea and motion sickness?

16. Turkmenistan, which is north of Iran, has which city as its capital?

The Bumper *Family* Quiz Book
Quiz 265

① What type of clothing is a 'snood'?

② Which African island nation's highest mountain is Mount Karthala?

③ What colour is Scooby Doo's collar? 💡

④ Fear of death or dead things is known as what?

⑤ The food pyramid contains grains, vegetables, fruits, dairy and what else?

⑥ Which early men's laced shoes first appeared in the 17th century?

⑦ What is an arpeggio?

⑧ Which of these units in the scientific measurement system is used to measure length: grams, pounds, seconds or metres? 💡

⑨ In 1988 Steffi Graf accomplished what tennis feat?

⑩ What geometric shape is the path of the Earth around the Sun?

⑪ Which famous author committed suicide in 1941 at age 59?

⑫ Which country has the west-most point in South America?

⑬ What does the name 'Iwo Jima' mean in Japanese?

⑭ Which English monarch immediately preceded James II?

⑮ Who discovered the rotating magnetic field that is the basis of Alternating Current?

⑯ Which film featured a character named Chappy Sinclair?

The Bumper Family Quiz Book
Quiz 266

① Where are the 2016 Olympic Games due to be held?

② What is the name of the heroine in Disney's *Hercules*? 💡

③ A carving of whose head decorated the Temple of Artemis at Ephesus?

④ The 1948 book, *Cry, the Beloved Country*, was written by whom?

⑤ Which *Spider-Man* actress appeared in *Interview With the Vampire* as a child?

⑥ What colourless brandy is made from cherries?

⑦ What medical term means 'pain resulting from insufficient blood to the heart'?

⑧ What designer famously said 'You have two eyes, so use them'?

⑨ Colombia shares which grassland plain with Venezuela?

⑩ In what year did boy band Westlife announce they were splitting?

⑪ In *The Rocker*, what is Robert's nickname?

⑫ What banana-shaped stick comes back to the thrower? 💡

⑬ Malta became an independent nation in which year?

⑭ Who directed the 1981 film *Das Boot*?

⑮ What was seen worldwide as the final defeat of European imperialism?

⑯ What three colours is the Apple iPhone 6 available in?

The Bumper Family Quiz Book
Quiz 267

1. What is the capital of Burundi?

2. What did the German ship *Emden* move on January 23, 1945, in World War 2?

3. Which Libyan leader announced in 2003 that his country would give up its weapons program?

4. In the 2006 film *Flushed Away*, what does Roddy get flushed into?

5. What type of tree grows from acorns?

6. The longest river in the world is located on what continent?

7. Which body coordinates the assignment of domain names and Internet protocol addresses?

8. Which material is commonly used in sculpture: charcoal, concrete or plaster?

9. What was the 1996 debut album from the Super Furry Animals?

10. Which Hindu god has the head of an elephant and the body of a man?

11. Norman Reedus plays which brother in *The Boondock Saints*?

12. What do you traditionally give for a twentieth anniversary?

13. In *Alice's Adventures in Wonderland*, what does Alice fall through?

14. Which dog can be black, brown or yellow: collie, labrador retriever or springer spaniel?

15. What is a dewlap on a dog?

16. What would you use chalk for in a game of snooker?

The Bumper *Family* Quiz Book
Quiz 268

1. Who was known as the *Sailor King*?

2. What is the general term pertaining to the blood vessels that supply the heart?

3. Who was the great middleweight boxer nicknamed 'Marvellous'?

4. Who wrote *The Day of the Triffids*?

5. Which Stuart Queen of England bore 18 children, of which none survived past childhood?

6. Which is a ribosome?

7. What sandal-like footwear were once made from car tyres?

8. Which country has Rome as its capital?

9. What is the name of a Mexican deep-fried pastry stick, rolled in sugar and served hot?

10. When you speak of a nation's currency, what are you talking about?

11. What is a 'hobbledehoy'?

12. Who plays Professor X in the *X-Men* trilogy?

13. In what year did Henry III become King of England?

14. Which of the following countries is not in the top 10 worldwide in terms of land area: Australia, Canada, Kazakhstan or Mexico?

15. Which author, born in 1922, wrote *Lucky Jim*?

16. From which US state does the continental divide enter Mexico?

The Bumper *Family* Quiz Book
Quiz 269

1. What condition do you have when you have a decreased red blood cell count?

2. By what familiar name was King George VI known to his family?

3. A phytotoxin is a poison produced from what?

4. What is the surface an artist uses to mix his colours called? 💡

5. Martha Wainwright sings with what band on a song called *Eyes Open*?

6. The medical term 'triple zero' refers to what?

7. How long did the Vandals spend destroying Rome in 455 AD?

8. What Swiss folk music involves making a high-low-high-low sound with your voice? 💡

9. The Pantanal, the world's largest tropical wetland, is primarily in which country?

10. Which fighter was the film 'Somebody Up There Likes Me' about?

11. Which of these films starred Jim Carrey: *Eddie*, *The Cable Guy* or *Aladdin*?

12. What did Jacob Schick patent in 1928?

13. The x-ray machine was first used to discover what?

14. What does 'unman' mean?

15. What happened in Tiananmen Square in 1989?

16. Jamaica is considered part of which continent?

The Bumper Family Quiz Book
Quiz 270

1. How many commandments were given to Moses?

2. In *One Flew Over the Cuckoo's Nest* what malady is the Chief faking?

3. Henry VII ascended the English throne in which year?

4. With what tool would a carpenter drive nails?

5. What is the main way the Cairo suburbs are connected?

6. RCA first introduced what speed of record in 1949?

7. What is the wire that gives off light in a light bulb called?

8. What major plot twist occurs at the end of Agatha Christie's *The Murder of Roger Ackroyd*?

9. What does the phrase 'Hasta la vista', said by the Terminator in the film of that name, mean?

10. Which country did the World Health Organization declare in 2000 had 'the best healthcare in the world'?

11. What type of domestic switch allows you to reset an electrical circuit?

12. Which sport uses the biggest ball?

13. Who was the first golfer to lose a play-off in all four Majors?

14. How many countries suffered major damage in the 2004 Indian Ocean tsunami?

15. In what country is the Taj Mahal?

16. Where does the Inca trail terminate?

The Bumper Family Quiz Book
Quiz 271

1. In which year did sprinter Darren Campbell win his first Olympic medal?

2. Which Australian bird can mimic the sound of almost anything?

3. In the film *Goodfellas*, what was Jimmy's nickname?

4. What is an area of grass in front of a house called: foyer, lawn, porch or stoop? 💡

5. Which software company makes *Powerpoint*?

6. What part of a flower are the 'calyx'?

7. Who ascended the English throne after the death of Mary I?

8. Where is *The Polar Express* going?

9. What is the tarantula's deadliest enemy?

10. What is the name of the European Union single currency that came into being in 1999? 💡

11. In what year did James II become King of England?

12. What kind of food is 'focaccia'?

13. What Australian artist recorded *Most People I Know Think That I'm Crazy* in October of 1972?

14. In tenpin bowling, what is a 'strike'? 💡

15. In *Lord of the Flies*, which character is called by the name 'Merridew'?

16. Atelophobia is the fear of what?

The Bumper Family Quiz Book
Quiz 272

1. In 1994, who was elected the first non-white President of South Africa?

2. In heraldry, what are the two types of fur?

3. Which word, meaning 'the act of bringing goods into a country', is the opposite of export? 💡

4. Which film won the 2006 Academy Award for Best Picture?

5. During what month does the *Orionids* meteor shower take place?

6. What race did court documents describe Nelson Mandela as: Asiatic, Bantu or Black?

7. Who wrote the 1941 book, *A Curtain of Green*?

8. What is the ability of fluids to flow through soil called?

9. The 'West Lothian question' concerns parliamentary matters between England and what other country?

10. Which part of a church is often made of stained glass? 💡

11. Who commissioned the Pantheon in Rome?

12. What was the name of Mussolini's Yacht in World War 2?

13. What is the highest point in Africa?

14. Which member of the Killers is the drummer?

15. What is a latke?

16. Who won the 1982 FIFA World Cup?

The Bumper Family Quiz Book
Quiz 273

1. What is the capital city of Bulgaria?

2. In what year was the lost Inca city of Machu Picchu found?

3. Who played William Shakespeare in the film *Shakespeare in Love*?

4. Riga is the capital of which country?

5. What is the name of the bell in the clock tower of London's Parliament building?

6. What decade is the hit single *All Out Of Love* by Air Supply from?

7. From what country does Fievel hail in the film *An American Tail*?

8. 'Frère Jacques, Frère Jacques, Dormez-vous? Dormez-vous?' is a children's song from what country?

9. Which of these animals does not produce milk that is used in cheese: cow, goat, horse or sheep?

10. The Central American nation of Costa Rica uses which currency?

11. When referred to in computer networking, what is a 'WLAN'?

12. What is the mythology of the Vikings called?

13. Which boxer won the World Boxing Council super-welterweight title in 2007?

14. What type of speleothems found in limestone caves grow upward from the floor?

15. What is a hundredth of a Danish krone called?

16. What common pollutant is formed when oxygen reacts with other compounds, particularly on hot days?

The Bumper Family Quiz Book
Quiz 274

1. What was the first operational jet-powered fighter aircraft in history?

2. Dublin is the capital of what country?

3. A spider has how many legs?

4. Which is the second letter of the Greek alphabet?

5. Brazil covers roughly what percentage of South America?

6. What is the highest point on Malta?

7. Approximately what percentage of the brain is water?

8. On which continent is Latvia located?

9. In what film did Johnny Depp play Gene Watson?

10. In Henry James' book *The Aspern Papers*, what was character Jeffery Aspern's occupation?

11. Tennis player Jo-Wilfried Tsonga comes from which country?

12. In 1991, what was made the official language of Puerto Rico?

13. Trinidad and Tobago were discovered by Columbus on his third voyage. What is their capital city?

14. Trypanophobia is the fear of what?

15. Which food nationality do tacos belong to?

16. In 1978, Robert K. Jarvik was credited with which invention?

The Bumper Family Quiz Book
Quiz 275

1. What is the capital city of Spain?

2. In zoology, what is an 'ocellus'?

3. What would a trumpeter do with a mute?

4. Where did John Lennon and Yoko Ono record the single *Give Peace A Chance*?

5. A Medieval illuminated manuscript is what type of object?

6. The Roman Empire reached its greatest land area under which Emperor?

7. Margaretha Zelle was a professional dancer of what discipline during World War 1?

8. Which of these drinks is not alcoholic: beer, milk, rum or vodka?

9. What footballer married pop star Cheryl Tweedy in 2006?

10. Which actor played William Black in *Clerks*?

11. Which part of an elephant's body has the most muscles?

12. What phenomenon explains why cyclohexatriene does not exist?

13. In which year was George III crowned King of the United Kingdom?

14. Who wrote *Waiting for the Mahatma*?

15. In terms of sushi and sashimi, what is 'toro'?

16. Belmopan is the capital of which country?

The Bumper Family Quiz Book
Quiz 276

1. Captain Henry Morgan used what island as a base of buccaneer operations?

2. In *Austin Powers*, which James Bond villain was Dr. Evil a parody of?

3. The natural hallucinogen psilocybin is found in what?

4. If it is now 1:15, what time was it one hour ago?

5. What is steam drawn deep from within the earth called?

6. Which King Henry was once Earl of Richmond?

7. In what year was heavyweight boxer Sinan Samil Sam born?

8. Who was Henry VIII's fifth wife?

9. Before she was a painter, Georgia O'Keeffe created art using what?

10. What is the Roman numeral for 100?

11. In what country did Indra Devi spend most of her final days?

12. What year did Salvador Dali paint 'Persistence of Memory'?

13. Who was the space-walking astronaut on *Gemini 10*?

14. What is *Leberkäse*?

15. What failed project was started in Australia at Humpty Doo, near Darwin, in 1956-57?

16. In golf, what is a 'toe'?

The Bumper Family Quiz Book
Quiz 277

1. Which Stuart monarch married William of Orange?

2. What are the two main colours on the Spanish flag?

3. What part of speech is 'terrify', meaning 'to fill with extreme fear'?

4. Which country was the first to host two World Cups?

5. What layer of the Earth is right below the crust?

6. The Western Ghats mountain range in India is also called what?

7. In which year did Edward VIII ascend the British throne?

8. Which English King died in Whitehall in January 1547?

9. In *One Flew Over The Cuckoo's Nest*, what character drowned in the pool?

10. What device would you use to manually open and close a circuit?

11. Which mammals use a pouch to continue their offspring's development once born?

12. Which 2005 film's plot is about a pair of committed womanizers who sneak into weddings to meet women?

13. Al Capone was sentenced to 11 years for what crime?

14. Which is the largest island still under Spanish rule?

15. Fillet steak comes from which cut of beef?

16. What was the name of the first commercially successful Australian-produced talkie film?

The Bumper Family Quiz Book
Quiz 278

1. When did footballer Alan Shearer score his first England hat-trick: 1993, 1997, 1999 or 2001?

2. Which was the first Bond film to not feature Q?

3. In Scotland, what is a 'brae'?

4. Which 2014 film stars Samuel L. Jackson, Scarlett Johansson and Chris Evans? 💡

5. To what country did Khrushchev send troops to brutally suppress a revolt in 1956?

6. What ancient people based their law on Hammurabi's Code?

7. What is the official name of Weezer's 'Green Album'?

8. What is the last word in the title of the famous book, *To Kill A ___*?

9. What theory describes that Earth is made of plates that move? 💡

10. The Chinese developed what fabric from worms?

11. Scotland was a sovereign state until what year?

12. Fear of cooking is known as what?

13. The 1965 film *Pierrot Le Fou* was directed by Jean-Luc Godard. To what phrase does *Le Fou* translate?

14. Where would you find the fictional Dracula's castle?

15. If you ordered 'Awabi' in a Japanese restaurant what would you get served?

16. In what era did dinosaurs live?

The Bumper Family Quiz Book
Quiz 279

1. Where is Pengrowth Saddledome located?

2. Which world leader travels in Air Force One?

3. What country's children does La Befana deliver gifts to?

4. Pharaoh Seti I was the father of which famous Egyptian monarch?

5. What 1989 Nine Inch Nails album does their song *Down In It* appear on?

6. The 1945 book titled, *Loving*, was written by whom?

7. Who was lured into the Gingerbread House by the Wicked Witch?

8. Which SI unit of absorbed radiation replaced the rad?

9. What character did Jack Palance play in the 1989 film *Batman*?

10. What city hosted the Summer Olympics in 1956?

11. Which town is furthest south in mainland Australia?

12. What was the last name of the Royal Family before George V changed it in 1917?

13. Which country withdrew from the Exchange Rate Mechanism on September 16, 1992?

14. Which Andrew Lloyd Webber musical re-opened in the West End in 2014?

15. What country hosted the 1988 UEFA European Football Championship?

16. What is the fastest-moving fish in the sea?

The Bumper Family Quiz Book
Quiz 280

1. In which country would you find Loch Ness, and possibly the mythical 'Loch Ness Monster'?

2. In the book *The Da Vinci Code*, what is Robert Langdon's profession?

3. Allison Goldfrapp appeared on the album *Maxinquaye* by what artist?

4. The acronym 'EU', when referring to a group of nations, stands for what?

5. What is the only country crossed by both the equator and the Tropic of Capricorn?

6. What type of animal is a cassowary?

7. In furniture, what is 'buhl'?

8. A flat drawing that shows what the earth looks like from above is called a what?

9. Which superhero has a small cameo in many episodes of *Seinfeld*?

10. What are the odds of rolling two six-sided dice and getting two sixes?

11. What is the best way to avoid contracting dengue fever along the Texas-Mexico border?

12. Which George W. Bush cabinet member wrote the book *Lessons from a Father to His Son*?

13. Who wrote the 1973 novel, *Crash*?

14. What is the nickname of the French national soccer team?

15. In what World War 2 North African battle was Rommel involved in?

16. Catagelophobia is the fear of what?

The Bumper Family Quiz Book
Quiz 281

1. Who directed the Oscar-nominated *Captain Phillips*?

2. Which of these is not a type of penguin: adele, gentoo, macaroni or telugu?

3. What is the traditional colour of royalty?

4. What band did Alvin Lee play in?

5. Which South American country has the highest elevation?

6. What is *Coq au vin*?

7. In what year did classic screen actor Bela Lugosi pass away?

8. How many sides does an octagon have?

9. Which country claims ownership of the Falkland Islands from the UK?

10. According to the nursery rhyme, who were 'all the King's horses and all the King's men' unable to put together again?

11. What does the Lord Chancellor sit on while presiding over the UK House of Lords?

12. Which cosmetics firm provided make-up services for the *I Love Lucy* TV show?

13. What was the official competition slogan of UEFA Euro 2012?

14. Which land animal lives the furthest north: arctic fox, canada goose or dung beetle?

15. In *The Hitchhiker's Guide to the Galaxy*, what is said to be the meaning of life?

16. What lake is near Villa La Angostura in Argentina?

The Bumper Family Quiz Book
Quiz 282

1. Where is the Golden Triangle?

2. Which long-reigning Tudor monarch never married?

3. What is 'teutophobia'?

4. If you say someone is 'underbred', what do you mean?

5. In text chat, what does BTW mean?

6. In which year did the Nazis hold their infamous exhibition of 'degenerate art'?

7. When a dog's tail is between its legs, it usually means what?

8. What is 4648 rounded to the nearest 1000?

9. In what US state is Wall Street located?

10. Which field of mathematics was prefigured by the 'Seven Bridges of Konigsberg' problem?

11. What country is directly to the north of Vietnam?

12. What breed of dog is known as the 'king of terriers'?

13. Who was 'Chief Big Wind' in World War 2?

14. Who plays Cyclops in the *X-Men* trilogy?

15. What was Italian footballer Claudio Gentile nicknamed?

16. Who wrote the sci-fi book *A Case of Conscience*?

The Bumper Family Quiz Book
Quiz 283

① What did American Carl Hertz introduce to Australia in 1896?

② Which is the longest river entirely within England?

③ What is the name of Donald Duck's girlfriend? 💡

④ What honorary position did Ted Hughes hold from 1984?

⑤ Where does the Hapsburg (ruling house of Austria 1282-1918) name come from?

⑥ The film *Jurassic Park III* was directed by whom?

⑦ In what year did TV ownership reach one million homes with television sets: 1773, 1814 or 1948? 💡

⑧ What is 'knar' an archaic word for?

⑨ Which Tudor monarch ascended the throne in January 1547, at the age of 9?

⑩ Which Bavarian castle did Walt Disney sculpt Cinderella's after?

⑪ Which of these types of tea is said to help settle an upset stomach: lemon, orange pekoe or peppermint?

⑫ What type of flower is an 'ixia'?

⑬ What is the name of the time period when glaciers covered most of the earth? 💡

⑭ What is the upper layer of earth called?

⑮ What company introduced the first programmable pocket calculator in 1974?

⑯ What year did tennis player Maria Sharapova turn professional?

Quiz 284

1. What role did Shawn Ashmore play in *X-Men*?

2. Who is the Roman goddess of love?

3. In which compass direction are the Andes mountains located in relation to Chile?

4. Aristotle tutored which person who would go on to conquer all of the then-known world?

5. What part of speech is 'piccolo', meaning 'a small flute'?

6. What is a 'xeric'?

7. Iceland is home to active volcanoes that spew what: concrete, ice, lava or slime?

8. How many of Magellan's five ships completed the voyage around the world?

9. What adaptation allows an organism to look like another in order to survive?

10. Which horse won the Grand National in 2010?

11. The Persian religious leader Zoroaster believed that nothing was more shameful than what?

12. In which country was iced tea first sold commercially?

13. Where did the alternative rock band Coldplay get its name?

14. What fluid-filled sac surrounds the human embryo?

15. What is the state flower of Florida?

16. Who wrote *The Hound of the Baskervilles*?

The Bumper Family Quiz Book
Quiz 285

1. In what city, the capital of Iraq, is Aladdin said to have found his magic lamp?

2. What is the best way to put out a pan fire on a stove?

3. What actor played the title character in *Hugo*?

4. What is the official language of Vietnam? 💡

5. In which James Bond film is Tunbridge Wells mentioned?

6. In what year did Tiger Woods become a professional golfer?

7. The image of an object when seen in a mirror is called what? 💡

8. What is the most popular sport in Peru?

9. Which animal, like humans, cries tears when distressed?

10. Where were 'Belgian' waffles invented?

11. How often did Bram Stoker visit Transylvania when writing *Dracula*?

12. The chariot route called 'The Appian Way' connected Ancient Rome with what other city?

13. Which emperor immediately preceded Trajan?

14. Who was the top Italian Ace of World War 2?

15. In Anne Rice's *The Witching Hour*, where did the Mayfair family live?

16. As of 2014, how many BRIT award nominations has Leona Lewis had?

The Bumper Family Quiz Book
Quiz 286

① Kung Pao chicken is a food item of what type of cuisine?

② What is the name of the top-flight professional soccer league in Turkey?

③ In the *James Bond* films, what country was *Oddjob* from?

④ In what century did Edmund Ironside become King of England?

⑤ Up to and including *Skyfall*, in how many feature films has Daniel Craig played James Bond? 💡

⑥ The Da Nang International Airport is in which country?

⑦ In Hawaii, what are 'ahi'?

⑧ To the nearest 100, how many Earth days does it take Mars to orbit the sun?

⑨ In text chat, what does JK mean? 💡

⑩ In Ancient Egyptian mythology, who was Osiris?

⑪ What were Confederate forces looking for when they entered Gettysburg in July 1863?

⑫ In which country is the Ho Chi Minh Trail?

⑬ What is a 'demoniac'?

⑭ In evolution, which period gave rise to the first mammals?

⑮ What is a dark area that light does not reach called? 💡

⑯ In 1962 Nelson Mandela went to Algeria to do what?

Quiz 287

(1) What happened to the B-25 'Old Feather Merchant' in New York on July 28, 1945, in World War 2?

(2) How is the constellation *Crux* known in English?

(3) According to the nursery rhyme, Little Bo-peep lost her what? 💡

(4) What did 2013 Presidential Medal of Freedom recipient Mario Molina win a Nobel Prize for?

(5) What does 'orotund' mean?

(6) If something is 'sanguineous', what is it?

(7) Which of these is a long-horned antelope: oryx, anteater or cassowary? 💡

(8) Which country hosted the FIFA World Cup in 2010?

(9) In what year was Darwin, in Australia's Northern Territory, almost destroyed by cyclone Tracy?

(10) What is an average delivery rate over a channel called?

(11) Fear of tornadoes and hurricanes is known as what?

(12) Who was the leader of Iraq during the 1980-1988 Iran-Iraq War?

(13) In *Star Wars: Revenge of the Sith*, who adopts baby Luke?

(14) What city is China's second largest in terms of population?

(15) Who was the muse of history in Greek mythology?

(16) The Darkness insist that they 'Believe in a Thing Called' what?

The Bumper Family Quiz Book
Quiz 288

1. What were all Roman people who were not slaves called?

2. What strong-smelling Japanese breakfast food is made from soya beans?

3. Which French philosopher pioneered the use of the letter 'x' to represent an unknown variable?

4. Which is the only vowel on the middle row of a computer keyboard?

5. The leading edge of an advancing cold air mass is known as what?

6. The Strait of Tiran separates the Red Sea from what other body of water?

7. In the film *Wild Hogs*, released in 2007, what was Doug Madsen's job?

8. To the nearest 10, how many Earth days does it take Venus to orbit the sun?

9. Which one of the following is not a London area airport: Luton, Crawley or Stansted?

10. Who wrote the sci-fi book *The Demolished Man*?

11. Which city hosted the 1992 Winter Olympic Games?

12. Who is the current editor of *Vogue* Magazine in the UK, as of 2014?

13. What was the name of the German aviator who flew his plane undetected into Red Square?

14. In music, what is a 'lacuna'?

15. Which European country's highest elevation point is Musala?

16. What woman was the last Pharaoh of Egypt?

The Bumper *Family* Quiz Book
Quiz 289

① Which designer invented a leather bag with a bamboo handle?

② What country are potatoes originally from?

③ What is the name of the limestone formation that hangs down from a cave ceiling?

④ How is the constellation *Aries* known in English?

⑤ Which empire did Egypt eventually become a part of?

⑥ In heraldry, what colour is 'sable'?

⑦ Who is Rudolph the Red-Nosed Reindeer's father?

⑧ During what war is the 2001 film *The Devil's Backbone* set?

⑨ What does 'to taw' mean?

⑩ What is polenta made from?

⑪ In comparing art to music, Wassily Kandinsky once said colour was what?

⑫ What All Saints member had a hit single called *TwentyFourSeven*?

⑬ Where does hail form?

⑭ Which King created the Babylonian Empire?

⑮ Which countries hosted the FIFA World Cup in 2002?

⑯ What is the term for a relaxation of tension between countries?

Quiz 290

1. In what year did Cyrus of Persia conquer the Median overlords and form the Persian Empire?

2. What do you call a room that uses projectors to show the night sky? 💡

3. Which of the following is actually a lizard: adder, corn snake or glass snake?

4. In geology, what is 'loess'?

5. VoIP refers to what technology?

6. Where in the ocean would you find lobsters living?

7. Who was not part of Ken Kesey's 'Merry Pranksters': Jack Kerouac, Jerry Garcia or Neal Cassady?

8. Who became heavyweight champion when Ali was forced to vacate it?

9. How often are the summer Olympic Games held? 💡

10. Where is the largest natural harbour in England?

11. Why did Vincent van Gogh paint his first self-portrait?

12. What A-list film star's first role was in *A Nightmare On Elm Street*?

13. The Andes, which run partly through Argentina, is what kind of natural formation?

14. Which winter vegetable is best described as looking like a small green ball?

15. What symbol is on the flag of Macedonia?

16. Who was the author of *Forty Days of Musa Dagh*, a novel recounting the Armenian Genocide?

The Bumper Family Quiz Book
Quiz 291

1. Vilnius is the capital of which country?

2. In which year was the independence of Egypt, a former British colony, first declared?

3. What was Pope Benedict XVI's real name? 💡

4. Which fruit is ninety per cent water?

5. Who won the Pichichi Trophy for being the top scorer in the 2011-12 season of the Spanish La Liga?

6. What is a long balloon filled with helium generally called?

7. Which London museum is located in Covent Garden Piazza?

8. What was the name given to the conflict between China and Britain from 1839 to 1842?

9. Which type of animal has hollow bones: bird, cat or dog?

10. Which month is the last in the year? 💡

11. What does *a posteriori* mean?

12. Who is the author of the book *The Deep*?

13. Where do crepes originally come from? 💡

14. London's Brick Lane was the centre of what 16th-century industry?

15. Who played Eve Moneypenny in *Skyfall*?

16. Which UK Prime Minister led the country during the majority of World War 2? 💡

The Bumper *Family* Quiz Book
Quiz 292

1. Who invented the FORTRAN computer programming language?

2. What does 'ersatz' mean?

3. What World War 1 German pilot said 'Find the enemy and shoot him down. Anything else is nonsense'?

4. What do Amazon call their free delivery service?

5. What geometric shape has five sides?

6. What *Harry Potter* character is also known as Moony?

7. What is the Greek name for the east wind?

8. Who defined the radius of a black hole?

9. What inanimate object sings *Tale as Old as Time* in Disney's *Beauty and the Beast*?

10. In which US state is 'Area 51' located?

11. The cake topping 'streusel' comes from a German word that means what?

12. Tijuana, Ensenada, Acapulco and Cancun are cities in what country?

13. In what year did Mary II become Queen of England?

14. Riyadh is the capital city of which Arab nation?

15. In golf's Ryder Cup, how many points are awarded for each match won?

16. Who played Neo in *The Matrix*?

The Bumper Family Quiz Book
Quiz 293

1. Who enforces the thoughtcrime laws in *Nineteen Eighty-Four*?

2. The Japanese flag is a circle of what colour on a white background? 💡

3. What causes the moon to shine?

4. How many of the ten 2010 World Cup stadia featured an indoor field?

5. A 2011 horror film centres around fictional events on what cancelled NASA mission?

6. On which continent are the Atlas Mountains?

7. Taquitos are included in which cuisine?

8. Which Saxon King was killed by William the Conqueror in 1066?

9. What was the most visited website in 2014, according to Alexa? 💡

10. The lower arm comprises which two bones?

11. Which of the following wars took place before World War 2: Korean War or Spanish-American War?

12. Who was Hedwig Potthast during World War 2?

13. What is the national flower of China?

14. On which island can you find Madang, Wewak, Fak Fak and Jayapura?

15. What form of focused light can be found in Frankie Goes to Hollywood's *Relax* lyrics?

16. In what two countries might you find 'bani' in your wallet?

The Bumper Family Quiz Book
Quiz 294

1. What is the second-best-selling UK Christmas single of all time?

2. Which of these dance styles is associated with Spain: clog dancing, disco dancing or flamenco dancing?

3. The Pyramids of Giza are in which city?

4. 'Canada' is an Indian word meaning what?

5. What makes the cell walls of plants rigid?

6. How long can tarantulas and mygalomorph spiders live?

7. Who is considered 'The Father of Modern French Cooking'?

8. What part of the ginger plant is used in cooking?

9. Which Czech supermodel was born on March 10, 1973?

10. Which US state's flower is the sunflower?

11. Which vitamin nourishes the skin?

12. Who discovered the Straits of Magellan?

13. Who was the famous botanist who travelled with Captain Cook on his first voyage?

14. Which country hosted the FIFA World Cup in 1982?

15. Which Queen of England died of smallpox in December 1694?

16. Which character in Disney's *Aladdin* was named after a Shakespearean character?

The Bumper Family Quiz Book
Quiz 295

① In what type of institution did the members of U2 originally meet?

② What was Disneyland Paris called originally? 💡

③ Who ascended the throne of England in February 1685?

④ What capital city is located at approximately 60 degrees north and 25 degrees east?

⑤ Which capital city has, as a scenic backdrop, the snow-capped Mount Wellington?

⑥ How many teeth does an adult cat usually have?

⑦ How many countries did the North Atlantic Treaty Organization formally admit in 2004?

⑧ What song does Phil wake up to each day in the film *Groundhog Day*?

⑨ Alan Schneider is known for being what?

⑩ Samurai warriors belong to which culture? 💡

⑪ Which Greek playwright wrote the three Theban plays, including *Antigone*?

⑫ In snooker, why would you take a rest?

⑬ How many moons does Eris have?

⑭ What do you call a word which is one of multiple hyponyms of another word?

⑮ In what year was the Big Mac introduced to the world?

⑯ What are the hair-like projections on the outside of cells called?

The Bumper Family Quiz Book
Quiz 296

1. What did Heinrich Himmler order removed from Paris on the eve of its liberation?

2. You can calculate the length of a hypotenuse using whose theorem?

3. Alitalia is the flag-carrier airline of which country?

4. A young cat is called what?

5. Which museum, first known as the Museum of Non-Objective Painting, opened in New York in 1939?

6. What is Captain Sparrow's first name in *Pirates of the Caribbean*?

7. Which Welsh children's television comedy featured three skeletons living together?

8. Which is the penultimate letter of the Greek alphabet?

9. What is a scientist who specializes in soil and crops called?

10. What does an immunosuppressive drug do?

11. What geographic distinction does the 1972 Sapporo Winter Olympics have?

12. Which scientist named oxygen?

13. What does the term 'atomic number', used in physics, mean?

14. Which zone separates the Chilean Coast Range from the Andes?

15. How can you start your day off with a faster-burning metabolism?

16. 'The Sleeping Gypsy' was created by which artist?

The Bumper *Family* Quiz Book
Quiz 297

1. What was the former capital of West Germany?

2. What is the only SI unit still defined by an artifact rather than a fundamental property?

3. What colour of tea is 'English Breakfast' tea?

4. What is the capital city of Sierra Leone?

5. What type of historical weapon was a 'fusil'?

6. In which year was Juan Peron first elected Argentina's President?

7. What is deterioration of a metal by chemical or electrochemical reaction with its environment?

8. Which Asian country's highest elevation point is Kula Kangri?

9. In what year was the artificial heart used for the first time?

10. In which sport might you do the crawl, backstroke or butterfly?

11. On a piano, what does a middle pedal do?

12. In the 'Twilight' books, what does Bella suffer from?

13. Which unit is used to measure the purity of gold?

14. Hungarian director Lajos Koltai's 2005 film *Fateless* takes place during what historical event?

15. Which singer informed us that 'My Life Would Suck Without You' in 2009?

16. What is the motto of the Olympic Movement?

The Bumper Family Quiz Book
Quiz 298

1. Arachnophobia is fear of what?

2. Where can you find a coral island called Lizard Island?

3. What website lets you send 'tweets'? 💡

4. Who is Caesar's wife in the 2014 film *Dawn of the Planet of the Apes*?

5. In what city would you find Vatican City, the home of the head of the Catholic Church?

6. Medically, what is an 'ictus'?

7. What is the largest country in North America?

8. In what event did Liz McColgan win a medal at the Seoul Olympics?

9. What does 'multigravidae' mean?

10. The first *Harry Potter* book was *Harry Potter and* what? 💡

11. What is your 'physiognomy'?

12. What revolutionary institution did Ted Turner establish in 1980?

13. Which British King was executed in January 1649?

14. What is another name for green beryl?

15. What is a *haricot vert*?

16. How many Primetime Emmys has writer and actress Mindy Kaling been nominated for, as of 2014?

The Bumper Family Quiz Book
Quiz 299

1. Antananarivo is the capital of which large island?

2. Zakumi, a green and gold lion, was the mascot for which year's World Cup?

3. What object is Lumiere in Disney's *Beauty and the Beast*?

4. Where is the Bass Strait, in which King and Flinders Islands can be found?

5. The Qinghai-Tibet railway connects Tibet with which country?

6. Which artist was nicknamed 'Jack the Dripper'?

7. Who were Shakespeare's twins named after?

8. Which is the word for the study of the ocean?

9. What object gives the titular character of *Green Lantern* his superpowers?

10. What enormous structures were used as burial tombs in Ancient Egypt?

11. What year did the first American go into orbit?

12. In archaeology, what is a 'cist'?

13. What is the name given to a line that connects all points of the same elevation on a map?

14. During the Middle Ages, who was the single largest owner of land?

15. What term describes a brief fluctuation in a VoIP transmission signal: jitter, murmur or quaver?

16. What is the Sikh holy text called?

The Bumper Family Quiz Book
Quiz 300

① What nickname was earned by Mary I for her persecution of Protestants?

② How tall is Big Bird on *Sesame Street*? 💡

③ What is the first name of Garfield's owner in the film *Garfield*?

④ In which part of the body is the 'ulna'?

⑤ Which muscles will benefit from doing push-ups?

⑥ The term *camera obscura* is from which language?

⑦ What type of reproduction do yeast cells use: budding, jumping or sprinting?

⑧ What is water in its solid form called? 💡

⑨ What World War 2 bomber was made entirely of wood, yet fast enough to outrun most enemy fighters?

⑩ How many miles long is the Indianapolis 500 car race?

⑪ Which of these heavy-set comedians was born and raised in Canada: Chris Farley, John Belushi or John Candy?

⑫ What is the capital of Chechnya?

⑬ What country was the scene of the Boxer Uprising of 1900?

⑭ Who famously said 'Facts do not cease to exist because they are ignored'?

⑮ Who is the Nutcracker's enemy?

⑯ Which dwarf planet is larger – Pluto or Eris?

The Bumper Family Quiz Book
Quiz 301

1. In emergency medicine, what does 'stat' mean?

2. What is the Kuiper belt?

3. From what language does the word 'kindergarten' originate? 💡

4. Which US state's flower is the rose?

5. In which medal position did Turkey finish in the 2002 FIFA World Cup?

6. In 1945, the United States dropped an atomic bomb on which two Japanese cities?

7. What are the geese doing in the song *The Twelve Days of Christmas*? 💡

8. What is the name of the strait that separates the two Japanese islands of Shikoku and Kyushu?

9. How is the song *99 Luftballons* better known in English?

10. Tempera paints are made by mixing pigments with what breakfast food?

11. Which famous golfer makes numerous cameos in the film *Happy Gilmore*?

12. What was a Roman *gladius*?

13. Into which ocean do most Chinese rivers empty?

14. In what year did Anne become Queen of England?

15. What does vitamin A do for your eyes?

16. Who banned Christmas carols in England from 1649-1660?

The Bumper Family Quiz Book
Quiz 302

1. What are gnocchi?

2. What is the capital of India?

3. What type of microscope uses light and two or more lenses to see specimens?

4. What does an astronaut experience in space that leads to muscle weakness? 💡

5. In biology, what are 'bacilli'?

6. Where was the treaty signed ending the Russo-Japanese War?

7. Princes Harry and William are members of what country's royal family? 💡

8. Brand's Hatch Farm has been hosting motor racing since what year?

9. What was Kevin Costner's *Waterworld* nicknamed during production?

10. Who was the fifth, and final, Tudor monarch?

11. Which royal dynasty preceded the Hanoverians?

12. On which continent is Japan located?

13. In Ancient Greece, how many obols would you get for one drachma?

14. Ruby and sapphire are gem forms of which mineral?

15. What country in Africa with Freetown as its capital uses the leone as its currency?

16. Who wrote *The Home and the World*?

The Bumper Family Quiz Book
Quiz 303

① Where on your body would you find the 'fovea'?

② Who won the World Snooker Championship in 2014?

③ What name does *Internet Explorer* give to its bookmark feature?

④ Which country borders 14 nations and crosses 8 time zones?

⑤ What is the usual Pimm's 'No.' sold?

⑥ In 1472, Leonardo da Vinci became a member of which Florentine guild?

⑦ What kind of animal is a burbot?

⑧ What is the most common programming language for web '/cgi' scripts?

⑨ Which planet orbits between Saturn and Neptune?

⑩ Which US territory is the largest and most southerly of the Mariana Islands?

⑪ What is the first name of the front-woman in the band Goldfrapp?

⑫ In what year did Great Britain defeat the Spanish Armada?

⑬ Who played Zorro in the 1940 film, *The Mark of Zorro*?

⑭ What was the name of the first artificial Earth satellite?

⑮ What is 'psychopathy'?

⑯ Which Stuart King was married to Anne of Denmark?

The Bumper Family Quiz Book
Quiz 304

1. What substance is industrially prepared by the Haber Process?

2. Who first used the term 'Iron Curtain'?

3. Which of the following is not a type of cheese: American, Cheddar, Gouda or Parisian?

4. Which fish is frequently incorrectly claimed to be immune to all known diseases?

5. Grant Wood created which of these famous paintings: American Gothic, La Grande Jatte or Water Lilies?

6. Which Chinese dynasty built the Forbidden City?

7. In football, what are 'Los Galacticos'?

8. Kirin Brewery was founded in what country?

9. What is the system consisting of the Earth's sun and the eight planets orbiting it called?

10. What Joy Division vocalist had an untimely death just before their second album was released?

11. The kwanza is an official currency for what nation?

12. Who was sworn in for a second term as minister of Pakistan in 1993?

13. Who was the bad guy in the James Bond film *For Your Eyes Only*?

14. Who leads American comedy series *New Girl*?

15. On which continent is the Netherlands located?

16. What season does the US word 'Fall' refer to in British English?

Quiz 305

1. What were Obama, Cameron and the Danish PM caught doing at Mandela's memorial service?

2. Who celebrated his 200th grand prix start at the 2008 Monaco Grand Prix?

3. Who wrote the 1927 book titled *Death comes for the Archbishop*?

4. Why was the Great Wall of China built?

5. What is the imaginary line that runs through the centre of the Earth called: axis, mode or pole?

6. In zoology, what is an 'ungulate' animal?

7. What year did Just Fontaine score a record 13 times in a single World Cup?

8. In which year was the first 'Miss Australia' contest held?

9. What song by Sigma, featuring Paloma Faith, reached number 1 in the UK chart in 2014?

10. Tandoor ovens are used for baking breads, such as naan, in what country?

11. How is an 'MPEG-4 Part 14' file usually better known?

12. How many states does Australia have?

13. In what year was Pluto reclassified as a 'dwarf planet'?

14. Beatrix Potter's Mrs Tiggy-Winkle is what kind of animal?

15. *The Birdcage*, starring Robin Williams, is a remake of which film?

16. What type of animal is a Nebelung?

The Bumper Family Quiz Book
Quiz 306

1. Which vitamins are acquired through sunshine?

2. What was the occupation of Vincent Van Gogh's brother?

3. What fruit is lemonade made from?

4. What is the white ball called in snooker?

5. In literary usage, what is a 'plaint'?

6. What is a group of animals of the same species living and working together called?

7. Who played *Gandhi* in the epic 1982 biographical film?

8. What vegetable is claimed to keep vampires away?

9. What act did Nelson Mandela enact in 1994 to reverse the Natives Land Act of 1913?

10. During the Second Crusade, which city did Saladin recapture?

11. In Shakespeare's *Much Ado About Nothing*, the comic style used most by Dogberry is known as what?

12. Who had Robert De Niro as the best man at her wedding?

13. In biology, what is an 'euglena'?

14. What island off the coast of Africa is the fourth-largest island in the world?

15. Which disease prompted UN warnings that 90 million Africans could be infected?

16. When attacked, what does the giant petrel bird use for defence?

The Bumper Family Quiz Book
Quiz 307

1. At what 'ETA' does the bulk of David Foster Wallace's *Infinite Jest* take place?

2. Who first devised a possible way to terraform Mars?

3. How many provinces does Canada have?

4. Which of the following capitals is not in Europe: Helsinki, Lisbon, Moscow or Tel Aviv? 💡

5. Which planet takes 243 Earth days for one of its own days to pass?

6. The chemotherapy drug Paclitaxel was first extracted from which tree?

7. In the Middle Ages, what were the 'liberal arts'?

8. What type of performance art is 'kabuki'?

9. In what year was Nelson Mandela convicted under the Suppression of Communism Act?

10. What is the amount left over when a number can't be divided equally? 💡

11. Which English King first earned the title *Fidei Defensor*, 'Defender of the Faith', from the Pope?

12. Women in what country wear chadris that cover their head and face in keeping with Islamic tradition?

13. What is the occupation of Catherine Zeta-Jones' character in the 2007 film *No Reservations*?

14. In what city does the title character in Usher and R. Kelly's *Same Girl* live?

15. Boxer Arturo Gatti was raised in Canada, but where was he born?

16. Which country has Tirana as its capital city?

The Bumper Family Quiz Book
Quiz 308

1. Mestizo people make up over 50% of the population of which North American nation?

2. What unusual feature does a polydactyl cat have?

3. On which bank of the Thames are the Houses of Parliament?

4. What was crime-solver Nancy Drew's boyfriend called? 💡

5. What is the leaf of a fern called?

6. What silhouette appears on the Canadian flag?

7. In 1653, who became Lord Protector, with the same authority as a King of England?

8. Which of these is a soil that is better to grow plants in: clay, loam, rocks or sand? 💡

9. In British slang, what is a 'nana'?

10. Who sculpted the 'Little Mermaid' statue in Copenhagen ?

11. Typically, where in the heart is a pacemaker located?

12. What is credited with cutting malaria deaths in half in Zambia between 2006 and 2008?

13. Krishna and Vishnu are Hindu gods worshipped principally in which country?

14. Camel's hair is a thick fibre sometimes used in all but which type of clothing: coats, dresses, suits or sweaters?

15. Who appeared as the Penguin's father in the film *Batman Returns*?

16. Who won the 1994 FIFA World Cup?

Quiz 309

① What is the state flower of Kansas?

② Which is the highest mountain in Scotland?

③ In text chat, what does LOL mean? 💡

④ In what year did the World Cup opening ceremony include 'human origami'?

⑤ What is the 'Vedomosti'?

⑥ Who was the gunpowder plotter who tried to blow up the UK parliament in 1605? 💡

⑦ What is the area on the lee side of a mountain that receives little rain called?

⑧ What do you call a triangle that has all three sides of equal length? 💡

⑨ Monks live in what?

⑩ Who plays Rogue in the *X-Men* trilogy?

⑪ Which Stuart monarch married Henrietta Maria, daughter of Henri IV of France?

⑫ What makes Jupiter's Great Red Spot?

⑬ What rock band is Pat Smear in?

⑭ In herbal medicine, garlic is used most commonly as what?

⑮ What was Disney's first animated feature film? 💡

⑯ Which country pioneered heart transplant surgery?

The Bumper Family Quiz Book
Quiz 310

1. During his Presidency, Nelson Mandela was known for wearing what kind of shirts?

2. Which food can be called 'marrowfat'?

3. Which of these is a nocturnal, giraffe-like animal: okapi or oryx?

4. Which film is about a prosecutor who leaks a false story that targets the son of a dead Mafia boss: *Absence of Malice* or *The Colour of Money*?

5. Which Libyan leader did Nelson Mandela appoint to the Order of Good Hope in 1998?

6. What is an artificial extension used to replace a missing body part called?

7. What is Georg Dreyman's profession in the 2006 film *The Lives of Others*?

8. What is the capital of the Caribbean Island that won its independence on August 6th, 1962?

9. What animal builds lodges, dams up rivers and has large front teeth for gnawing?

10. Who wrote *All Quiet on the Western Front*?

11. What element gives the diamond its blue colour?

12. What is a 'schmo', in US slang?

13. Who was the youngest person to become ruler of England?

14. A picture that has a wide unbroken view of an area is called what?

15. What 'army' was founded in London's East End in 1865?

16. What did the 1848 gutta-percha golf ball replace?

The Bumper Family Quiz Book
Quiz 311

1. In which country was the boxer Lucian Bute born?

2. Which actress performed in both *Dragonheart* and *Johnny Mnemonic*?

3. What is another name for an African camel?

4. *Metamorphosis* is a famous novella by which author?

5. Which series of car-racing films stars Vin Diesel?

6. Peru's main exports are copper, zinc and what precious metal?

7. The period of waning light from the time of sunset until dark is called what?

8. Who were the newcomers to the Indus Valley between 2000 and 1500 BC: Aryans, Mongols, Persians or Romans?

9. What was the name of the boat that carried Charles Darwin on his historic journeys?

10. What is a 'deva'?

11. Who killed Blondi, Adolf Hitler's dog?

12. Nintendo's first coin-op arcade game was what type of game?

13. Where is the 'Fertile Crescent' located?

14. In what year did Oscar de la Renta debut his accessories line?

15. What was the name of King Arthur's wizard friend?

16. What do you call the self-replicating, DNA-containing genetic structures of cells?

The Bumper Family Quiz Book
Quiz 312

1. Which company created the *Athlon* brand name?

2. Who was President of Mexico from 2006-2012?

3. How many arms plus tentacles does a squid have?

4. A higher-resolution digital image is made up of more what?

5. What length was the 2014 Tour De France?

6. Bangui is the capital of which country?

7. In what year was *Sleepless in Seattle* released?

8. What does 'BMI' stand for?

9. In heraldry, what colour is 'gules'?

10. What are the traces of animals and plants left in rocks called?

11. What did Ashoka the Great have dug all along the roads in his kingdom?

12. What became Canada's official winter sport in 1994?

13. Which horse won the Grand National in 2013?

14. What French impressionist painter lived from 1840-1926?

15. What does the dish 'chicharron' consist of?

16. What is the national religion of Indonesia?

The Bumper *Family* Quiz Book
Quiz 313

1. Which of these is a lake situated in Bolivia: Lake Titicaca, Lake Pando or Lake Yungas?

2. On which continent is Lithuania located? 💡

3. The disease ichthyosis causes what?

4. The production of art with stones, leaves and dirt is called what?

5. Which James Bond actor was in *Mrs Doubtfire*?

6. What is the capital city of Guatemala?

7. What was the final score in the first international soccer match ever played?

8. Which comedian voices Lord Business in *The Lego Movie*? 💡

9. What company attempted to take over Gucci?

10. What Australian animal has fingerprints very similar to those of humans?

11. Margarine was first patented, in France, during which year?

12. Business data centres started moving towards what type of remote storage in the late 2000s?

13. What profession is Hulk Hogan best known for?

14. Which musical theatre show features a love triangle between Eponine, Cosette and Marius?

15. What Cuban prison did the US take Taliban and Al-Qaeda prisoners to?

16. During what month does the *Perseids* meteor shower take place?

The Bumper Family Quiz Book
Quiz 314

1. What is the name of the 1997 short film made by the musical group Portishead?

2. On which notable date was William I crowned? 💡

3. What military leader is quoted as saying 'I came, I saw, I conquered'?

4. What does the file extension .TIFF stand for?

5. What mountain will you see when visiting Cape Town, South Africa?

6. In the *Harry Potter* series, who owns the wand shop?

7. In what year did Ireland join the United Kingdom?

8. Who made the first successful aeroplane flight over the English Channel?

9. What do the five rings on the Olympic flag symbolize? 💡

10. How old was Pele when he scored a hat-trick in the 1958 World Cup final?

11. How much did the largest meteorite that plunged into the Earth in 2002 weigh?

12. Aruba is a constituent country of which Kingdom?

13. Edouard Manet was an Impressionist with elements of what other style?

14. Which nationality do mancha manteles belong to?

15. What did Max give up his medical career to do in the 2006 French film *If You Love Me, Follow Me*?

16. What two colours are on the flag of Greece?

The Bumper Family Quiz Book

QUIZ 1

1. PRI; 2. Blue with white bandages; 3. Whoopi Goldberg; 4. Uganda; 5. Canada; 6. Lion; 7. Eel; 8. *Dreaming With A Broken Heart*; 9. Maputo; 10. Rubeus; 11. The White Rabbit; 12. Lithium-ion batteries catching fire; 13. Muriel Spark; 14. Dada; 15. *A Midsummer Night's Dream*; 16. St. Louis

QUIZ 2

1. A type of pottery; 2. Darkness; 3. Flamingo; 4. Floating; 5. Chlorofluorocarbons; 6. Six; 7. Parallel; 8. 3800m (12,460ft); 9. Charles II; 10. Thorns; 11. Steve Jobs; 12. Twice a year; 13. 1970; 14. Battleship Row; 15. Juno; 16. Andrew Motion

QUIZ 3

1. 57 miles; 2. Josip Simunic; 3. Europe; 4. White; 5. Kiribati; 6. 15%; 7. Ed Harris; 8. Koala; 9. Finely ground and roasted coffee boiled with sugar; 10. A god or good spirit; 11. Cindy Crawford; 12. John Curtin; 13. Hard to interpret; 14. A formal sitting room; 15. Quito, Ecuador; 16. Baud

QUIZ 4

1. The Crimean War; 2. *Crowded House*; 3. A seamless join between two phrases; 4. Migrating; 5. Lodestone; 6. Vitamin C; 7. A sudden blow to the face; 8. Jean-Paul Sartre; 9. Morocco; 10. 1.5 biscuits each; 11. Chicken; 12. 2002; 13. Ouagadogou; 14. Painting; 15. 1138; 16. *Medea*

QUIZ 5

1. Okeh, by Gene Krupa; 2. The Zambezi; 3. Henry VII; 4. Pride Park; 5. FedEx; 6. Turkey; 7. 3.6m (12ft); 8. Bollywood; 9. Four; 10. President; 11. Nolan Bushnell; 12. Thakur; 13. Bridge; 14. Oman and Saudi Arabia; 15. Asia; 16. Cricket

The Bumper Family Quiz Book

QUIZ 6

1. Single Lens Reflex; 2. Hulk; 3. Tsunami; 4. 1898; 5. Luis Aragones;
6. South Africa; 7. Through its knees; 8. African elephant; 9. Russia;
10. Static; 11. Back in the UK; 12. Concerning fishing; 13. Blue;
14. Thomas A. Swift's electric rifle; 15. The Bottom; 16. Tommy Franks

QUIZ 7

1. Internet Message Access Protocol; 2. Blue and white;
3. Microbiologist; 4. William McKinley High School; 5. 630; 6. Muscle
doesn't turn to fat; 7. Light welterweight; 8. Italy; 9. 1884; 10. A reef;
11. Edvard Munch; 12. Tunis, Tunisia; 13. Sunscreen; 14. Stillwater;
15. Washing; 16. Bats

QUIZ 8

1. Atlantic; 2. Wood; 3. Scarlett Johansson; 4. Anaconda; 5. Light;
6. Jean Navarre; 7. Florence Nightingale; 8. 1980s; 9. Malaysia;
10. Driver's race number; 11. Religion; 12. Italy; 13. Michael
Fassbender; 14. Somali Shilling; 15. Tequila, grenadine and orange
juice; 16. Pre-revolution village

QUIZ 9

1. Kenya; 2. Orchid; 3. 13th or 15th; 4. A boxed potato/Meat stew;
5. Swollen; 6. I want you back; 7. *Thriller*; 8. 146 BC; 9. Venezuela;
10. Four; 11. 1872; 12. California Redwood; 13. Algerian War;
14. Monkeys; 15. Picture element; 16. Abdel-Aziz Ibn Saud

QUIZ 10

1. Red Rum; 2. A cloth measure; 3. Mayor; 4. Demeter; 5. Sandstone;
6. *Chinnampo*; 7. Floral; 8. William III (William of Orange); 9. Clifford
Simak; 10. Neon Jungle; 11. Jeffrey Donovan; 12. 100 days old;
13. Champagne; 14. Seven years; 15. 45 mph; 16. *The Black Cauldron*

The Bumper Family Quiz Book

QUIZ 11

1. Mars; 2. Adam; 3. Pol Pot; 4. 65%; 5. Red, yellow, green and blue;
6. Mayor of Toronto; 7. Having an obnoxious smell; 8. A spatula;
9. Salt cod and hard tack bread; 10. Roberto Baggio; 11. 5524 miles
(8,891km); 12. Brother; 13. Kiribati; 14. Rhea; 15. Lion and eagle;
16. Winston Smith

QUIZ 12

1. Jacob Marley; 2. Rose; 3. A simultaneous occurrence; 4. They are
used to fund wars; 5. Hertz; 6. George Harrison; 7. 10, Downing Street;
8. Jupiter; 9. James Woods; 10. Sochi, Russia; 11. More than 50%;
12. Leif Erikson; 13. 1914; 14. The Scream; 15. Sahara; 16. Field Of
Dreams

QUIZ 13

1. *Carpool Guy*; 2. Smothered; 3. Maritime Pollution Protection Act;
4. Sealed With A Kiss; 5. French; 6. Amen; 7. Mardi Gras; 8. A badger;
9. Portraits; 10. Denmark; 11. Libya; 12. It decreases; 13. Taiwan;
14. His son, Richard Cromwell; 15. Italy; 16. Love

QUIZ 14

1. *Man of Steel*; 2. Asia; 3. In real life; 4. Millefiori; 5. Bolero; 6. Cornea;
7. 10-14 days; 8. Alcoholism; 9. Vertex; 10. Pacific ring of fire; 11. 1967;
12. Neptune; 13. 1483; 14. Kate Moss; 15. Red, white and blue;
16. *Estonia Ferry*

QUIZ 15

1. Denmark; 2. Aslan; 3. Nutmeg; 4. Bill Clinton; 5. Oxygen; 6. *No
Country for Old Men*; 7. Frunze; 8. White; 9. What I can't afford;
10. Chicago; 11. Birmingham; 12. RMS *Titanic*; 13. Adult insect;
14. Mammal; 15. David Brin; 16. Twice

The Bumper *Family* Quiz Book

QUIZ 16

1. St Joseph; 2. A lime; 3. Bilby; 4. Shi Huandi; 5. Algarve;
6. Bhutan; 7. Heptagon; 8. Italy; 9. Light; 10. Termite; 11. Meg Ryan;
12. Blancmange; 13. South-East Asia; 14. It has toxic levels of vitamin
A; 15. 1945; 16. Irene Nemiorvsky

QUIZ 17

1. Simple tennis game; 2. Comoros; 3. Bridge; 4. Chickens; 5. Fattened
duck or goose liver; 6. Read, recite; 7. System and software
configuration files; 8. Larry King; 9. A loaf of French bread; 10. Australia;
11. 12; 12. Imagine or conceive something; 13. Matthew Maury;
14. Bahrain; 15. Small blue bow and a horseshoe; 16. Lord Howe Island

QUIZ 18

1. A unit of type equal to 12 points; 2. Atlantic Ocean; 3. Dancing;
4. Soya flour and sugar; 5. Front; 6. Toronto; 7. Kiln; 8. Helicopter;
9. Comoros; 10. 1975; 11. Mexican; 12. A noisy reveller; 13. Gala;
14. Mallorca; 15. Emperor Nero; 16. Hypotenuse

QUIZ 19

1. 1666; 2. Wilco; 3. *Bambi*; 4. Ocelot; 5. Peter the Great; 6. The
Elder Wand; 7. David Coulthard; 8. Hermann Goering; 9. Patterns;
10. Spanish; 11. Henry James; 12. 12; 13. Mongoose; 14. Palm;
15. Sundarbans Delta; 16. Green, white and orange

QUIZ 20

1. Oak tree; 2. Camel; 3. Mrs Peacock; 4. *The Hurt Locker*; 5. Bledisloe
Cup; 6. Pittwater, New South Wales; 7. Sarah Breathnach; 8. No
problem; 9. Three; 10. A coarse grass, native to Spain and North Africa;
11. Night; 12. Carbon dioxide; 13. Johnny; 14. Malaysia; 15. Potato;
16. Chair height

The Bumper Family Quiz Book

QUIZ 21

1. Painting; 2. *Drop Zone*; 3. Macduff; 4. Justin Timberlake; 5. Great Ocean Road; 6. Greece; 7. Enteral; 8. Lions; 9. Judaism; 10. 1961; 11. Jan Mayen Island; 12. Cleopatra; 13. Okra; 14. Bollettieri Tennis Academy; 15. Australian Terrier; 16. Talbot

QUIZ 22

1. Rice cooker; 2. 2011; 3. *Sons Of The Silent Age*; 4. Skulk; 5. Libya; 6. Navel; 7. Nile; 8. A poet; 9. Scottish Terrier; 10. At the moment; 11. 327; 12. Winning Olympic Gold; 13. Bonsai; 14. Over 200 years; 15. Lima; 16. Dominika Cibulkova

QUIZ 23

1. Joe Louis; 2. 12 inches; 3. Sea; 4. Clive Barker; 5. Ellipse; 6. Ian Fleming; 7. IBM; 8. Duckling; 9. Four; 10. Pineapples; 11. Sudden enlightenment; 12. Two; 13. Ulaanbataar; 14. Cayman Islands; 15. Karl Doernitz; 16. Parsley, lemon zest and garlic

QUIZ 24

1. Daniel Defoe; 2. Face lift; 3. Croatia; 4. 2009; 5. All sides are of equal length; 6. Harry Shearer; 7. Leonardo da Vinci; 8. Japan; 9. Ten years; 10. Antimatter; 11. Cuba; 12. *South Side*; 13. Suriname; 14. Karma yoga; 15. Red and white; 16. Mexico

QUIZ 25

1. Microsoft Network; 2. Iris; 3. Ten; 4. Ireland; 5. Anthony Michael Hall; 6. Yourself; 7. 1831; 8. *Million Dollar Baby*; 9. Three; 10. A nomenclature; 11. North America; 12. Ronald Reagan; 13. Jean-Paul Sartre; 14. 457m (1,500 feet); 15. Andy Thomas; 16. Perfume

The Bumper Family Quiz Book

QUIZ 26

1. A two-pronged dagger; 2. Olivetti; 3. Fur pouch worn with a kilt; 4. Spiked helmets worn by Germans; 5. Coughing; 6. Soup; 7. *Tobermory*; 8. Windward Passage; 9. Anthony Daniels; 10. Newark Liberty, New York; 11. Lycans; 12. China; 13. The Water Bearer; 14. Cat; 15. Gauchito; 16. *Pride (in The Name of Love)*

QUIZ 27

1. Philip II; 2. 1960; 3. Buttons; 4. *Off the Wall*; 5. Eternal Life; 6. Andes mountains; 7. Larger-than-life statues; 8. Dust in the air; 9. S; 10. *The Tortoise and the Hare*; 11. 4; 12. Thomas E. Dooley; 13. Fila; 14. Metal; 15. Goblin; 16. Artemis

QUIZ 28

1. 1992; 2. *Land of Hope and Glory*; 3. Kuwait; 4. Blue; 5. Miss Scarlett; 6. Tunisia; 7. A cheese; 8. Isothermic; 9. In the inner ear; 10. Pound; 11. Haemostatic; 12. Curious; 13. A broad sash worn with a kimono; 14. 1957-58; 15. The leaves are chewed as a stimulant; 16. Tiger

QUIZ 29

1. 19th century; 2. Cap; 3. The Amazon; 4. The Acorn Archimedes; 5. 0; 6. A score of one over par; 7. Mike Myers; 8. Hector Mercedes; 9. Dull and gloomy; 10. Coin; 11. Mongolians; 12. Ureter; 13. HIV / AIDS; 14. Author; 15. Bangladesh; 16. 5 hours

QUIZ 30

1. Iqaluit; 2. Penne; 3. Neil Armstrong; 4. Radiant; 5. A fish; 6. Sir Steve Redgrave; 7. Gilbert Gottfried; 8. Jasper and Horace; 9. Tony Blair; 10. 1959; 11. 1999; 12. Imperial Hotel; 13. Athena rescues him; 14. Vietnam; 15. Port Moresby; 16. Black and white

The Bumper Family Quiz Book

QUIZ 31

1. With their jaws; 2. Bucharest; 3. Bamboo; 4. 1553; 5. DVI;
6. Spherical; 7. Sales tax (or VAT); 8. Cristiano Ronaldo; 9. 800; 10. The
Vikings; 11. Reunion; 12. Play brightly; 13. Golf; 14. Samoa; 15. Altair;
16. Alto

QUIZ 32

1. Picasso; 2. Take an x-ray; 3. Chronic; 4. Mother and father;
5. Hungary; 6. Haiti; 7. A coin; 8. A heart; 9. The Bug War; 10. Pale
Saints; 11. Alan Shepard; 12. Asexual reproduction; 13. Brazil; 14. The
Spanish Armada; 15. *The King's Speech*; 16. Leo III

QUIZ 33

1. Southampton; 2. Avocado; 3. A year; 4. 3 feet; 5. Hydrogen and
oxygen; 6. James Puckle; 7. Kevin Chapman; 8. Nero; 9. Grey-haired
with age; 10. Gaston; 11. Melbourne, Australia; 12. Middle sister; 13. A
finger; 14. Poverty reduction; 15. Hit the earth's surface; 16. The Mona
Lisa

QUIZ 34

1. A sauce of crushed basil leaves, pine nuts, garlic, Parmesan cheese
and olive oil; 2. Eight; 3. Richard Neville; 4. 26; 5. Beetroot; 6. Must take
insulin to stay alive; 7. Armenia; 8. Yellow with red ribbons; 9. Seven;
10. 1900; 11. 1066; 12. Stamps; 13. *Pictures at Eleven*; 14. Galatasaray;
15. Evelyn Waugh; 16. Concave

QUIZ 35

1. Croquembouche; 2. Talons; 3. A time zone; 4. Children; 5. James
II; 6. They were a stranger; 7. *The Pirates of The Caribbean*; 8. 16th;
9. Russia; 10. Corvette; 11. Staves; 12. Parhelia; 13. Penguins;
14. Stratus; 15. John Surtees; 16. New Zealand

The Bumper Family Quiz Book

QUIZ 36

1. Helen; 2. Avocados; 3. I don't know; 4. Diode; 5. Fingerprint scanner;
6. Saul Bellow; 7. Hinder or preclude a denial; 8. Procter & Gamble;
9. Atlantic; 10. A brain; 11. Leg muscles; 12. Anne Boleyn; 13. Peru;
14. *Bleach*; 15. Guadalajara; 16. 1980

QUIZ 37

1. Peabody; 2. Petroleum; 3. 1960; 4. Depository Bank Of Zurich;
5. *Dumbo*; 6. BC; 7. Ohrdruf; 8. Drawing; 9. Hekla; 10. Environment
Canada; 11. Blue Planet Aquarium; 12. Bob the Builder; 13. An Eskimo
knife; 14. Cantonese; 15. 1936; 16. Dull-looking, old-fashioned women

QUIZ 38

1. Algeria; 2. Salman Rushdie; 3. Muggle; 4. A poult; 5. Eldrick
Woods; 6. Colonization; 7. French and Arabic; 8. Pride; 9. Michelle
Trachtenberg; 10. An African antelope; 11. James I (also known as
James VI of Scotland); 12. ARM; 13. 1954; 14. Stained-glass window;
15. Humerus; 16. Jigsaw Sudoku

QUIZ 39

1. Canada; 2. Coloured faxes; 3. Edvard Munch; 4. *Wreck-It Ralph*;
5. *To Kill A Dead Man*; 6. Hawaii; 7. Wellington, New Zealand;
8. Oxygen; 9. Sejant; 10. J and K; 11. Bob Hoskins; 12. Charlotte
Brontë; 13. Brazil; 14. Brazil; 15. Second; 16. Lithium

QUIZ 40

1. 1999; 2. 1814; 3. Sydney; 4. Bacterium; 5. A full grown male deer;
6. Eternity; 7. Eric; 8. *Monster's Ball*; 9. Asia; 10. 1891; 11. Poison;
12. Older works of art; 13. *True Blood*; 14. 1909; 15. Hamilton;
16. Donna

The Bumper Family Quiz Book

QUIZ 41

1. Jack Sears; 2. A weasel; 3. Right; 4. The North Pole; 5. Blue crown conure; 6. To stick together in a clump; 7. White; 8. Iceland; 9. *War Of The Worlds*; 10. *Killing in the Name*; 11. Suriname; 12. A dancer; 13. Toltecs; 14. A lime; 15. Immigrants; 16. 1869

QUIZ 42

1. Tehran; 2. *Harry Potter and the Goblet of Fire*; 3. Kit Harrington; 4. The oceans; 5. St Andrew; 6. Flooding of the Nile river; 7. Hughie Gallacher; 8. 19; 9. A white Siamese; 10. *Wayne's World*; 11. Canada; 12. A caveman; 13. Sister; 14. Elevation; 15. Four; 16. *The Seven Year Itch*

QUIZ 43

1. Helots; 2. Submarine; 3. Edward Jenner; 4. 1066; 5. Sarafina; 6. Salt; 7. 221B, Baker Street; 8. Detroit; 9. Will Arnett; 10. Zach Braff; 11. Braising; 12. Adobe Reader; 13. Ayers Rock; 14. Samuel O'Reilly; 15. Russia; 16. 64

QUIZ 44

1. *Ride With The Devil*; 2. Eight; 3. Religious items and clothing; 4. Orange with a blue hat; 5. South-Western Townships; 6. Iceland; 7. Stella Gibbons; 8. Denmark; 9. His father's; 10. Guilder; 11. Two; 12. Cats; 13. Pound; 14. Of the eye socket; 15. Cream; 16. Taproot

QUIZ 45

1. Hyper Text Transfer Protocol; 2. Pacific; 3. 103 miles (166km); 4. Lotus; 5. Tower of London; 6. E.M. Forster; 7. Peach Schnapps; 8. Blue and yellow; 9. Cleo; 10. David Boreanaz; 11. Izod Lacoste; 12. Wales; 13. Zagreb; 14. Pearl; 15. 1952; 16. Solar panels

The Bumper *Family* Quiz Book

QUIZ 46

1. Starbucks; 2. Juan Mata; 3. *X-Men: First Class*; 4. Silvester;
5. Bat; 6. Simple Minds; 7. US Airways; 8. Irrigation; 9. Magnesium;
10. Portugal; 11. 1888; 12. *Get Shorty*; 13. Converts a domain name
into an IP address number; 14. A hot, Mediterranean wind; 15. 5th of
May; 16. Iris Murdoch

QUIZ 47

1. Selfie; 2. A speck; 3. United Kingdom; 4. Germany; 5. Pasta;
6. Byzantium; 7. Nelly Furtado; 8. Algeria; 9. New York; 10. *The Lego
Movie*; 11. Tbilisi; 12. Henry VIII; 13. Saltwater crocodile; 14. Outlook or
probable outcome; 15. Radio City Music Hall; 16. Ape

QUIZ 48

1. Seoul, South Korea; 2. Trinidad; 3. Iocaste; 4. Be right back;
5. Icebergs; 6. 1943; 7. Chromebooks; 8. A tenth; 9. Vespasian; 10. The
main constituents of natural fats and oils; 11. Finland; 12. Kingdom of
Lesotho; 13. *Running On Empty*; 14. Anne Hathaway; 15. 100-mile;
16. Rosetta Stone

QUIZ 49

1. *Sour Times*; 2. Scotland; 3. Australia; 4. Germany; 5. Venus; 6. 1994;
7. Sphere; 8. Pablo Picasso; 9. Spraint; 10. Six; 11. Stem; 12. *Batman
and Robin*; 13. 8 hours; 14. Nigeria, as the local chief; 15. The Taliban;
16. Cancer

QUIZ 50

1. Yuri Gagarin; 2. Human capital; 3. 1983; 4. Pineapple and ham;
5. One month; 6. Michael Faraday; 7. Turin, Italy; 8. An open cart;
9. Seven; 10. A Middle-Eastern honeyed sweet; 11. Afghanistan;
12. Ottawa, Ontario; 13. One; 14. *The Lion, The Witch And The
Wardrobe*; 15. *Dry*; 16. Bonnie

The Bumper Family Quiz Book

QUIZ 51

1. Brazil; 2. Steep-sided gully; 3. 1987; 4. St Patrick; 5. Glinda; 6. Body building; 7. Flappers; 8. 4; 9. Largest country; 10. White; 11. 1975; 12. His father; 13. 21 miles (33.8km); 14. 1; 15. Australia; 16. Hydrogen and helium

QUIZ 52

1. Melbourne; 2. *Luna 1*; 3. Orange; 4. James Cook; 5. Henry II; 6. Koba; 7. 1996; 8. Quartz; 9. Three; 10. Flowers; 11. Bering Sea; 12. Confusion; 13. A preface, or a preamble to a speech; 14. A fine or compulsory payment; 15. Aids in the absorption of calcium; 16. *One*

QUIZ 53

1. Horse; 2. Anaphylaxis; 3. Pea; 4. Ruby slippers; 5. George Cross; 6. Nitrogen; 7. Anna Wintour; 8. Domitian; 9. An ordered list of historic moments; 10. Antoine; 11. Fear of wasps; 12. St. Paul's Cathedral; 13. Acid rain; 14. France; 15. Jan Hus; 16. His garden

QUIZ 54

1. Commonly used herbs; 2. 13; 3. *Submarine*; 4. 60; 5. 1087; 6. The Kookaburra; 7. Gabrielle; 8. Project Paperclip; 9. Switzerland; 10. Abbey Road, London; 11. George Clooney; 12. Palestine; 13. 1954; 14. Sundew; 15. Jodhpur; 16. Feudal lord

QUIZ 55

1. Downdraught; 2. Greg Norman; 3. New Zealand; 4. Throwback Thursday; 5. 1150; 6. Denmark; 7. *The Little Mermaid*; 8. Daniel Keyes; 9. Senegal; 10. Ned Kelly; 11. He fell into a circus cart full of them; 12. Mohandas Gandhi; 13. Potato; 14. Adverse; 15. Tzatziki; 16. Three

The Bumper Family Quiz Book

QUIZ 56

1. Charles Townshend; 2. Wrinkles; 3. Bucky Larson; 4. Decagon;
5. A confused mixture; 6. Indian rupee; 7. Seoul, South Korea;
8. Renaissance artists; 9. It floats; 10. Stockholm, Sweden; 11. Duff
Stuff; 12. Cartographer; 13. 1.70m (5ft7in); 14. Alsatian bread; 15. Go to
Santa!; 16. A good heart and a good mind

QUIZ 57

1. Tertiary; 2. Panthalassa; 3. San Francisco; 4. Length; 5. Your head;
6. *Everybody*; 7. Hadrian; 8. Observatory; 9. India; 10. Syria; 11. 1930;
12. Stone bottom; 13. Tokyo, Japan; 14. Robert Redford; 15. Let's Do
It!; 16. Mascarpone

QUIZ 58

1. Lateral; 2. South American hummingbird; 3. Atlanta; 4. Adolf
Eichmann; 5. Circle; 6. Karachi; 7. Jimmy Cliff; 8. *Pinocchio*; 9. Tsetse
fly; 10. Texas; 11. London; 12. Gary Lineker; 13. Nike; 14. Bo Xilai;
15. Roller derby; 16. Joseph Heller

QUIZ 59

1. Aaron Eckhart; 2. Red; 3. Haider al-Abadi; 4. 1975; 5. Franklin
D. Roosevelt; 6. Mexico City; 7. Hair colour; 8. Atlantic and Pacific;
9. Aviary; 10. Polly; 11. Cape Verde; 12. Project Mercury; 13. To pay
heed to something; 14. Rabbit; 15. Jane Seymour; 16. The Beatles

QUIZ 60

1. Antoninus Pius; 2. Methane, carbon monoxide, fluorine;
3. Calendar; 4. Renesmee; 5. 1915; 6. Victoria; 7. Eight; 8. Angstroms;
9. Grasshopper; 10. Italy; 11. 1994; 12. Musical speeds; 13. He burned
most Chinese books in 213 BC; 14. Pagoda; 15. 1960s; 16. Apollo

The Bumper Family Quiz Book

QUIZ 61

1. Bly; 2. 32; 3. Jane Seymour; 4. Biogenesis; 5. Affected religious sentiment; 6. Klee; 7. Tallinn; 8. To darken, poetically; 9. Cl; 10. Jordan; 11. Nasser; 12. Beach Volleyball; 13. Catherine Of Aragon; 14. Its muscular foot; 15. *Bad*; 16. Angola

QUIZ 62

1. Slash and burn farming; 2. Paris; 3. Swirlie; 4. Control Unit and Arithmetic Logic Unit; 5. PlayStation; 6. Selwyn College; 7. Shere Khan; 8. Man-eating lions; 9. Biodegrade; 10. *Toy Story*; 11. Giuseppe Meazza; 12. A malaria outbreak; 13. Bank; 14. Vermont; 15. Fear; 16. Two

QUIZ 63

1. Chickpeas; 2. Pacific Ocean; 3. Mocha; 4. A grape; 5. Boers; 6. 1969; 7. Jonathan Taylor Thomas; 8. Lying face upwards; 9. Plankton; 10. 1915; 11. Neil Armstrong; 12. Swing across a creek; 13. 3; 14. Banana; 15. 20; 16. Tim Curry

QUIZ 64

1. James Marsters; 2. Speedy Gonzales; 3. Caribbean; 4. Black; 5. Continents; 6. Malawi; 7. Play loudly; 8. Herbie; 9. Warm and excessively humid weather; 10. Amortization; 11. Water erosion; 12. Six; 13. Animals; 14. Green and white; 15. 1900s; 16. Philippines

QUIZ 65

1. Land; 2. 120; 3. Thames Barrier; 4. Black; 5. *Monster-In-Law*; 6. 1798; 7. U2; 8. Lean tuna; 9. Sleep; 10. Peach; 11. *Sabrina, The Teenage Witch*; 12. 1970s; 13. 1kg; 14. One; 15. Black, yellow and red; 16. Nelson Mandela

The Bumper *Family* Quiz Book

QUIZ 66

1. Frank Oz; 2. Darkroom; 3. Theodore Roosevelt; 4. Prince Charming; 5. Eritrea; 6. 4,000 miles; 7. Cameroon; 8. Conduct impulses and reflexes; 9. John Terry; 10. Ichthyosaur; 11. The soft palate; 12. He's a very theatrical actor; 13. Last vehicle in a convoy; 14. Casca; 15. Switzerland; 16. Michael Stich

QUIZ 67

1. Potts Point, Sydney; 2. Aluminium; 3. Eileen Collins; 4. Thomas; 5. The police; 6. *Vulcan*; 7. Bogota; 8. Pink; 9. 1949; 10. Ophelia; 11. John Terry; 12. Dairy; 13. Siberian Forest Cat, or Moscow Semi-longhair; 14. *Chromecast*; 15. 1861; 16. Blinks

QUIZ 68

1. Red and white; 2. Bradley Cooper; 3. *Friends*; 4. They have rings on the tail that rattle as a warning; 5. Syria; 6. Park Ranger; 7. Mars; 8. True; 9. Leopard; 10. Grey ghost; 11. Kuwait; 12. Dear Kitty; 13. Aloe Vera; 14. Pop-up; 15. Manchester United; 16. Neptune

QUIZ 69

1. Bram Stoker; 2. Superman; 3. Carrot; 4. Spain; 5. Nitrogen; 6. Roland Garros; 7. June; 8. Cindy Crawford; 9. Grampian; 10. Mary I; 11. My Little Girl; 12. Dash; 13. 2004; 14. Puffin; 15. African; 16. Georg Solti

QUIZ 70

1. Noble gas; 2. The Open Championship; 3. Because these are the first six letters on the top row; 4. Hattie and Olive; 5. Guinea; 6. Pound of flour, sugar, butter and eggs; 7. Mausoleum; 8. 6; 9. Ghana; 10. Tourism; 11. Ernst Leitz; 12. JXL; 13. Carbon dioxide; 14. South Korea; 15. The Nabateans; 16. Calcium

The Bumper Family Quiz Book

QUIZ 71

1. 1879; 2. Albania; 3. Krakow; 4. 53cm (21inches); 5. It's being kicked by the toe; 6. *Fallen*; 7. France; 8. Chicken Kiev; 9. Cars; 10. Michael Richards; 11. Africa; 12. 1902; 13. Aphrodite; 14. Three; 15. Send Mail Transfer Protocol; 16. Moon bear

QUIZ 72

1. *Our Happy Hardcore*; 2. 80%; 3. Iker Casillas; 4. 15; 5. Sinclair Lewis; 6. Kiel; 7. A nickname for the B-52; 8. English; 9. *Apollo 8*; 10. *Majora's Mask*; 11. Gulf of Oman; 12. Mountain-range depression; 13. Rose; 14. A caller tells them; 15. Religion; 16. Francois Truffaut

QUIZ 73

1. The UK and Argentina; 2. Green, white and red; 3. Everyman's Right; 4. 1972; 5. Football Association; 6. Karachi; 7. Too $hort; 8. Family tree; 9. Steve Jobs; 10. Germany; 11. Arthur Guinness; 12. Frank Borman; 13. Denmark; 14. Addends; 15. Bird; 16. Fulcrum

QUIZ 74

1. Suharto; 2. Raptor; 3. Weatherfield; 4. Portsmouth; 5. Oxygen; 6. Captain Vidal; 7. Insignificant people; 8. Sparta; 9. Acorns; 10. Bacteriophage; 11. Otto Von Bismarck; 12. Scissor Sisters; 13. Jean Rhys; 14. 12; 15. Kidneys; 16. New York, the Big Apple

QUIZ 75

1. Martinique; 2. Biogas; 3. Nuremburg; 4. Orca; 5. Premature burial; 6. At a moderate speed; 7. More than 1000 years; 8. Pen; 9. *Like a Prayer*; 10. School; 11. Macy's; 12. Bradley Cooper; 13. Liberia; 14. Surrealism; 15. David Garcia; 16. 1377

The Bumper *Family* Quiz Book

QUIZ 76

1. Genus and species; 2. AFC Ajax; 3. Titus; 4. Europe; 5. A pack animal; 6. Zambezi; 7. *Dirty Dancing*; 8. 1642; 9. Sending email; 10. Breadsticks; 11. A vampire; 12. A trumpet skirt; 13. Norway; 14. Stop the exercise; 15. The use of liposuction to accentuate specific body features; 16. The Royal Archives

QUIZ 77

1. 1936; 2. Henry VI; 3. Great Barrier Reef; 4. Auckland; 5. Accurate; 6. London; 7. Rodin; 8. Apps; 9. The moon; 10. *Titanic*; 11. Grazzi; 12. Dale Earnhardt Jr.; 13. Elizabeth I; 14. Turbulence; 15. Rotini; 16. Northern

QUIZ 78

1. Belize; 2. A sea; 3. Lake Titicaca; 4. 18th; 5. 1944; 6. The resistance; 7. Simplistic; 8. Pomeranian; 9. Ray; 10. *Frozen*; 11. Newman; 12. Ozone layer; 13. 1905; 14. *East 8*; 15. 2 hours and 40 minutes; 16. Nena

QUIZ 79

1. Metro-Goldwyn-Mayer; 2. The Silence; 3. Futile; 4. England; 5. Leaching; 6. Bosnia and Herzegovina; 7. Greyhound; 8. Darwin; 9. Queen Street; 10. Winning; 11. Hoisin sauce; 12. Looking the same; 13. 31; 14. Crab; 15. Noble gas; 16. End

QUIZ 80

1. Rumba; 2. Lech Kaczynski; 3. Autograph; 4. Orlando Bloom; 5. Borussia Dortmund; 6. John O'Hara; 7. Dehydration; 8. A large, flat hill with steep sides surrounded by plains; 9. Carrot; 10. Fiesta; 11. Bloodhound; 12. 1980s; 13. In pithy, memorable phrases; 14. Freising, Bavaria; 15. Hanoi; 16. Freedom of worship

The Bumper Family Quiz Book

QUIZ 81

1. Bangladesh; 2. *The Lion King*; 3. Muscle tissue disease; 4. The Game; 5. A hooligan or petty criminal; 6. Canada; 7. A flash flood; 8. James I (also known as James VI of Scotland); 9. 1666; 10. 33; 11. *Skyfall*; 12. Stirring it too often; 13. Alan Shepard; 14. Percolate; 15. Cpl. Hicks; 16. Robert A. Heinlein

QUIZ 82

1. Boron; 2. Also Known As; 3. Sand; 4. 19; 5. Government of National Unity; 6. Desperation; 7. Tom Hanks; 8. Kevin McHale; 9. Lalibela; 10. Venezuela; 11. 1884; 12. Edward VI; 13. Google; 14. Efficacy; 15. Accidents; 16. Romania

QUIZ 83

1. Butlers; 2. *American Beauty*; 3. Cinco de Mayo; 4. *Bring It All Back*; 5. Sucrose; 6. Russia; 7. *Lightroom*; 8. Edward VI; 9. A building material made from recycled paper; 10. The Union Jack/Flag; 11. Robert Campin; 12. Christianity; 13. Moray eel; 14. Laos; 15. Workers' Party of Korea; 16. Traditional Mexican scarf

QUIZ 84

1. Siberia; 2. Canada; 3. Donna Karan; 4. Pittsburgh; 5. *Tangled*; 6. A large-eyed South American monkey; 7. Trisha; 8. Japan; 9. *Harry Potter and the Half-Blood Prince*; 10. *Louisburg*; 11. Virginia Woolf; 12. Cayenne; 13. Ernest Rutherford; 14. Rum; 15. Octagon; 16. 2002

QUIZ 85

1. Atoll; 2. Cyprus; 3. Amber; 4. Johannesburg; 5. Sindelfingen; 6. Lancashire; 7. Compass; 8. Adverb; 9. Blood clotting within blood vessels; 10. Sarah Michelle Gellar; 11. *No Country for Old Men*; 12. Abdominal; 13. Red and white; 14. GameBoy; 15. Echidna; 16. Coincident

The Bumper Family Quiz Book

QUIZ 86

1. 1909; 2. Russia; 3. In a flower; 4. Pegasus; 5. Plain; 6. Jonas Salk;
7. Oscar de la Renta; 8. Calf; 9. A plant with edible tubers; 10. 1950;
11. Mary Steenburgen; 12. Climate map; 13. iPhone 4; 14. Kidney;
15. November; 16. Wellington, New Zealand

QUIZ 87

1. Christopher Columbus; 2. Heteronym; 3. Bridge; 4. Pangaea; 5. Italy;
6. Eastern diamondback; 7. Lasagna; 8. Butter chicken; 9. Letters;
10. Elizabeth I; 11. John F Kennedy, New York; 12. 1958; 13. Google;
14. Crystal; 15. Vaduz; 16. Jakarta

QUIZ 88

1. Australia; 2. Taste buds; 3. Lemel; 4. The Netherlands; 5. Monica
Seles; 6. Incan; 7. 1461; 8. Soprano; 9. Malawi; 10. Fight fairly; 11. Tap;
12. Raymond Chandler; 13. iPhone 5S; 14. Wrist; 15. China and Taiwan;
16. *Working Class Hero*

QUIZ 89

1. It may contain raw eggs; 2. Rembrandt; 3. A record; 4. Photograph;
5. 34 (add the last two numbers); 6. XVI (16); 7. 2; 8. Bala; 9. July; 10. At
all; 11. Jamie Whincup; 12. Scotland; 13. Three; 14. The country at the
centre of the world; 15. A very fast passing note in music; 16. Robert
Redford

QUIZ 90

1. Cross; 2. Liberia; 3. Oil; 4. Strawberry; 5. Eel roll; 6. 1810; 7. Round
Table; 8. Aliens; 9. Jean Dubuffet; 10. East; 11. 50 years; 12. Helps
develop red blood cells; 13. Faeces; 14. *The Tempest*; 15. 158;
16. Sino-Tibetan

The Bumper *Family* Quiz Book

QUIZ 91

1. Sergio Ramos; 2. France; 3. Croque monsieur; 4. Digital representation of a person; 5. Germany; 6. First Street; 7. Matt Hooper; 8. Far north; 9. Binder; 10. Mexico; 11. 336; 12. Scuba diving; 13. Komnenos; 14. Copacabana; 15. Pandas; 16. A long-tailed bird of the cuckoo family

QUIZ 92

1. Spam; 2. A molecule built from repeating similar units; 3. Joff Ellen; 4. East; 5. Si; 6. Albania; 7. Nikola Tesla; 8. On hillsides; 9. Cleveland, Ohio; 10. Pharaoh; 11. Positive; 12. Adam West; 13. 2001; 14. Mixture of fresh water and salt water; 15. A train; 16. Ray Harryhausen

QUIZ 93

1. Sculpture; 2. Marine; 3. Blackboard; 4. Five years; 5. Six and a half; 6. John Ronald Reuel; 7. Nicolaus Copernicus; 8. Tisane; 9. Red; 10. Median; 11. Hindu religious teacher; 12. 16; 13. Bowl; 14. Amsterdam; 15. Armando; 16. Glendale Toy Museum

QUIZ 94

1. Mahatma Gandhi; 2. Tarantula killer; 3. Monsoon; 4. Jack Traven; 5. Renounce armed struggle; 6. Subdivision of a legion; 7. Khartoum; 8. Tutu; 9. Ginny; 10. Peregrine falcon; 11. 1998; 12. A small island; 13. Red, White, Black and Yellow; 14. Truffles; 15. *Bangerz*; 16. Chile

QUIZ 95

1. A type of wheat grain; 2. Zambia and Zimbabwe; 3. Dog; 4. 1999; 5. Orange; 6. Six; 7. King Jil; 8. 1961; 9. Polar bear; 10. 5ive; 11. 1; 12. Nile; 13. Time; 14. Meat and dairy; 15. About 13 kilotons; 16. Italian

The Bumper *Family* Quiz Book

QUIZ 96

1. Iron; 2. iPhone 6 and 6 Pro; 3. Adam; 4. Frank and Joe; 5. Gillette;
6. Firewall; 7. December 26th to January 6th; 8. Alice Springs;
9. Hydrogen; 10. Pots; 11. Olive; 12. Cranberry juice; 13. 1843;
14. Darwin; 15. 1 billion; 16. Henry Hudson

QUIZ 97

1. Cheese; 2. Canada; 3. A force sent to liberate POWs in Germany;
4. Toto; 5. A conductor or eminent musician; 6. Atlanta, United
States; 7. Red; 8. An opossum; 9. Ray; 10. Comet Shoemaker-Levy 9;
11. Barry; 12. Col. Tibbits; 13. Nika Revolt; 14. Pinocchio; 15. Taiwan;
16. Laser

QUIZ 98

1. Kundan; 2. Rice cooked in coconut milk; 3. Nala; 4. Mutt; 5. COO;
6. Ireland; 7. 180; 8. Emerac; 9. America; 10. Elizabeth I; 11. The
Fantastic Four; 12. *Scream*; 13. BSL (British Sign Language); 14. 500;
15. Thomas Edison; 16. One

QUIZ 99

1. iPhone 5S and 5C; 2. Cook; 3. Large eyes; 4. Excretory system;
5. Insect; 6. Queens' College; 7. Roger Davies; 8. 1413; 9. Jordan and
Israel; 10. Torchwood; 11. One; 12. Peruvians; 13. Lake Kariba; 14. Six;
15. St George; 16. 1lb (450g)

QUIZ 100

1. 16 hr 3 min; 2. Reptile; 3. Mouse; 4. Bagpipes; 5. Spanish; 6. Sit
down heavily; 7. Warrens; 8. South Africa; 9. Janus, a Roman god;
10. The Dark Destroyer; 11. Sodium chloride; 12. Tall, conical cap,
or a crown; 13. Munchkins; 14. In the dungeon; 15. Suleyman;
16. Bangladesh

The Bumper *Family* Quiz Book

QUIZ 101

1. Puck; 2. Jack; 3. Barley; 4. 17 years old; 5. Reverend Green;
6. Ukraine; 7. Selenium; 8. Germany; 9. 442nd Combat Team;
10. Josef Craig; 11. Standard deviation; 12. A small flag; 13. Vinegar;
14. Stationary front; 15. Red; 16. Ferdinand Magellan

QUIZ 102

1. Malorie Blackman; 2. Queen Alexandra; 3. Purple; 4. Lewis
Hamilton; 5. Dick Costolo; 6. Graves; 7. 1960s; 8. Ursula; 9. Hedgehog;
10. Pacific; 11. Inappropriate; 12. TRIM5-alpha; 13. Fairchild
Semiconductor; 14. 1981; 15. Marble; 16. Mary Jane

QUIZ 103

1. Beef; 2. Prokaryotic; 3. Scribes; 4. Bipedal; 5. Apple trees; 6. The
Volga; 7. Industrial Revolution; 8. A squidger; 9. Italy; 10. Caribbean
Sea; 11. Anne Rice; 12. Chief Medical Examiner; 13. Cycling;
14. Bullseye; 15. Backstreet Boys; 16. Fine Gael

QUIZ 104

1. Dushanbe; 2. San Francisco; 3. Trade winds; 4. Yeast extract;
5. Australia; 6. Significant life change; 7. Both are; 8. 240mph
(386km/h); 9. Carol Ann Duffy; 10. Mark; 11. Fernando de La Rua;
12. Trees; 13. Softball; 14. Scandinavia; 15. Belief in absolute moral
truths; 16. Catherine The Great

QUIZ 105

1. The Cult; 2. Theo Walcott; 3. March; 4. Tom Hulce; 5. A large
travelling bag; 6. Materialism; 7. Rum; 8. Rajah; 9. 1997; 10. Cuneiform;
11. It can play musical chords; 12. Rarotonga; 13. Pisces; 14. Less is
more; 15. Bedrock; 16. Sun

The Bumper Family Quiz Book

QUIZ 106

1. Purple, black and white; 2. Pope John Paul II; 3. Structured Query Language; 4. Kenya; 5. Fermentation; 6. Italian; 7. Coal; 8. The Time Vortex; 9. 5; 10. Carter Burwell; 11. A half-note; 12. 1949; 13. Herpetophobia; 14. Three; 15. James Rodríguez; 16. Abuja

QUIZ 107

1. India; 2. Sushi; 3. Berlin; 4. Icarus; 5. Patterns in Earth's magnetic field; 6. Wilkie Collins; 7. Mexican; 8. *On Her Majesty's Secret Service*; 9. Nine Inch Nails; 10. Blue; 11. Friedrich Paulus; 12. Carnation; 13. Proverb; 14. Force exerted by a stretched spring; 15. Hydrogen; 16. Wood

QUIZ 108

1. Glasgow; 2. Steven Seagal; 3. Trousers; 4. 5th largest; 5. South Korea; 6. Isometric; 7. Ursula K. Le Guin; 8. Konrad Adenauer; 9. Please; 10. Fifth Harmony; 11. It Increases; 12. World War 2; 13. Spain; 14. Keel extension; 15. He can engulf himself in flames; 16. Beans

QUIZ 109

1. Beef; 2. Georgia; 3. Soap; 4. St Paul's Cathedral; 5. 110mph; 6. Humanism; 7. Abidjan; 8. Genius; 9. 2; 10. The Football Factory; 11. Ethiopia; 12. Picasso; 13. Bolivia; 14. Peru; 15. Tiberius; 16. Wren

QUIZ 110

1. 1896; 2. 'Bob's Big Boy', a restaurant mascot; 3. Two; 4. Mary I; 5. XIV; 6. Georgia; 7. *Angels and Demons*; 8. Helium; 9. A clock; 10. Safari; 11. Mayapan; 12. Sinead O'Connor; 13. *Pieces of You*; 14. Meteorology; 15. The Palace of Holyroodhouse; 16. 1967

The Bumper *Family* Quiz Book

QUIZ 111

1. Colin Farrell; 2. Asia; 3. A pod; 4. Australian Open; 5. *My Humps*;
6. Curry bread; 7. Chinese two-stringed bowed instrument; 8. Europe;
9. Theodore Dreiser; 10. Rapid Eye Movement; 11. 7%; 12. A species;
13. Spanish; 14. 1947; 15. Sodium; 16. Taken by paratroopers in gliders

QUIZ 112

1. Innsbruck, Austria; 2. Root; 3. Mercedes-Benz; 4. A crown;
5. Indonesia; 6. *Rocky*; 7. Dale Crover And Chad Channing; 8. Pig;
9. Centrarchids; 10. 7 days; 11. 11.3 years; 12. Brahma; 13. Douglas
Adams; 14. Eggs; 15. Germany; 16. Bangladesh

QUIZ 113

1. Square; 2. Gold; 3. Asia; 4. Operation Overlord; 5. Ernie; 6. Acorn
System 75; 7. A zero calorie drink; 8. Jim Carrey; 9. Austin Mahone;
10. Sodium; 11. 1327; 12. Tom Simpson; 13. Jasmine; 14. Ljubljana;
15. *Mr & Mrs Smith*; 16. ZX80

QUIZ 114

1. Henley Street; 2. Sudan and Afghanistan; 3. Husky; 4. 20; 5. Mary I;
6. *Quadrophenia*; 7. Ada Lovelace; 8. A thin, puckered, all-cotton fabric;
9. Wish you were here; 10. 40%; 11. A long, operatic song for solo
voice; 12. The Uffizi; 13. A mishmash or confused mixture; 14. Sweden;
15. Venus; 16. Rouen

QUIZ 115

1. A supporting stalk; 2. 1773; 3. From the beginning; 4. *Aladdin*;
5. Commodore; 6. English Team Captain; 7. Chapter 12; 8. No distance;
9. Atlantic; 10. Jordan; 11. Africa; 12. Auditory; 13. Portugal; 14. Boron;
15. Addressing the whole person; 16. William III (William of Orange)

The Bumper *Family* Quiz Book

QUIZ 116

1. Cairo, Egypt; 2. Ghia; 3. Phnom Penh; 4. Thermometer;
5. Heidelberg, Germany; 6. Hosted a TV chat show; 7. Cats; 8. Green;
9. Pantothenic Acid; 10. King Frederick II; 11. Sausages; 12. *Wings*;
13. Mount Vesuvius; 14. Hermann Goering; 15. Greek; 16. Hurricane

QUIZ 117

1. Opossum; 2. Birds; 3. Lindsay Lohan; 4. Rolling on the floor laughing;
5. 1861; 6. 12; 7. 16; 8. Tony Blair; 9. France; 10. Chinese; 11. An arch-
shaped cue support; 12. 15%; 13. Victor Verster Prison; 14. Richard III;
15. Edna St. Vincent Millay; 16. Kneading

QUIZ 118

1. The Tiger; 2. It is open vertically down the front; 3. Ecuador; 4. Iraq;
5. Apricot; 6. A substance made by worker bees to feed queen
bees; 7. Hypermiling; 8. The beach; 9. Natural gas; 10. Moscow;
11. Royal Albert Hall; 12. Couchant; 13. Toni Braxton; 14. Mosquitoes;
15. Minerva; 16. Migraine

QUIZ 119

1. Daveigh Chase; 2. 1922; 3. China; 4. 24; 5. 6; 6. Bellerophon;
7. Aurora; 8. Diana Spencer; 9. Microscope; 10. Chinua Achebe;
11. Hibiscus; 12. Porno For Pyros; 13. Boeing 757-300; 14. Someone
who studies ocean plants and animals; 15. Buster Douglas; 16. Mexican

QUIZ 120

1. Buoyancy; 2. 20; 3. In a tree; 4. King Henry VIII; 5. A whole number
and a fraction; 6. The Earth and the Sun; 7. Queen's Day, a national
holiday; 8. Drizzle; 9. Clive Staples; 10. Messerschmitt Me 210;
11. Netherlands; 12. LA Galaxy; 13. Idina Menzel; 14. Hypotension;
15. Monosaccharides; 16. Dr Tony Hill

The Bumper Family Quiz Book

QUIZ 121

1. Bosnia; 2. Julia Roberts; 3. A word or phrase that reads the same both forwards and backwards; 4. *Dr. 90210*; 5. Blue whale; 6. Bat; 7. Milk; 8. Kiev; 9. Land of the Angles; 10. New York Cosmos; 11. Nassau; 12. Carbon dioxide; 13. A peasant farmer wealthy enough to own a farm; 14. Dili; 15. 32; 16. 0

QUIZ 122

1. Boeing 737; 2. Comply or Die; 3. Falcon; 4. Malta; 5. A werewolf; 6. The armadillo; 7. *Swear It Again*; 8. Hugh Jackman; 9. *I Want To Break Free*; 10. Chin Shih Huang; 11. Continental Hyatt Hotel; 12. Lunar eclipse; 13. Solar; 14. Westeros and Essos; 15. An accusation or charge; 16. Argentina

QUIZ 123

1. Napoleon; 2. Optical Character Recognition, or image-to-text conversion; 3. Richard III; 4. Europe; 5. Purple; 6. Christmas Island; 7. David Trezeguet; 8. Flood; 9. Antiseptic; 10. The Harp; 11. 1994; 12. Equator; 13. Alt; 14. George Town; 15. *The Fast and The Furious*; 16. Three

QUIZ 124

1. Domenico and Stefano; 2. Salford; 3. Fluorine; 4. Ron Perlman; 5. Obtuse; 6. Protean; 7. Compass (or a pair of compasses); 8. Atlantic Ocean; 9. Italy; 10. Brussels sprout; 11. Respiratory Disease; 12. Sir Terry Wogan; 13. Drums; 14. Australia; 15. Tombs; 16. *Valentine's Day*

The Bumper *Family* Quiz Book

QUIZ 125

1. Corona; 2. The Space Shuttle; 3. *Kiss*, by Prince; 4. London;
5. Trumpet; 6. *Alpha Canis Majoris*/The Dog Star; 7. The Clash;
8. Prunes; 9. Cristiano Ronaldo; 10. Every four years; 11. 1960;
12. Bangladesh; 13. A stork brings him; 14. The end part of a
composition; 15. Sun Yat-Sen; 16. Bangladesh

QUIZ 126

1. Heart attack; 2. Thanks; 3. 1982; 4. Metamorphosis; 5. *War Of
The Worlds*; 6. The Vedas; 7. Painting; 8. Nocturnal; 9. The Beast;
10. Gender segregation in some religious societies; 11. James Joseph
Sylvester; 12. Moisturizing; 13. Pennsylvania; 14. Pan-Arab Newspaper;
15. Gregg Wallace and John Torode; 16. Petrarch

QUIZ 127

1. Louis Pasteur; 2. The names of the five Great Lakes; 3. 1215;
4. *Apollo 8*; 5. A beginner, or novice; 6. *Run The Road*; 7. James II;
8. George Washington; 9. Widow Twankey; 10. Valhalla; 11. Assassinate
a senator; 12. Carbon; 13. Raphael; 14. Tonga; 15. His father-in-law;
16. 50 Cent

QUIZ 128

1. Router; 2. Iceland; 3. Madagascar; 4. A woman; 5. Artichokes;
6. Mexico; 7. A hangar; 8. Quinoa; 9. Lockiophobia; 10. A peasant;
11. Steven Spielberg; 12. Très chic; 13. Kimono; 14. Bone mass; 15. Sir
Derek Jacobi; 16. Giuseppe Signori

The Bumper *Family* Quiz Book

QUIZ 129

1. Ivory Coast; 2. Reddish-brown American wildcat; 3. Loch Ness Monster; 4. Bullmastiff; 5. Sydney Harbour Bridge; 6. 1995; 7. An infant less than four weeks old; 8. Vasco Da Gama; 9. Smoke cigarettes; 10. Gold rings; 11. Jon Favreau; 12. Diagonally; 13. Humpback whales; 14. A treatment with no effect; 15. Jalal Talabani; 16. Snakes

QUIZ 130

1. Asia; 2. Jelena Gencic; 3. *Dear Jessie*; 4. 8; 5. Fisher-Price; 6. Paloma; 7. Stendhal; 8. Sergio Garcia; 9. 1,330 miles (2,140km); 10. Moult; 11. May; 12. Madagascar; 13. 11; 14. Akira Kurosawa; 15. Typhoon; 16. Speaking in public

QUIZ 131

1. Madame Tussauds; 2. Thunderbirds; 3. Mutton; 4. 57.3 degrees; 5. Fragrant harbour; 6. Segmented worm; 7. Left to right, top to bottom; 8. *The Princess and the Frog*; 9. Ellie; 10. 1509; 11. Nick Bolletieri's; 12. Vitamin K; 13. Different versions; 14. Austria; 15. A photon; 16. Al Pacino

QUIZ 132

1. A sixteenth note; 2. John Cade; 3. *Wolf Hall*; 4. Mythology; 5. London, Belfast, Edinburgh and Cardiff; 6. Kabul; 7. Tuberculosis; 8. 1066; 9. Pinto; 10. Talia Balsam; 11. Rice; 12. Jon Cryer; 13. Arctic tundra; 14. Beijing, China; 15. Dublin; 16. Bizet

QUIZ 133

1. Benazir Bhutto; 2. Avignon; 3. Manny, Sid And Diego; 4. 10 years; 5. One; 6. Ruth Wakefield; 7. 440; 8. Skunky; 9. Tom Cruise; 10. El Salvador; 11. London Waterloo; 12. Gyro; 13. Rutherford B. Hayes; 14. Great Dane; 15. Lithium; 16. A fragrant essential oil

The Bumper *Family* Quiz Book

QUIZ 134

1. Complete Works of Shakespeare; 2. Red Bull-Renault; 3. Vincent;
4. Mrs White; 5. The Koran; 6. Uruguay; 7. A sceptre; 8. Knot;
9. Blowfish; 10. Divorced couple; 11. Black; 12. Gave him a pig's tail;
13. *Columbia*; 14. Franz Kline; 15. Large, Irish coracle; 16. Spain

QUIZ 135

1. 35 days; 2. February 29th; 3. Earthquake; 4. It will contract; 5. Frank;
6. Ludwig Boltzmann; 7. A very short or missing tail; 8. Russell
Brand; 9. Charles II; 10. Juliet Landau; 11. Milk; 12. Amadou Ahidjo;
13. Australia; 14. An unscrupulous lawyer; 15. Peter Capaldi; 16. Atlanta

QUIZ 136

1. Roy Hodgson; 2. William the Conqueror; 3. 1944; 4. *I Would Die 4
U*; 5. Red; 6. B2; 7. Farley Mowat; 8. Mammoth; 9. Nuclear energy;
10. Haiti; 11. 3.5%; 12. 1956; 13. On the head of a clover; 14. 18;
15. Entertainment; 16. ICANN

QUIZ 137

1. The *App store*; 2. Martin Sheen; 3. Eucalyptus leaves; 4. Ceausescu;
5. Serbia; 6. Bluebottle; 7. The repeated elliptical course of an object
about a star or planet; 8. Toblerone; 9. Venezuela; 10. Tennessee
Williams; 11. *HMS Belfast*; 12. Cornelius; 13. Book of Common Prayer;
14. Chanel No. 5; 15. *Chicago*; 16. Alofi

QUIZ 138

1. Certificate of Deposit; 2. Kent; 3. 1 January, 1901; 4. Courage;
5. 1976; 6. Approving; 7. Slippery surface; 8. Canopy; 9. Ireland;
10. Baffin Island; 11. Meningitis; 12. Albania; 13. Tommy Flanagan;
14. Rat tail; 15. Halloween; 16. Kinetic energy

The Bumper *Family* Quiz Book

QUIZ 139

1. Carl Sagan; 2. 1887; 3. Crayons; 4. Philippines; 5. Nematoda;
6. Lleyton Hewitt; 7. Prince Ali; 8. Leigham; 9. Sun Yat-Sen; 10. Sheath
around the spinal cord; 11. *Going Out Too*; 12. Chicken wings;
13. Technetium; 14. Small, South American monkey; 15. A priest of
Amiens and a key figure during the First Crusade; 16. Uzbekistan

QUIZ 140

1. Facebook; 2. Tadpoles; 3. Bhutan; 4. *Enterprise*; 5. Charon;
6. England; 7. Mercury; 8. Argentina; 9. Length times width times
height; 10. Sunset; 11. White blood cell; 12. Alchemy; 13. Juventus;
14. El Salvador; 15. Ctrl + V; 16. Captain Phillips

QUIZ 141

1. Richard Gere; 2. Elizabeth I; 3. Litre; 4. Colombia; 5. Clint Eastwood;
6. Russia; 7. Bahrain; 8. Uruguay; 9. 1432; 10. Supernumerary;
11. Herring; 12. France; 13. The Lake District; 14. Slipknot; 15. Pillbox;
16. Colour blindness

QUIZ 142

1. Alcatraz; 2. Three; 3. Patella; 4. Hera; 5. Alveoli; 6. 21 years;
7. Nick Park; 8. Pedometer; 9. Lack of; 10. A lyric poet; 11. Rowan
Atkinson; 12. New York City; 13. Gambia; 14. 1989; 15. Lionel Messi;
16. Saraswati

QUIZ 143

1. Sergio Leone; 2. The Black Eyed Peas; 3. Sturgeon eggs; 4. Ford;
5. Florida; 6. Pluto; 7. Martha Stewart; 8. Saturn; 9. Yoghurt; 10. Vixen;
11. Mass erosion of the US Great Plains; 12. Heel wound; 13. Kyoto;
14. Elvis Presley; 15. Paul Baer; 16. Ted Hughes

The Bumper *Family* Quiz Book

QUIZ 144

1. Mexican; 2. *Final Cut Pro*; 3. Boston, Massachusetts; 4. Tick bird; 5. Jane Lynch; 6. Newcastle United; 7. Weight; 8. Ramesses II; 9. Pacific Ocean; 10. Niue; 11. Joyeux Noel; 12. Jason Isaacs; 13. Pitchfork; 14. *Bringing Down The House*; 15. Deep rhythmic breathing; 16. Lech Walesa

QUIZ 145

1. 777 miles (1,250km); 2. Leytonstone, England; 3. Red; 4. Jethro Tull; 5. Konrad Heiden; 6. 2 days; 7. 2002; 8. By singing; 9. Suzanne; 10. *Mulan*; 11. English; 12. Bucket; 13. An Ancient Greek gold or silver coin; 14. Scream; 15. Inu; 16. Von Braun

QUIZ 146

1. A hot pot; 2. London Heathrow; 3. Particle; 4. 19; 5. Berlin; 6. ENIAC; 7. Salman; 8. Pink; 9. Drafting; 10. A tropical tree; 11. Atlantic Ocean; 12. An instrument used to measure water depth; 13. The Queen; 14. Play with sharp accents; 15. Third; 16. Japan

QUIZ 147

1. They are both dentists; 2. Oxalic; 3. Ruby red; 4. Land attached to a manor that was retained for the owner; 5. Yahoo; 6. Four couples or eight dancers; 7. Thunder and lightning; 8. The Yellow Brick Road; 9. Olive oil; 10. Madagascar; 11. Christopher Lloyd; 12. Arcade; 13. A revolutionary; 14. Ben Affleck; 15. The Nigerian Nightmare; 16. North Korea

The Bumper *Family* Quiz Book

QUIZ 148

1. Pedal bone (or distal phalanx, third phalanx or P3); 2. Acid rain;
3. Mayotte; 4. 24; 5. Mexico; 6. Heyday; 7. Fusses; bustles; 8. Steak
and shrimp; 9. Guilds; 10. *NSYNC; 11. Afterimage; 12. *D.O.A.*;
13. Sparrow; 14. Bundesrat; 15. Tibetan Buddhism; 16. *So Red the
Rose*

QUIZ 149

1. Guillermo del Toro; 2. Battle of Tapae; 3. Cyan, magenta and yellow;
4. Octagon; 5. Shovels; 6. The Duke of Wellington; 7. 68 AD; 8. Wales;
9. Echo; 10. A sudden coup; 11. Roger Federer; 12. Ireland; 13. Retina;
14. *Rollerball*; 15. Pumpkin seeds; 16. Toni Braxton

QUIZ 150

1. José María Olazábal; 2. Cooking the syrup; 3. *A Single Man*;
4. Sparkling wine; 5. Below 120; 6. Peasants; 7. Once a year; 8. An
archipelago; 9. Rainbow lorikeet; 10. Present from birth; 11. Toadstool
veils; 12. Poseidon; 13. Eleanor Catton; 14. Rugby; 15. Thames; 16. A
Plan To Get Us Out Of Here

QUIZ 151

1. *Enchanting*; 2. Mozambique; 3. Mask; 4. Mumble; 5. Islam;
6. Muhammad; 7. Acuity; 8. British explosives; 9. 4; 10. *The Giaour*;
11. Scotland; 12. Lima bean; 13. Czech Republic; 14. Antarctic;
15. Backbone; 16. Go back to the beginning

QUIZ 152

1. San Marino; 2. *Do They Know It's Christmas?* by Band Aid; 3. Face;
4. Nitrogen; 5. All I Want Is You; 6. Almond paste; 7. It's behind you!;
8. Chris Tucker; 9. *The Adventure of Link*; 10. A soft-shelled clam;
11. Brookings, Oregon; 12. India; 13. The public; 14. 1809; 15. Grey
wolf; 16. Charles Dickens

The Bumper Family Quiz Book

QUIZ 153

1. Aryan; 2. Flour; 3. Richard Nixon; 4. Pick me up; 5. Massachusetts;
6. Azurite and Malachite; 7. Switzerland; 8. *American Beauty*;
9. Sauerkraut; 10. Poet Laureate; 11. A musical instrument; 12. Arnold;
13. Linux; 14. A hopping desert rodent; 15. Vitamin C deficiency; 16. Ali
Khamenei

QUIZ 154

1. Pacific Coast Championships, 2006; 2. Lion; 3. Krakow; 4. Cheetah;
5. The Pencil Musuem; 6. The tailbone; 7. Dianna Agron; 8. Hamburg;
9. A painter; 10. Mummification; 11. Gildor Inglorion; 12. Jupiter;
13. Tesco; 14. 1981; 15. North; 16. *Versificator regis*

QUIZ 155

1. Nepal; 2. 1960s; 3. Spain; 4. Irish; 5. USA; 6. Pope Benedict XVI;
7. Commerce; 8. 34; 9. Indigestible plant parts; 10. Sirloin steak; 11. *Ice
Age*; 12. The Valentines; 13. *Treasure Island*; 14. Chlorine; 15. Pretty
Boy; 16. January

QUIZ 156

1. 58%; 2. Single Lens Reflex; 3. 1995; 4. Franklin W. Dixon; 5. An
image file; 6. John Young and Thomas Mattingly; 7. Golden Ball;
8. Emerald; 9. Shark; 10. Michael Keaton; 11. Web editing; 12. 1294;
13. Straits of Malacca; 14. A salamander; 15. Sicily; 16. St Nicholas

QUIZ 157

1. Fine art; 2. Northern lights; 3. Six; 4. Henry VII; 5. Heteroccus;
6. Sausage meat; 7. The Muses; 8. Cosecant; 9. Core; 10. Lions;
11. Half Baked; 12. Australia; 13. Fatigue; 14. India; 15. Kansas;
16. Volcanoes

The Bumper *Family* Quiz Book

QUIZ 158

1. Five; 2. Camel; 3. January; 4. In Croatia and Bosnia and Herzegovina; 5. Alvin; 6. Aristotle; 7. July–September; 8. Andrew Gross; 9. Monaco; 10. Thursday Island; 11. Ylvis; 12. 64 bit; 13. 2 weeks; 14. The beaver; 15. Grilled fish; 16. 1990

QUIZ 159

1. Ayatollah Khomeini; 2. In an 'L' shape, 2 squares one way and 1 square perpendicularly; 3. US Open; 4. Robert Penn Warren; 5. Cirrus; 6. Crispin Glover; 7. *Little Red Riding Hood*; 8. Athens; 9. *Voyager*; 10. Femur; 11. Lindisfarne; 12. Michael Pare; 13. Hue; 14. Medenham Hall; 15. 540 degrees; 16. Ascorbic acid

QUIZ 160

1. Along the Indus river; 2. Blue cheese; 3. Condensed milk; 4. Eros; 5. 1973; 6. Peninsula; 7. Toyger; 8. Excessive interest rates; 9. Jon Voight; 10. *Hakuna Matata*; 11. National Union of Mineworkers; 12. The Cottonmouth; 13. Taro root; 14. Turkey; 15. When pigment separates from water; 16. *White Light/White Heat*

QUIZ 161

1. Adidas; 2. The reigning monarch; 3. Sonar; 4. Lemon; 5. West Germany; 6. Silver; 7. Magma; 8. Mikhail Gorbachev; 9. Wheat noodles; 10. Harper Lee; 11. Source area; 12. Ford; 13. Hamid Karzai; 14. Steve McQueen; 15. Argentina; 16. A puncture, tear or hole

QUIZ 162

1. *Premiere*; 2. 1953; 3. Egypt; 4. Cersei Lannister; 5. Talk to you later; 6. Armoured Recovery Vehicle; 7. Red, green and blue; 8. Muscle; 9. A fish; 10. I; 11. *East China Sea*; 12. Archie Moore; 13. Florida; 14. A close-fitting jacket or doublet; 15. Lychee; 16. Randy Newman

The Bumper *Family* Quiz Book

QUIZ 163

1. Athena; 2. A temporary fortification; 3. Smear; 4. Less than; 5. Paul McCartney; 6. Gandalf the Grey; 7. The Scream of Nature; 8. May 5th; 9. Divot; 10. 14; 11. Mercator; 12. Nicolaus Copernicus; 13. Palace of Westminster; 14. Test pilot; 15. USS *Nautilus*; 16. *Ocarina of Time 3D*

QUIZ 164

1. Discontent; 2. Matter; 3. A tidal wave; 4. Pablo Picasso; 5. India; 6. Joey Archer; 7. Lebanon; 8. Queenstown; 9. Waves; 10. Pope Julius I; 11. Brown; 12. Corgi; 13. Ashton Kutcher; 14. 1925; 15. Wine; 16. Sea of Tranquility

QUIZ 165

1. Taxi driver; 2. Metabolism; 3. Sir William Hamilton; 4. Echidna and platypus; 5. Caribbean; 6. Godthab; 7. *Runaway Bride*; 8. Alec Gilroy; 9. Redfish; 10. 0; 11. South Africa; 12. *Ugly Betty*; 13. 4; 14. Mars; 15. Joan Baez; 16. One day before symptoms appear

QUIZ 166

1. George VI; 2. A party or feast; 3. Increase in multiple births; 4. Litas; 5. Hibernate; 6. A topographic map; 7. Dutch; 8. Blarney; 9. Jack Johnson; 10. Mushu; 11. Long and thin; 12. Less than 80.; 13. Anne; 14. Memphis; 15. 1980; 16. Black, white and grey

QUIZ 167

1. Brazil; 2. Swan; 3. *Argo*; 4. Manila; 5. *Hercules*; 6. The queen of the fairies; 7. Life after death; 8. Speed; 9. A weasel; 10. Friend; 11. Tee off; 12. Shiva; 13. Australian sheepdog; 14. Mosaic; 15. Geoffrey of Anjou; 16. 3.6m (11 feet 10 inches)

The Bumper Family Quiz Book

QUIZ 168

1. Los Angeles; 2. Mayan; 3. Periodic table; 4. Tobey Maguire; 5. A cold tomato soup; 6. Asia; 7. Leeds Castle; 8. Jack White and Alicia Keys; 9. 100; 10. Balthazar, Caspar and Melchior; 11. Mach 6; 12. Peter Pan; 13. *Excel*; 14. Francis Forde; 15. All clear; 16. Moves rapidly while whirring

QUIZ 169

1. *Pay It Forward*; 2. Cape Town; 3. 3; 4. Petrochemicals; 5. Pulsar; 6. France; 7. 1947; 8. 1998; 9. Purple-grey; 10. Lizard; 11. Air resonating; 12. Sydney Harbour Bridge; 13. Monterey squid; 14. None; 15. Norma Jean Mortenson; 16. Wickes

QUIZ 170

1. In the Netherlands; 2. Kilt; 3. *Shakespeare in Love*; 4. Richard Hughes; 5. Grid; 6. C = 5/9 x (F - 32); 7. Dido; 8. Relating to the leg; 9. Platinum; 10. Mayfair; 11. Harriet Ann Jacobs; 12. Feet and legs; 13. Mary I; 14. James Hunt; 15. Soviet Union; 16. Spanish

QUIZ 171

1. Rich Text File, an early formatted text document; 2. Six hours; 3. Il Codino; 4. Professor Plum; 5. Kathy Bates; 6. A number from which another is subtracted; 7. A week; 8. SI; 9. 62.8cm (24.7in); 10. Grampians; 11. Spike Milligan; 12. Streets intersected at right angles; 13. Long Term Debt; 14. Pointillism; 15. Sunspots; 16. *Calypso*

QUIZ 172

1. Waltz; 2. Vitamin C; 3. Jeremy Piven; 4. Cape Verde Islands; 5. Xbox; 6. Vesta; 7. An Extra Flap Of Fur On Cats; 8. She had been set on fire; 9. William the Conqueror; 10. Mixing batter; 11. Hermes; 12. Producing; 13. *Office 365*; 14. Comparethemarket.com; 15. MGM's financial issues; 16. 1781

The Bumper *Family* Quiz Book

QUIZ 173

1. Adrianna Pennino; 2. October; 3. Sao Tome and Principe; 4. Steely Dan; 5. The Bank Of England; 6. George Washington; 7. Corundum; 8. Automatic Teller Machine; 9. 116 years; 10. José Mourinho; 11. Brisbane; 12. Landed a plane in Red Square; 13. Tara; 14. He was talented in many areas; 15. El Principe Ponceno; 16. 1,000 volts

QUIZ 174

1. A unicellular blue-green alga; 2. 180, in 85 countries; 3. *12 Years a Slave*; 4. 50 gallons; 5. A Poetic Genius; 6. Claridge's; 7. Assets minus liabilities; 8. Fig; 9. Carbon; 10. 1912; 11. Universal Serial Bus; 12. Henry VII; 13. Prince Edward Island; 14. Pataliputra; 15. 2.5cm (1 inch); 16. Bahrain

QUIZ 175

1. Hippopotamus; 2. Nine years; 3. Princess Grace, wife of the Prince of Monaco; 4. Follow Friday; 5. 1961; 6. Land of the dead; 7. Orange; 8. Pineapple; 9. Oceanographers; 10. The George Cross; 11. Flannery O'Connor; 12. Tours; 13. Based on theory, not practice; 14. 1997; 15. An eighth note; 16. Rome

QUIZ 176

1. *Thriller*; 2. 21; 3. Japan; 4. Espresso with milk foam; 5. Land's End; 6. Mary II; 7. Honoré de Balzac; 8. It rotates; 9. 1952; 10. France; 11. St. John's; 12. Aloe; 13. United Arab Emirates; 14. Ballabriggs; 15. Puff adder; 16. Blind date

QUIZ 177

1. Valley of Mercy; 2. Dachshund; 3. A play; 4. Giraffe; 5. Regina; 6. William P. Blatty; 7. Pancreas; 8. Area; 9. 1977 Pontiac Firebird; 10. 115; 11. Indira Point; 12. Brooke Shields; 13. Very, very fast; 14. 4; 15. Fruit cooked in a sugar syrup; 16. 1981

The Bumper Family Quiz Book

QUIZ 178

1. John Irving; 2. A solid swelling of clotted blood within tissue;
3. Thailand; 4. Las Vegas; 5. Photosynthesis; 6. Shi Hyun Ahn;
7. Japanese ceremonial tea pottery; 8. 3,300; 9. Holly; 10. Papa
Roach; 11. 1903; 12. Oval; 13. *SS Athenia*; 14. Octagon; 15. Nose job;
16. Ecuador

QUIZ 179

1. Lebanon; 2. Paraguay; 3. Apartment or house; 4. Max Shreck;
5. Cognac; 6. Pup; 7. Sydney, Australia; 8. Mandy Moore; 9. Antecede;
10. A wide, open v-shape; 11. Germany; 12. *Overload*; 13. Eight nights;
14. Absolute date; 15. Plymouth Argyle; 16. 1934

QUIZ 180

1. Cronus; 2. *Swan Lake*; 3. National Assembly; 4. Purple with a green
bow; 5. Lion; 6. Mark Antony; 7. 802.11b; 8. Domain name server;
9. Piers Polkiss; 10. Rosettes; 11. Cameroon; 12. Tazo; 13. Chirpa;
14. Italy; 15. Top Croatian Ace; 16. 1994

QUIZ 181

1. Elizabeth I; 2. Pumpkin; 3. 27 times larger; 4. A sonic boom; 5. Speed
of light; 6. About 322 feet taller; 7. Chewing gum; 8. Oil; 9. Red;
10. At the lowest level; 11. Toronto; 12. Nathan Lane; 13. Sweet wine;
14. Thames; 15. National debt; 16. Lebanon

QUIZ 182

1. Thomas Gainsborough; 2. *The Hunchback of Notre Dame*; 3. *Friends*;
4. Mariana Trench; 5. Hindi; 6. Not genuine; 7. Meat and grain groups;
8. Opaque; 9. Bjorn Borg; 10. Martin Luther; 11. Anthony; 12. The Great
Bear; 13. Thabo Mbeki; 14. Anyone; 15. Botswana; 16. Boggart

The Bumper Family Quiz Book

QUIZ 183

1. John Dryden, in 1688; 2. Magnet; 3. Hartsfield-Jackson International Airport, Atlanta, US; 4. African National Congress; 5. Aristotle's Lantern; 6. Kids' screams; 7. Peru; 8. Moonface; 9. Jacuzzi; 10. 1.3 billion years; 11. 1958; 12. A promoter; 13. Second fermentation; 14. Iraq; 15. 12; 16. Spain

QUIZ 184

1. Asparagus; 2. Joan Brandwyn; 3. Shel Silverstein; 4. Woodstock '94; 5. Autumn; 6. The Thirty Years War; 7. Mexico; 8. Tadpole; 9. Recycling; 10. Battle of Bosworth; 11. Virgin Galactic; 12. Not responding to treatment; 13. Kazakhstan; 14. Antioxidants; 15. A cupboard in the wall; 16. Opium

QUIZ 185

1. South America; 2. Mushroom; 3. 52; 4. Pituitary gland; 5. Spain; 6. Chile; 7. Black, red and yellow; 8. Transylvania; 9. Mexican; 10. Crab claw; 11. Three; 12. Seamounts; 13. North Korea; 14. Aethelred; 15. 20; 16. Pulitzer Prize

QUIZ 186

1. 1979; 2. Lord Voldemort; 3. Tiberius; 4. Cow; 5. Berlin; 6. 11; 7. Professor Charles Xavier; 8. Easel; 9. London Eye; 10. Dim lighting; 11. Solar storms; 12. Silver; 13. Attempting to hitchhike; 14. Likely lads; 15. 1; 16. Hungary

QUIZ 187

1. A holy man; 2. Madagascar; 3. Pyeongchang, South Korea; 4. Spring; 5. Little Bourke; 6. 1982; 7. Vitamin B1; 8. Afghanistan; 9. Blue; 10. Mercury; 11. Benedick; 12. Statant; 13. Punk; 14. Acini di pepe; 15. Good heart; 16. The Who

The Bumper Family Quiz Book

QUIZ 188

1. Russia; 2. Jack Kerouac; 3. London; 4. Italy; 5. NTSC;
6. Argentina; 7. Japan; 8. Drink of strength; 9. 47; 10. Haematophagy;
11. Mendelssohn; 12. A bull; 13. *The Village*; 14. Three; 15. Meat;
16. Teeth

QUIZ 189

1. Bunga bunga parties; 2. Ian Fleming; 3. Nate Mendel; 4. A fish; 5. A
hollow grass stem; 6. Caspian Sea; 7. Living room; 8. A ring; 9. Robert
Gascoyne-Cecil, 3rd Marquess of Salisbury; 10. Monitor; 11. 48 miles
(77.1km); 12. Climatology; 13. Kenneth Branagh; 14. Reptile; 15. Or
Nearest Offer; 16. Death by hanging

QUIZ 190

1. Ian McKellen; 2. Atomic; 3. *The Wiz*; 4. Brazil; 5. Blood-red;
6. 1943; 7. Hardened tree sap; 8. Flopsy, Mopsy and Cotton Tail;
9. David Mamet; 10. Art Vandelay; 11. Vitellius; 12. 2002; 13. Grapes;
14. Foxglove; 15. Comb filter; 16. Georgian

QUIZ 191

1. Dear Leader; 2. Gmail; 3. Typically authentic; 4. Thomas Anderson;
5. Manta ray; 6. Grey; 7. *Windows* 3.0; 8. Pakistan; 9. Fry it in a bit
of butter or oil; 10. Red; 11. Cytologist; 12. Portsmouth, England;
13. England, Africa and America; 14. Snake; 15. Miguel Indurain;
16. Barkhad Abdi

The Bumper Family Quiz Book

QUIZ 192

1. Highest rainfall; 2. Raphael Santi; 3. Pudu; 4. A stone meteorite; 5. 3; 6. Clinical trial; 7. Afroman; 8. Taino; 9. The Masters; 10. A word that sounds the same as another but has a different meaning; 11. Deimos; 12. Specially coloured robes; 13. Length, especially of fabric; 14. Peace of Augsburg; 15. Strategic Homeland Intervention, Enforcement and Logistics Division; 16. 64

QUIZ 193

1. John Grisham; 2. Scotland; 3. Andrew Davis; 4. Mauritius; 5. Blocks out ultra violet rays from the sun; 6. Diamond; 7. Salt Lake City, United States; 8. *The Smurfs*; 9. Second Boer War; 10. Stripper; 11. 2007; 12. Organism; 13. Italian; 14. Jamie Oliver; 15. Suri Cruise; 16. A snowman

QUIZ 194

1. Anterior; 2. Echidna (spiny anteater); 3. *A Moment Like This*; 4. Flavian amphitheatre; 5. Abraham Lincoln; 6. 31; 7. Mills Bomb; 8. Age 2; 9. Elizabeth Banks; 10. Africa; 11. The Twins; 12. A type of subatomic particle; 13. Violet; 14. Steve Martin; 15. Oxbow lake; 16. Mexican

QUIZ 195

1. 1969; 2. Baseball player; 3. Saint Kitts and Nevis; 4. Pearl; 5. *Twilight*; 6. Greg Sacks; 7. Red; 8. Boundary stone; 9. Relates map distance to actual distance; 10. *Salyut*; 11. Torshavn; 12. Spanish Netherlands; 13. Malta; 14. Gnocchi; 15. Bing; 16. 17

The Bumper Family Quiz Book

QUIZ 196

1. Frank Lloyd Wright; 2. Alison Brie; 3. Wolfgang Puck; 4. Russia;
5. Graham Greene; 6. 82; 7. Orange; 8. Joan of Arc; 9. *Gladiator*;
10. Corporal punishment; 11. Hanoi; 12. Hash; 13. David Calderhead;
14. Mars; 15. Edvard Munch; 16. The US flag

QUIZ 197

1. Todd Field; 2. New South Wales; 3. Cuba; 4. Kurt Cobain; 5. France;
6. Strong, cold Adriatic wind; 7. The agony of the leaves; 8. Kangaroo
Island; 9. Jack Nicklaus Trophy; 10. A giant shark; 11. 1999;
12. Zinedine Zidane; 13. 'Eat fresh'; 14. Eastern hognose; 15. Waist;
16. Stonehenge

QUIZ 198

1. 1958; 2. World War 1; 3. Avatar; 4. Lenny Montana; 5. Charles
I; 6. Post Office Protocol; 7. *Beauty and the Beast*; 8. In the north;
9. Oriental rat flea; 10. Isaac Mizrahi; 11. *...Baby One More Time*;
12. Pan fried veal fillet; 13. 3.57m x 1.78m (11ft 8.5in x 5ft 10in); 14. A
lake; 15. Jupiter; 16. Sydney Brenner

QUIZ 199

1. Paraguay; 2. Porsche; 3. Samosas; 4. Four; 5. Kits; 6. Treating burns;
7. 104; 8. 10th century; 9. China's Sorrow; 10. To the west; 11. Olmecs;
12. Apex; 13. 25 years; 14. Krist Novoselic; 15. John Glenn; 16. A buffet

QUIZ 200

1. The Ghost; 2. Northern Mariana Islands; 3. Kiwi; 4. Six; 5. *Blurred
Lines*; 6. Old Customs, Old Culture, Old Habits and Old Ideas;
7. Blackpool; 8. 3; 9. London; 10. C.S. Lewis; 11. 2010; 12. Marduk;
13. Biological warfare; 14. Thin, transparent dress fabric; 15. Black
mamba; 16. The dollar

The Bumper *Family* Quiz Book

QUIZ 201

1. 1985; 2. Raccoon; 3. Blackish-brown; 4. *Bolt*; 5. Ireland;
6. Hippocrates; 7. Epic; 8. Florida; 9. Marcel Proust; 10. Nucleus;
11. John Adams; 12. Nickel-cadmium battery; 13. Steffi Graf; 14. The repeal of laws; 15. The Bible; 16. Romano-Italic

QUIZ 202

1. Alaska; 2. East Timor; 3. Scotland; 4. *Fantasia*; 5. Noble gas;
6. 1943; 7. Caraway seeds; 8. Scale; 9. Suriname; 10. Rene Mathis;
11. Bratislava; 12. 58 hours, 35 minutes and 58 seconds; 13. Nurse of the Mediterranean; 14. 2 Far; 15. Gravitational constant; 16. Denmark

QUIZ 203

1. Neptune Collonges; 2. *Amerika*; 3. 29; 4. 1-3%; 5. Sir Joshua Reynolds; 6. Learned behaviour; 7. Majuro; 8. A cooperative association of smallholders; 9. Milking; 10. Emilio Butragueno; 11. *Gloster Meteor*;
12. Andy Warhol; 13. Louis-Frantois Cartier; 14. A conch shell; 15. Asia;
16. Celine Dion

QUIZ 204

1. Zero; 2. Portugal; 3. Robert Pattinson; 4. Guillermo del Toro; 5. Fear of popes; 6. Chile; 7. Joss Whedon; 8. *Proxima Centauri*; 9. 2012, for *Rolling in the Deep*; 10. Pierre Bonnard; 11. Bone marrow; 12. Finland;
13. Henry Clay; 14. It will melt; 15. Oscar de la Renta; 16. Pekingese

QUIZ 205

1. Karachi; 2. 1727; 3. *Blackbird*; 4. Emily; 5. Eggnog; 6. Impressionism;
7. *Slumdog Millionaire*; 8. Gold; 9. 16; 10. Silk; 11. Boris Pasternak;
12. Royal Liverpool Golf Club; 13. The Scales; 14. Paprika;
15. Hinduism; 16. South-East Asia

The Bumper Family Quiz Book

QUIZ 206

1. Miuccia; 2. 1962; 3. Minoan; 4. Bat; 5. Ulnar nerve; 6. 1930s;
7. Euclid; 8. A united Ireland; 9. Eyesight; 10. *When I Get You Alone*;
11. Dome-shaped Buddhist shrine; 12. Dark blue; 13. Treaty of
Westphalia; 14. Kristin Otto; 15. Belarus; 16. 10 principles

QUIZ 207

1. Indian Rhinoceros; 2. Mark Zuckerberg; 3. Jean-Bertrand
Aristide; 4. Jackie Stewart; 5. Chisel; 6. Insects; 7. Ceres; 8. Jay-Z;
9. Rhytidectomy; 10. England; 11. Three; 12. Calvin Klein; 13. 7;
14. Kuwait; 15. 1981; 16. Frank Lloyd Wright

QUIZ 208

1. Twelve; 2. Elizabeth Gaskell; 3. Between 250-300; 4. *A Knight's Tale*;
5. 0.05; 6. Sirius, also known as the Dog Star; 7. Spain; 8. George
and Bess; 9. Mary I; 10. India; 11. He was missing both legs; 12. 22;
13. Actress; 14. Meryl Streep; 15. Philtrum; 16. Summer

QUIZ 209

1. Christopher Lee; 2. 1979-1990; 3. Mr Tickle; 4. Singularity; 5. Near
Runnymede; 6. Mary; 7. Iraq; 8. Albert Camus; 9. Seven; 10. Ecuador;
11. Bhutan; 12. Gary Lineker; 13. Cellulose; 14. Pablo; 15. 1949;
16. Bread

QUIZ 210

1. Charly Gaul; 2. Kidneys; 3. 6.6 litres (7 quarts); 4. Take That;
5. Cumulus; 6. He was stuck in bed for surgery; 7. 1960; 8. Passant;
9. You; 10. The key to what the symbols on the map mean; 11. Tobe
Hooper; 12. Laying mines; 13. Charles I; 14. Amylase; 15. Atlantic;
16. *Hands All Over*

The Bumper Family Quiz Book

QUIZ 211

1. 1932; 2. *Cats*; 3. Solar flare; 4. Food that observes Jewish food laws; 5. Macedonia; 6. Sartorius; 7. Robin Hood; 8. Frances; 9. 500 to 1; 10. Sherlock Holmes; 11. *The Prime of Miss Jean Brodie*; 12. Astronomical Unit; 13. Lower Nubia; 14. Pop Art; 15. Plato; 16. Raisins, peanut butter and celery

QUIZ 212

1. Alpaca; 2. Canada; 3. Sunflower; 4. The Grinch; 5. Six; 6. Egypt; 7. 1885; 8. George Eliot; 9. A tank; 10. Hexagon; 11. 4 zeros; 12. Kathmandu; 13. Microsoft's; 14. Lee Petty; 15. *Access*; 16. Christopher Pratt

QUIZ 213

1. CHD; 2. Nadine Gordimer; 3. A composer; 4. Touch the heart; 5. Religious events; 6. North America and Asia; 7. Ang Lee; 8. Best friends forever; 9. Mick Mannock; 10. Los Angeles; 11. Angela Stanford; 12. Three; 13. 1979; 14. Colorado; 15. From sea to sea; 16. Short-legged, strong horse; or also a swan

QUIZ 214

1. Seattle; 2. John Constable; 3. Ton; 4. Peel it; 5. *Delivery Man*; 6. Lake District, Cumbria; 7. Square; 8. Mars; 9. Changing shirts; 10. 5,631; 11. The pot; 12. Ammut; 13. Tate Modern; 14. Poland; 15. Blue-white; 16. Jimmy Page

QUIZ 215

1. Paul Azinger; 2. Hyrax; 3. Australian Capital Territory; 4. Lexicographer; 5. A stunned and unresponsive state; 6. Latvia; 7. Owlet; 8. Avalanche; 9. *Amazon Fire TV*; 10. *Courageous*; 11. Robbie Williams; 12. Orion; 13. Puerto Rico; 14. European Railway Agency; 15. 1818; 16. *Dogma*

The Bumper Family Quiz Book

QUIZ 216

1. Vagus; 2. Cells; 3. Eye; 4. Manchester City; 5. Vincent van Gogh; 6. The Bull; 7. To feed tin miners underground; 8. Iraq; 9. Prince Charmont; 10. The Renaissance; 11. Their retirement; 12. Phillip of Macedonia; 13. James and Lily; 14. Generous One; 15. Janus; 16. William Hague

QUIZ 217

1. Belgium; 2. Colonel Mustard; 3. A roofed colonnade or classical portico; 4. Hypnos; 5. Guns N' Roses; 6. Nobel Prize; 7. The Body; 8. Solid; 9. Haemophobia; 10. Mental and physical control; 11. Papua New Guinea; 12. Samurai Sudoku; 13. Sauerkraut; 14. *The Hurt Locker*; 15. David; 16. A third eyelid

QUIZ 218

1. 1903; 2. Asian nursemaid; 3. Blood cholesterol; 4. *Ice Age*; 5. Steven; 6. Half a byte; 7. Angela Lansbury; 8. Asia; 9. 5/8; 10. The tank; 11. 1399; 12. Bright green; 13. Capacitor; 14. One; 15. North America; 16. Dwain Chambers

QUIZ 219

1. Rome; 2. Chicago; 3. Too long; didn't read; 4. Danny DeVito; 5. Maya Angelou; 6. Freeview; 7. *Crazy in Love*; 8. Bolivia; 9. Bhutan; 10. Cocaine; 11. Tim Berners-Lee; 12. Student doctor; 13. Platypus; 14. Golf; 15. 15-17 mph; 16. Virgin

QUIZ 220

1. 1801; 2. Rings; 3. Miles Gloriosus; 4. 93 miles (150km); 5. 112 Ocean Avenue; 6. Germanicus; 7. Barn; 8. Beijing; 9. Ribonucleic acid; 10. Jimmy Carter; 11. Kiribati; 12. Verbal; 13. In the middle ear; 14. Salvador Dali; 15. Constipation; 16. *Just Dance*

The Bumper *Family* Quiz Book

QUIZ 221

1. Reflex; 2. Very long, when referring to a word; 3. Six; 4. Mars and Jupiter; 5. Perth; 6. Trevor Francis, Jimmy McIlroy and Michael Owen; 7. Bakery products; 8. A small marble; 9. A right-angled triangle; 10. Kenya; 11. Scandinavia; 12. George III; 13. Film director; 14. Algeria; 15. Poet Laureate; 16. The River Gambia

QUIZ 222

1. 1942; 2. FALSE; 3. A broken branch; 4. Saudi Arabia; 5. Mandy Moore; 6. Personal Computer; 7. Rajasthan; 8. Pain; 9. Midnight; 10. Photoperiodism; 11. Convent; 12. California; 13. Torque; 14. *Remember Two Things*; 15. 1922; 16. Serafina

QUIZ 223

1. Dr. Dre; 2. Matthew McConaughey; 3. *iTunes*; 4. Distance; 5. Grapefruit; 6. Canada; 7. Adidas; 8. Net; 9. Clocks; 10. The chicken; 11. Snow and ice; 12. Atomic number; 13. *Appointment At Samarra*; 14. Agriculture; 15. Bundesliga; 16. Richelle Mead

QUIZ 224

1. Patrick Henry Roark; 2. Mozzarella; 3. *The White Tiger*; 4. Monopoly; 5. Landscape; 6. Tokyo; 7. 2am Wednesday; 8. A Malay dagger with a wavy blade; 9. 1917; 10. Swaziland; 11. Two; 12. Jack Nicklaus; 13. Data; 14. Roman peace; 15. Excessive blood sugar; 16. Animals in War Memorial

QUIZ 225

1. Florida; 2. Temperature; 3. Chris Pratt; 4. Argentina; 5. Arwen; 6. 2005; 7. Appaloosa; 8. *Tarzan*; 9. Gwyneth Paltrow; 10. True; 11. Plants and animals; 12. Bergamot orange; 13. Prince Rogers Nelson; 14. Kublai Khan; 15. A fermented cereal drink; 16. Mon Mome

The Bumper *Family* Quiz Book

QUIZ 226

1. 1988; 2. John Travolta; 3. 5m (16ft); 4. F. Scott Fitzgerald;
5. ARG; 6. Iraqi Special Tribunal; 7. The light colour of unbleached
linen; 8. Africa; 9. Paris, France; 10. Ray Ban; 11. *The Eiffel Tower*;
12. Argentina; 13. Television Network President; 14. Charles II;
15. Hypocalcemia; 16. The dinar

QUIZ 227

1. Songhai; 2. Atlantic; 3. *Pocahontas*; 4. London Gatwick; 5. Cocos
(Keeling) islands; 6. A flat, marshy headland in Essex; 7. Shoes; 8. *A
Wrinkle In Time*; 9. Tantalus; 10. *The Big Lebowski*; 11. Kinshasa;
12. 660 feet; 13. Great; 14. City guards; 15. Krypton; 16. 22

QUIZ 228

1. Italian; 2. Surface currents; 3. Lightning rod/conductor; 4. Jordan;
5. Counting machine; 6. Amazon basin; 7. *Creep*; 8. 10; 9. Communist;
10. Green; 11. Katey Sagal; 12. Spitfire; 13. Jamie; 14. 1932;
15. Charles Goodyear; 16. Restricted

QUIZ 229

1. The Dead Sea Scrolls; 2. Thank you very much; 3. Wembley Stadium;
4. Benito Mussolini; 5. All the colours; 6. Japanese; 7. Lobster;
8. *Winnie the Pooh*; 9. India; 10. James I (also known as James VI of
Scotland); 11. A pointed tool used for making holes for seeds; 12. Zero;
13. Tea; 14. Liechtenstein; 15. Vancouver, Canada; 16. Bichon Frise

QUIZ 230

1. He turns into a werewolf when he sees the moon; 2. Argentina;
3. Music; 4. Manila; 5. Mockingjay; 6. Cri-Kee; 7. Rain; 8. Concave;
9. Italy; 10. Termites; 11. An Asian ornamental honeysuckle; 12. Former
Prime Minister of Israel; 13. 1950s; 14. 13 goals; 15. Snap!; 16. A ban

The Bumper *Family* Quiz Book

QUIZ 231

1. *Braveheart*; 2. Canada; 3. 1; 4. Proteins; 5. Moose; 6. Netherlands;
7. Crossbow; 8. Protein; 9. Scotland; 10. Avocados and olives;
11. Sally; 12. George I; 13. Richard III; 14. Asmara; 15. McLovin;
16. Bird (a Eurasian partridge)

QUIZ 232

1. San Francisco; 2. *On My Own*; 3. *Bockscar*; 4. Idris Elba; 5. 1997;
6. *Girl*; 7. Hugs and kisses; 8. Anaconda; 9. Ashmolean Museum;
10. Numbersixvalverde; 11. William III (William of Orange); 12. 2 weeks;
13. San Salvador; 14. 5 years; 15. Australia; 16. Germany

QUIZ 233

1. Three; 2. Fleurieu; 3. 1990s; 4. Airway; 5. *Men in Black II*; 6. *The Music of The Night*; 7. 100; 8. Princess Alexandra; 9. Disney; 10. Brain and liver; 11. Latin; 12. Ron Howard; 13. Transliterating Japanese into the Roman alphabet; 14. Gozo; 15. Africa; 16. Lignite

QUIZ 234

1. Spartacus; 2. Turkey; 3. Carrots on a stick; 4. St. Patrick's Day;
5. Spinach; 6. Perfume; 7. Singer, dancer or actor; 8. Coal; 9. 17th;
10. Brazil; 11. William Snape; 12. Earth; 13. Algeria; 14. Stereocyte;
15. Acorn Archimedes/Risc PC range; 16. 1989

QUIZ 235

1. The USA; 2. United Kingdom; 3. Nitrogen; 4. Apartheid; 5. Panda;
6. The mouse; 7. Hedwig; 8. Augusta National Golf Club; 9. True;
10. 741 AD; 11. Poseidon; 12. Zoran Djindjic; 13. Sucks to be you;
14. He is hanged; 15. Dublin; 16. Roberto Baggio

The Bumper *Family* Quiz Book

QUIZ 236

1. Robert Louis Stevenson; 2. McDonald's; 3. Utah; 4. Rain;
5. Three; 6. Ice cube; 7. 1982; 8. Nutrient; 9. Lebanon; 10. Cuckoo;
11. Pterodactyl; 12. Edris Stannus; 13. 40; 14. Red and white;
15. Septagon; 16. Anne

QUIZ 237

1. Lost nets continuing to catch fish; 2. North; 3. Ernest Hemingway;
4. Lisbon; 5. Pacific Ocean; 6. New York Cosmos; 7. The marketplace;
8. *American Beauty*; 9. Athens, Greece; 10. Evergreen; 11. Badger dog;
12. *Dancing Barefoot*; 13. German and Italian prisoners; 14. Animal
feed; 15. Dar-Es-Salaam; 16. Fear of the colour yellow

QUIZ 238

1. Goalkeeper coach; 2. The Great Dog; 3. Olive oil; 4. Nepal; 5. Fear of
going bald; 6. Grammar and music; 7. 1917; 8. Norwegian Ridgeback;
9. Australia; 10. Peanut; 11. London, UK; 12. Podgorica; 13. Rodney
Copperbottom; 14. Ctrl + O; 15. Skeleton; 16. Alpha

QUIZ 239

1. 1959; 2. A stainless steel structure rising 192m (630ft) high in St.
Louis, Missouri; 3. Something wasn't right here; 4. His home; 5. A ram;
6. Giraffe; 7. Spain; 8. Parental controls; 9. USSR; 10. A prism; 11. J.
G. Ballard; 12. Catherine of Aragon; 13. Scott Verplank; 14. Edward VI;
15. Solemnly renounce it; 16. Los Angeles

QUIZ 240

1. The break; 2. Stairs or steep slopes; 3. 1941; 4. Chocolate; 5. Under
a sink or other bathroom fitting; 6. Melbourne; 7. Silk; 8. Spine; 9. On
the ocean floor; 10. 10; 11. A metal rod used in glassmaking; 12. Ctrl +
X; 13. Zefram Cochrane; 14. Lima beans and maize; 15. Scarborough;
16. 2005

The Bumper Family Quiz Book

QUIZ 241

1. Bradycardia; 2. Kirsty Hume; 3. The Gambia; 4. Dunes; 5. Kala;
6. With; 7. Valerie Solanis; 8. Too much information; 9. Cuscus;
10. Three; 11. South Africa; 12. Butterfly; 13. Leeds; 14. It gets chewier;
15. Bill Clinton; 16. *To Kill A Mockingbird*

QUIZ 242

1. 1864; 2. Mesopotamia; 3. 7; 4. Height above sea level; 5. Professor
of linguistics; 6. 5; 7. Makes bones stronger; 8. Chimney; 9. Morocco;
10. Big; 11. Military use of harmful agents; 12. Simon; 13. Spiracles;
14. *Mai the Psychic Girl*; 15. Switzerland and Vatican City; 16. Castries

QUIZ 243

1. Linkin Park; 2. Pulsar; 3. Scar; 4. A writing system for blind people;
5. Greece; 6. Rhinoplasty; 7. Virginia Woolf; 8. Idina Menzel; 9. Elizabeth
I; 10. North; 11. Sun-dried tomatoes; 12. Seven; 13. Kigali; 14. Terry
Bradshaw; 15. Relating to deductive reasoning; 16. Stockholm

QUIZ 244

1. Poison Ivy; 2. Robin Williams; 3. Telemetry; 4. Protects against injury
and insulates the body; 5. Pago Pago; 6. Filfla; 7. Writes commercial
jingles; 8. Madonna; 9. Voting; 10. Switzerland; 11. About 1760
to around 1830; 12. Tudor rose; 13. Grosvenor House; 14. Ronnie
O'Sullivan; 15. Zeus; 16. Homemade cake

QUIZ 245

1. Nepal; 2. Kenya; 3. Sodium; 4. Colour; 5. No coastline at all;
6. Francis I; 7. Cardiff; 8. Franz Kafka; 9. Yellow; 10. *Sputnik*;
11. Sunspots; 12. Mr White; 13. Fully crossed; 14. Friends of theirs
worked in a pet shop; 15. Nigel Mansell; 16. 1100

The Bumper Family Quiz Book

QUIZ 246

1. Krona; 2. 1913; 3. Solid; 4. Putumayo; 5. Eating shrimp; 6. Radium; 7. Venus; 8. *Fantasia 2000*; 9. Liam Neeson; 10. Ashton Eaton; 11. An animal shelter, or pigeon coop; 12. *The Blinding*; 13. Mung; 14. Light; 15. Five years; 16. Charles V

QUIZ 247

1. Diameter; 2. Moscow, Minsk, Montevideo; 3. 1944; 4. Occasion; 5. 5th of May; 6. Sir Christopher Wren; 7. Diego Maradona; 8. They didn't move; 9. Denmark; 10. Arthur C. Clarke; 11. LeBron James; 12. Guyana; 13. Herbert Hoover; 14. Connoisseur of wine; 15. Soldiers' coffins; 16. Ventricles

QUIZ 248

1. Greek Letter 'Chi'; 2. Socrates; 3. Nine candles; 4. A spiced porridge; 5. Ernest Hemingway; 6. Stimuli; 7. Scallop; 8. Romania; 9. Vietnamese; 10. Jane; 11. Cygnet; 12. 1950; 13. Roman; 14. Taa II; 15. Red, green and white; 16. 10000

QUIZ 249

1. Gordon Brown; 2. Oscar the Grouch; 3. Orchid; 4. Fausto Coppi; 5. Galileo; 6. Newton-metres; 7. Rubeus; 8. Wind; 9. John Williams; 10. Dropped/hanging ceiling; 11. *Honey*; 12. June 10, 1940; 13. Indo-Gangetic; 14. Aids in iron absorption; 15. Gulf of Mexico; 16. Stonefish

QUIZ 250

1. *The Book of Mormon*; 2. Edge; 3. Making money; 4. Landscaping; 5. Soy sauce; 6. *Rockferry*; 7. Poland; 8. Rubbing two pieces of wood together; 9. 1685; 10. Royal Liverpool; 11. Crust; 12. Relax strained muscles; 13. Orleans; 14. *12 Years a Slave*; 15. 1962; 16. Albania

The Bumper *Family* Quiz Book

QUIZ 251

1. *Othello*; 2. Charles II; 3. Slazenger; 4. Plan B; 5. Hedgehunter; 6. War;
7. Poland; 8. Bruno Mars; 9. Green; 10. A moving fluid; 11. Chameleon;
12. Massive air assault involving 9000 aircraft; 13. The River Thames;
14. Ireland; 15. Pez; 16. Kara Kum Desert

QUIZ 252

1. Stephen King; 2. An ornamental shrub of the rose family; 3. Banana;
4. Greenkeeper; 5. 8; 6. Arabic; 7. SPecial Executive for Counter-
intelligence, Terrorism, Revenge, Extortion; 8. Charles II; 9. *Meet the
Robinsons*; 10. 9; 11. 1 mile (1.6km); 12. Auckland; 13. Byron Bay, New
South Wales; 14. Jackfruit; 15. Bankruptcy; 16. Sulphuric acid

QUIZ 253

1. Mechanical energy; 2. Royal Automobile Club; 3. 'How you doin'?';
4. Oh my God/goodness; 5. A sleeveless priest's garment; 6. James
Joyce; 7. Botany; 8. Ebro; 9. Spain; 10. Red and white; 11. 1904;
12. Sculptor; 13. Carolyn Keene; 14. Richard Nixon; 15. Aubergine;
16. Truth University

QUIZ 254

1. Rann of Kutch; 2. Sheep; 3. Ligaments; 4. Elizabeth Bowen; 5. Large
African stork; 6. Erosion; 7. Snapchat; 8. 46664 Campaign; 9. Dino Zoff;
10. A hot pepper; 11. Poetry; 12. *Pearl Harbor*; 13. Play very quietly;
14. Children's garden; 15. Sao Francisco; 16. Steady Ground

QUIZ 255

1. Vanessa Redgrave; 2. Boot; 3. The centre point of the earthquake;
4. Paul McCartney; 5. Know Thyself; 6. Largest; 7. 1976; 8. Rotation;
9. Dr Black; 10. Denmark; 11. Sheridan Le Fanu; 12. 15 litres (4 gallons);
13. New Zealand; 14. Amazon rainforest; 15. Royal Victoria; 16. White

The Bumper *Family* Quiz Book

QUIZ 256

1. Switzerland; 2. Fat; 3. Anne; 4. *Photoshop*; 5. A vacuum; 6. Onions;
7. Scotland; 8. Swimming; 9. Africa; 10. A mongrel dog; 11. *Super Size
Me*; 12. Robert A. Heinlein; 13. Being Salvador Dali; 14. Jack Nicklaus;
15. Helium; 16. A hill in Cornwall

QUIZ 257

1. Marcel Duchamp; 2. Chopsticks; 3. Digestive gland; 4. 10 years old;
5. 26; 6. Gezira and Roda; 7. Tide tables; 8. William Hartnell; 9. Algeria;
10. Veins in the eye; 11. Athena; 12. Thomas Wolfe; 13. 10 million;
14. Fort Caroline; 15. Fifteen Years; 16. Public Image Ltd

QUIZ 258

1. Bhutan; 2. Logarithmic function; 3. Green And Red; 4. Admiral
Horatio Lord Nelson; 5. 1989; 6. Dr. Spock; 7. Emily Brontë; 8. *Make
You Feel My Love*; 9. *Tangled*; 10. Wolverine; 11. *Illustrator*; 12. January
30th, 1972; 13. *Tricolore*; 14. To touch an enemy and prove bravery;
15. France; 16. David Toms

QUIZ 259

1. Rose; 2. Daimler-Benz; 3. An elf's child; 4. Newfoundland;
5. Blue; 6. Vitamin B3; 7. Lost Sheep; 8. Achilles; 9. Destiny's Child;
10. Cooking; 11. The Black Sea; 12. Tom Clancy; 13. 2000; 14. Pain;
15. Luxembourg; 16. Telescopes

QUIZ 260

1. Chewing gum dispensers; 2. Brazil; 3. West Sussex; 4. Pilots;
5. Edward Norton; 6. A quartz crystal; 7. 1921; 8. Leopard; 9. A
palindrome; 10. 1946; 11. Jamestown; 12. Rize tea; 13. Mars;
14. Cristiano Ronaldo; 15. *Genie in a Bottle*; 16. Maroon 5

The Bumper *Family* Quiz Book

QUIZ 261

1. Menes; 2. Idealization; 3. Sesame seeds; 4. Buckingham Palace;
5. India; 6. In the Kingdom of Far, Far Away; 7. Rose; 8. A partridge in
a pear tree; 9. A long, belted tunic; 10. Andorra; 11. Plaque; 12. Acre;
13. Unix; 14. American and Australian; 15. Night Watchman; 16. Ludwig

QUIZ 262

1. Russia; 2. Z; 3. A dog; 4. Spain; 5. Eight; 6. Ferromagnetic;
7. Leaping; 8. David Villa; 9. Asia; 10. Edelweiss; 11. Roberto
Bolano; 12. 1911; 13. Pele and Diego Maradona; 14. Santa Fe;
15. Chromosome; 16. Expressionism

QUIZ 263

1. Kennington, London; 2. Marseille; 3. Steam; 4. Moses; 5. Simon
Khan; 6. 1908; 7. South Australia, Australia; 8. Roots; 9. The equator;
10. Central and South America; 11. *If You Leave*; 12. Mexican;
13. *Amsterdam*; 14. Fibre; 15. A small, forest-dwelling monkey;
16. Chimpanzee

QUIZ 264

1. The Archer; 2. Cannoli; 3. A UK Prime Minister; 4. Praia; 5. 3; 6. Peter
Parker; 7. A flute; 8. Bobby Jones' putter; 9. Puerto Rico; 10. Eric Carle;
11. Holdfast; 12. Rio Grande; 13. A protruding stomach; 14. Turnus;
15. Ginger; 16. Ashgabat

QUIZ 265

1. An ornamental hairnet, hood or scarf; 2. Comoros; 3. Blue;
4. Necrophobia; 5. Meat and beans; 6. Oxfords; 7. A chord with spread-
out notes; 8. Metres; 9. Won the Golden Slam; 10. Ellipse; 11. Virginia
Woolf; 12. Peru; 13. Sulphur Island; 14. Charles II; 15. Nikola Tesla;
16. *Iron Eagle*

The Bumper Family Quiz Book

QUIZ 266

1. Rio de Janeiro, Brazil; 2. Megara; 3. Medusa; 4. Alan Paton;
5. Kirsten Dunst; 6. Kirsch; 7. Angina; 8. Anne Klein; 9. Llanos;
10. 2011; 11. Fish; 12. Boomerang; 13. 1964; 14. Wolfgang Petersen;
15. Suez Canal crisis; 16. Silver, gold and space grey

QUIZ 267

1. Bujumbura; 2. The bodies of Field Marshall Hindenburg and his
wife; 3. Muammar Qaddafi; 4. The sewer; 5. Oak; 6. Africa; 7. ICANN;
8. Plaster; 9. *Fuzzy Logic*; 10. Ganesh; 11. Murphy McManus;
12. China; 13. Rabbit hole; 14. Labrador retriever; 15. The pendulous
skin under the throat; 16. Coating the tip of your cue for better grip

QUIZ 268

1. William IV; 2. Coronary; 3. Marvin Hagler; 4. John Wyndham; 5. Anne;
6. A binding particle in the cytoplasm of a cell; 7. Huaraches; 8. Italy;
9. Churro; 10. Money; 11. A clumsy and gawky youth; 12. Patrick
Stewart; 13. 1216; 14. Mexico; 15. Kingsley Amis; 16. New Mexico

QUIZ 269

1. Anaemia; 2. Bertie; 3. Plants; 4. Palette; 5. Snow Patrol; 6. Absence
of pulse, respiration and blood pressure; 7. Twelve days; 8. Yodelling;
9. Brazil; 10. Rocky Graziano; 11. *The Cable Guy*; 12. The electric razor;
13. A bullet in a body; 14. To emasculate; 15. Mass demonstrations for
democracy took place, which were later crushed; 16. North America

QUIZ 270

1. 10; 2. Deafness; 3. 1485; 4. Hammer; 5. Bridges; 6. 45rpm;
7. Filament; 8. The narrator is revealed as the murderer; 9. See you
later; 10. France; 11. Circuit breaker; 12. Basketball; 13. Greg Norman;
14. 11; 15. India; 16. Machu Picchu, Peru

The Bumper *Family* Quiz Book

QUIZ 271

1. 2000; 2. Lyrebird; 3. The Gent; 4. Lawn; 5. Microsoft; 6. Protective flower sepals; 7. Elizabeth I; 8. North Pole; 9. Spider-hunting wasp; 10. Euro; 11. 1685; 12. Bread; 13. Billy Thorpe; 14. When you knock down all of the pins with a single ball; 15. Jack; 16. Imperfection

QUIZ 272

1. Nelson Mandela; 2. Ermine and vair; 3. Import; 4. *The Departed*; 5. October; 6. Bantu; 7. Eudora Welty; 8. Permeability; 9. Scotland; 10. The windows; 11. Marcus Agrippa; 12. *Aurora*; 13. Mount Kilimanjaro; 14. Ronnie Vannucci Jr.; 15. A potato pancake; 16. Italy

QUIZ 273

1. Sofia; 2. 1911; 3. Joseph Fiennes; 4. Latvia; 5. Big Ben; 6. 1980s; 7. Russia; 8. France; 9. Horse; 10. Costa Rican colon; 11. Wireless Local Area Network; 12. Norse; 13. Floyd Mayweather, Jr.; 14. Stalagmites; 15. An ore; 16. Ozone

QUIZ 274

1. Messerschmitt Me 262; 2. Ireland; 3. Eight; 4. Beta; 5. 50%; 6. Ta'dmejrek; 7. 85 per cent; 8. Europe; 9. *Nick of Time*; 10. Poet; 11. France; 12. Spanish; 13. Port of Spain; 14. Injections; 15. Mexican; 16. Jarvik-7 artificial heart

QUIZ 275

1. Madrid; 2. A simple eye; 3. Place it in the end of the trumpet; 4. In bed; 5. Book; 6. Trajan; 7. Belly dancing; 8. Milk; 9. Ashley Cole; 10. Scott Mosier; 11. Trunk; 12. Aromaticity; 13. 1761; 14. R.K. Narayan; 15. Tuna belly; 16. Belize

The Bumper Family Quiz Book

QUIZ 276

1. Jamaica; 2. Blofeld; 3. Toadstools; 4. 12:15; 5. Geothermal steam; 6. Henry VII; 7. 1974; 8. Catherine Howard; 9. Charcoal and pastels; 10. C; 11. Argentina; 12. 1931; 13. Mike Collins; 14. A German 'liver cheese'; 15. Rice cultivation; 16. Tip of a golf club head

QUIZ 277

1. Mary II; 2. Red and yellow; 3. Verb; 4. Mexico; 5. Mantle; 6. Sahyadri; 7. 1936; 8. Henry VIII; 9. Cheswick; 10. Switch; 11. Marsupials; 12. *Wedding Crashers*; 13. Tax evasion; 14. Mallorca; 15. Tenderloin; 16. *Diggers*

QUIZ 278

1. 1999; 2. *Live and Let Die*; 3. Hillside; 4. *Captain America: The Winter Soldier*; 5. Hungary; 6. Mesopotamians; 7. *Weezer*; 8. Mockingbird; 9. Plate tectonics theory; 10. Silk; 11. 1707; 12. Mageirocophobia; 13. The Madman; 14. Transylvania; 15. Abalone; 16. Mesozoic

QUIZ 279

1. Canada; 2. The US President; 3. Italy; 4. Ramesses II; 5. *Pretty Hate Machine*; 6. Henry Green; 7. Hansel and Gretel; 8. The gray; 9. Boss Grissom; 10. Melbourne; 11. Port Pirie, South Australia; 12. Saxe-Coburg-Gotha; 13. The UK; 14. *Evita*; 15. West Germany; 16. Sailfish

QUIZ 280

1. Scotland; 2. Symbologist; 3. Tricky; 4. European Union; 5. Brazil; 6. Bird; 7. Patterned material used for inlaying; 8. Map; 9. Superman; 10. 1 in 36; 11. Try to Avoid Mosquito Bites; 12. John Ashcroft; 13. J.G. Ballard; 14. Les bleus; 15. Medenine, Tunisia; 16. Being ridiculed

The Bumper Family Quiz Book

QUIZ 281

1. Paul Greengrass; 2. Telugu; 3. Purple; 4. Ten Years After; 5. Bolivia;
6. Chicken with wine; 7. 1956; 8. Eight; 9. Argentina; 10. Humpty
Dumpty; 11. The Woolsack; 12. Max Factor; 13. Creating History
Together; 14. Arctic fox; 15. The number 42; 16. Espejo Lake

QUIZ 282

1. South-East Asia; 2. Elizabeth I; 3. Fear of Germany or German
things; 4. They are rude; 5. By the way; 6. 1937; 7. They're scared;
8. 5000; 9. New York; 10. Topology; 11. China; 12. Airedale; 13. General
Montgomery; 14. James Marsden; 15. The Beast; 16. James Blish

QUIZ 283

1. Motion pictures; 2. Thames; 3. Daisy Duck; 4. Poet Laureate; 5. A
castle near Aargau, Switzerland; 6. Joe Johnston; 7. 1948; 8. A tree
knot; 9. Edward VI; 10. Neuschwanstein; 11. Peppermint; 12. South
African iris; 13. Ice Age; 14. Topsoil; 15. Hewlett Packard; 16. 2001

QUIZ 284

1. Bobby Drake/Iceman; 2. Venus; 3. East; 4. Alexander The Great;
5. A noun; 6. Very dry; 7. Lava; 8. One; 9. Mimicry; 10. Don't Push
It; 11. Lying; 12. USA; 13. From a book of poetry; 14. Amniotic sac;
15. Orange blossom; 16. Arthur Conan Doyle

QUIZ 285

1. Baghdad; 2. Put the lid over the pan; 3. Asa Butterfield;
4. Vietnamese; 5. *On Her Majesty's Secret Service*; 6. 1996; 7. A
reflection; 8. Soccer; 9. Elephant; 10. Luxembourg; 11. Never;
12. Brindisi; 13. Nerva; 14. Adriono Visconti; 15. New Orleans;
16. Seven

The Bumper *Family* Quiz Book

QUIZ 286

1. Chinese; 2. Super Lig; 3. South Korea; 4. 11th century; 5. Three;
6. Vietnam; 7. Large tuna; 8. 700 (687 days); 9. Just kidding; 10. God
of life and death; 11. Shoes; 12. Vietnam; 13. A possessed person;
14. Permian; 15. Shadow; 16. Guerrilla training

QUIZ 287

1. It crashed into the Empire State Building; 2. The Southern
Cross; 3. Sheep; 4. Chemistry; 5. Pretentious; 6. Containing blood;
7. Oryx; 8. South Africa; 9. 1974; 10. Throughput; 11. Lilapsophobia;
12. Saddam Hussein; 13. Owen and Beru Lars; 14. Beijing; 15. Clio;
16. Love

QUIZ 288

1. Citizens; 2. Natto; 3. Descartes; 4. A; 5. Cold front; 6. Gulf of Aqaba;
7. Dentist; 8. 220 days (224.7 days); 9. Crawley; 10. Alfred Bester;
11. Albertville, France; 12. Alexandra Shulman; 13. Mathias Rust; 14. A
silent pause; 15. Bulgaria; 16. Cleopatra

QUIZ 289

1. Guccio Gucci; 2. Peru (and north-west Bolivia); 3. Stalactite; 4. The
Ram; 5. Roman; 6. Black; 7. Donner; 8. The Spanish Civil War; 9. To
prepare skins for leather; 10. Maize flour/cornmeal; 11. A keyboard;
12. Melanie Blatt; 13. Clouds; 14. Hammurabi; 15. South Korea and
Japan; 16. Detente

QUIZ 290

1. 550 BC; 2. Planetarium; 3. Glass snake; 4. Fine, yellowish-grey loam;
5. Voice transmission over the Internet; 6. The ocean floor; 7. Jack
Kerouac; 8. Jimmy Ellis; 9. Every four years; 10. Poole; 11. He couldn't
afford models; 12. Johnny Depp; 13. Mountain range; 14. Brussels
sprout; 15. The sun; 16. Franz Werfel

The Bumper *Family* Quiz Book

QUIZ 291

1. Lithuania; 2. 1922; 3. Joseph Aloisius Ratzinger; 4. Watermelon; 5. Lionel Messi; 6. Blimp; 7. London Transport Museum; 8. First Opium War; 9. Bird; 10. December; 11. Based on known facts; 12. Peter Benchley; 13. France; 14. Brick-making; 15. Naomie Harris; 16. Winston Churchill

QUIZ 292

1. John Backus; 2. Not genuine; 3. Manfred von Richthofen/The Red Baron; 4. *Amazon Prime*; 5. Pentagon; 6. Remus Lupin; 7. Eurus; 8. Schwarzschild; 9. Mrs Potts the teapot; 10. Nevada; 11. Something scattered or sprinkled; 12. Mexico; 13. 1689; 14. Saudi Arabia; 15. 1; 16. Keanu Reeves

QUIZ 293

1. The Thought Police; 2. Red; 3. Reflected sunlight; 4. 1; 5. *Apollo 18*; 6. Africa; 7. Mexican; 8. Harold II; 9. Google.com; 10. Radius and ulna; 11. Spanish-American War; 12. Himmler's Mistress; 13. Plum blossom; 14. New Guinea; 15. Laser beams; 16. Romania or Moldova

QUIZ 294

1. *Mary's Boy Child* by Boney M; 2. Flamenco dancing; 3. Cairo; 4. Big village; 5. Cellulose; 6. Up to 25 years; 7. August Escoffier; 8. Root; 9. Eva Herzigova; 10. Kansas; 11. E; 12. Magellan; 13. Joseph Banks; 14. Spain; 15. Mary II; 16. Iago

QUIZ 295

1. High school; 2. Euro-Disney; 3. James II; 4. Helsinki, Finland; 5. Hobart, Tasmania; 6. 30; 7. Seven; 8. *I Got You Babe*; 9. A Broadway director; 10. Japanese; 11. Sophocles; 12. To support the end of your cue; 13. One; 14. Cohyponym; 15. 1968; 16. Cilia

The Bumper *Family* Quiz Book

QUIZ 296

1. A tapestry from the Louvre; 2. Pythagoras's; 3. Italy; 4. A kitten;
5. The Guggenheim; 6. Jack; 7. *Funnybones*; 8. Psi; 9. Agronomist;
10. Suppresses the body's immune response; 11. First Winter Olympics
in Asia; 12. Lavoisier; 13. Number of protons in an atom; 14. Central
Valley; 15. Add some morning cardio; 16. Henri Rousseau

QUIZ 297

1. Bonn; 2. The kilogram; 3. Black; 4. Freetown; 5. A light musket;
6. 1946; 7. Corrosion; 8. Bhutan; 9. 1963; 10. Swimming; 11. Keeps
current notes sounding; 12. Low self-esteem; 13. Carat; 14. The
Holocaust; 15. Kelly Clarkson; 16. Faster, Higher, Stronger

QUIZ 298

1. Spiders; 2. Near Australia's Great Barrier Reef; 3. Twitter; 4. Cornelia;
5. Rome; 6. A seizure or stroke; 7. Canada; 8. 10,000m; 9. Has been
pregnant at least twice; 10. *The Philosopher's Stone*; 11. Your set
of facial features; 12. Cable News Network (CNN); 13. Charles I;
14. Emerald; 15. A thin, green bean; 16. Six

QUIZ 299

1. Madagascar; 2. 2010; 3. A candlestick; 4. Of the south coast of
Australia; 5. China; 6. Jackson Pollock; 7. Hamnet and Judith Sadler;
8. Oceanography; 9. A ring; 10. Pyramids; 11. 1962; 12. An ancient
stone coffin or burial chamber; 13. Contour; 14. Catholic Church;
15. Jitter; 16. Guru Granth Sahib

QUIZ 300

1. Bloody Mary; 2. 2.49m (8ft 2in); 3. Jon; 4. Forearm; 5. Pectoralis,
triceps, and deltoids; 6. Latin; 7. Budding; 8. Ice; 9. *Mosquito*; 10. 500;
11. John Candy; 12. Grozny; 13. China; 14. Aldous Huxley; 15. The King
of Mice; 16. Eris

The Bumper *Family* Quiz Book

QUIZ 301

1. Immediately; 2. A region of the Solar System beyond Neptune;
3. Germany; 4. New York; 5. 3rd place; 6. Hiroshima and Nagasaki;
7. Laying eggs; 8. Bungo; 9. *99 Red Balloons*; 10. Egg yolks; 11. Lee
Trevino; 12. A sword; 13. Pacific; 14. 1702; 15. Protects the surface of
the cornea; 16. Oliver Cromwell

QUIZ 302

1. Potato and pasta dumplings; 2. New Delhi; 3. Compound Light
Microscope; 4. Weightlessness; 5. Rod-shaped bacteria; 6. Portsmouth,
New Hampshire; 7. The UK; 8. 1950; 9. Fishtar; 10. Elizabeth I;
11. The Stuarts; 12. Asia; 13. Six; 14. Corundum; 15. Sierra Leone;
16. Rabindranath Tagore

QUIZ 303

1. Inside the eye; 2. Mark Selby; 3. Favourites; 4. Russia; 5. No. 1;
6. Painters' guild; 7. A fish; 8. Perl; 9. Uranus; 10. Guam; 11. Allison;
12. 1588; 13. Tyrone Power; 14. *Sputnik 1*; 15. A mental illness or
disorder; 16. James I (also known as James VI of Scotland)

QUIZ 304

1. Ammonia; 2. Winston Churchill; 3. Parisian; 4. Shark; 5. American
Gothic; 6. Ming; 7. Expensive Real Madrid players; 8. Japan;
9. The Solar System; 10. Ian Curtis; 11. Angola; 12. Benazir Bhutto;
13. Kristatos; 14. Zooey Deschanel; 15. Europe; 16. Autumn

QUIZ 305

1. Taking a selfie; 2. Giancarlo Fisichella; 3. Willa Cather; 4. To keep
invaders out; 5. Axis; 6. A hoofed animal; 7. 1958; 8. 1925; 9. *Changing*;
10. India; 11. MP4; 12. Six; 13. 2006; 14. Hedgehog; 15. *La Cage aux
Folles*; 16. A long-haired Russian blue cat

The Bumper *Family* Quiz Book

QUIZ 306

1. Vitamins D and K; 2. Art dealer; 3. Lemons; 4. Cue ball; 5. A lamentation; 6. A society; 7. Sir Ben Kingsley; 8. Garlic; 9. Land Restitution Act; 10. Jerusalem; 11. Malaprop; 12. Stephanie Seymour; 13. Single-celled, green, freshwater organism; 14. Madagascar; 15. HIV; 16. Regurgitated food

QUIZ 307

1. The Enfield Tennis Academy; 2. Robert Zubrin; 3. 10; 4. Tel Aviv; 5. Venus; 6. Yew; 7. Trivium and quadrivium studies; 8. Stylized Japanese drama; 9. 1952; 10. Remainder; 11. Henry VIII; 12. Afghanistan; 13. Chef; 14. Atlanta; 15. Italy; 16. Albania

QUIZ 308

1. Mexico; 2. Extra toes; 3. North bank; 4. Ned Nickerson; 5. Frond; 6. Maple leaf; 7. Oliver Cromwell; 8. Loam; 9. A silly person; 10. Evard Erickson; 11. Right atrium; 12. Insecticide-treated mosquito nets; 13. India; 14. Dresses; 15. Paul Reubens; 16. Brazil

QUIZ 309

1. Sunflower; 2. Ben Nevis; 3. Lots of love, or lots of laughs, or laughs out loud; 4. 2002; 5. A Russian business newspaper; 6. Guy Fawkes; 7. Rain shadow; 8. Equilateral triangle; 9. Monasteries; 10. Anna Paquin; 11. Charles I; 12. A storm; 13. Foo Fighters; 14. Antibacterial; 15. *Snow White and the Seven Dwarfs*; 16. South Africa

QUIZ 310

1. Madiba shirts; 2. Processed peas; 3. Okapi; 4. *Absence of Malice*; 5. Muammar Gaddafi; 6. Prosthesis; 7. Playwright; 8. Kingston; 9. Beaver; 10. Erich Remarque; 11. Boron; 12. A fool; 13. Henry VI; 14. Panorama; 15. The Salvation Army; 16. The 'feathery' golf ball

The Bumper Family Quiz Book

QUIZ 311

1. Romania; 2. Dina Meyer; 3. Dromedary; 4. Franz Kafka; 5. *The Fast and the Furious*; 6. Gold; 7. Dusk; 8. Aryans; 9. *Beagle*; 10. Hindu god; 11. Dr. Werner Haase; 12. Racing game; 13. Iraq; 14. 2001; 15. Merlin; 16. Chromosomes

QUIZ 312

1. AMD; 2. Felipe Calderon; 3. 10; 4. Pixels; 5. 2277 miles (3664 km); 6. Central African Republic; 7. 1993; 8. Body Mass Index; 9. Red; 10. Fossils; 11. Wells; 12. Ice hockey; 13. Auroras Encore; 14. Claude Monet; 15. Pork rinds; 16. Islam

QUIZ 313

1. Lake Titicaca; 2. Europe; 3. Scaly skin; 4. Earth Art; 5. Pierce Brosnan; 6. Guatemala City; 7. 0-0; 8. Will Ferrell; 9. LVMH; 10. Koala; 11. 1869; 12. Cloud storage; 13. Wrestling; 14. *Les Miserables*; 15. Guantanamo Bay; 16. August

QUIZ 314

1. *Road Trip*; 2. December 25, 1066; 3. Julius Caesar; 4. Tagged Image File Format; 5. Table Mountain; 6. Ollivander; 7. 1801; 8. Louis Bleriot; 9. The five major continents; 10. 17; 11. 300 kg (660 lb); 12. Kingdom of the Netherlands; 13. Realism; 14. Mexican; 15. Start a rock band; 16. Blue and white